graphic arts encyclopedia

other reference works of interest

Aljian PURCHASING HANDBOOK

American Society of Tool and Manufacturing Engineers MANUFACTURING PLANNING AND ESTIMATING HANDBOOK

Baumeister and Marks STANDARD HANDBOOK FOR MECHANICAL ENGINEERS

Brady MATERIALS HANDBOOK

Callender TIME-SAVER STANDARDS

Condon and Odishaw HANDBOOK OF PHYSICS

Conover GROUNDS MAINTENANCE HANDBOOK

Dichter HANDBOOK OF CONSUMER MOTIVATIONS

Dunn INTERNATIONAL HANDBOOK OF ADVERTISING

Fink and Carroll STANDARD HANDBOOK FOR ELECTRICAL ENGINEERS

Grant HACKH'S CHEMICAL DICTIONARY

Greenwald McGRAW-HILL DICTIONARY OF MODERN ECONOMICS

Heyel THE FOREMAN'S HANDBOOK

Korn and Korn MATHEMATICAL HANDBOOK FOR SCIENTISTS AND ENGINEERS

Lange HANDBOOK OF CHEMISTRY

Lasser BUSINESS MANAGEMENT HANDBOOK

Markus ELECTRONICS AND NUCLEONICS DICTIONARY

Maynard HANDBOOK OF BUSINESS ADMINISTRATION

Maynard TOP MANAGEMENT HANDBOOK

Melcher and Larrick PRINTING AND PROMOTION HANDBOOK

Merritt STANDARD HANDBOOK FOR CIVIL ENGINEERS

Perry ENGINEERING MANUAL

Schmidt CONSTRUCTION LENDING GUIDE

Stanley HANDBOOK OF INTERNATIONAL MARKETING

Stephenson HANDBOOK OF PUBLIC RELATIONS

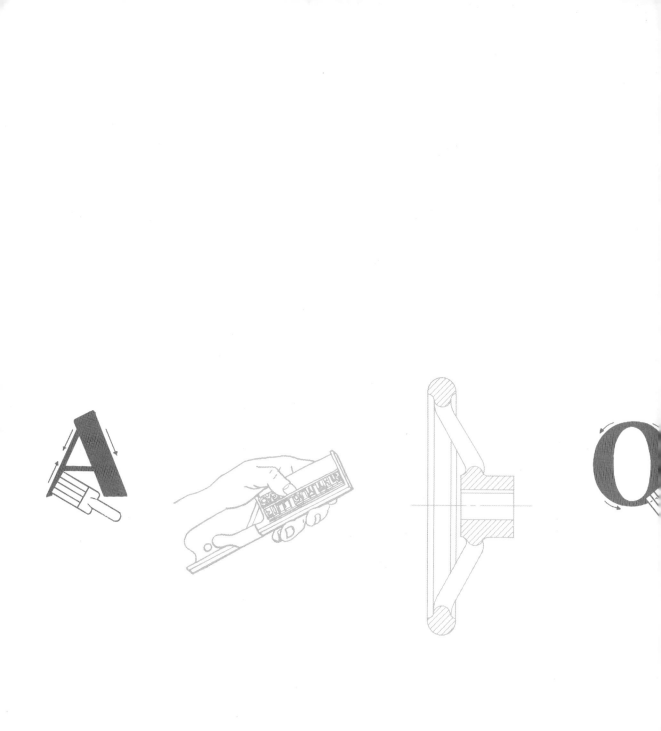

George A. Stevenson

Director, Graphic Arts Research Center, Garden Grove, Calif.

graphic arts encyclopedia

new york   McGRAW-HILL BOOK COMPANY

san francisco   toronto   london   sydney

graphic arts encyclopedia

Copyright © 1968 by McGraw-Hill, Inc. All Rights Reserved.
Printed in the United States of America. No part of this
publication may be reproduced, stored in a retrieval system, or
transmitted, in any form or by any means, electronic,
mechanical, photocopying, recording, or otherwise, without the
prior written permission of the publisher. *Library of Congress
Catalog Card Number 67–24445*

61287

34567890 **VHVH** 754321069

This book is dedicated to my wife Iileen, my son Chris, and to my daughter Jorlene. Understanding is the manifestation of true affection.

board of consultants

Cecil W. Birnbaum — *The Circle Studio, Huntington Beach, California*

Carl D. Buchanan — *C. D. Buchanan & Associates, Santa Monica, California*

Arthur E. Gleason — *Graphic Arts Research Center, Garden Grove, California*

Henri A. Lindeman — *Lindeman Advertising and Associates, Costa Mesa, California*

Jerry F. McCosky — *Graphic Arts Research Center, Garden Grove, California*

Arthur F. Meier — *Space Tools Corporation, Los Angeles, California*

The *Graphic Arts Encyclopedia* is designed to provide basic understanding and practical guidance in the reproduction of words and pictures. As such, it deals with (1) the products and tools with which an image is formed, (2) the kind of image, and (3) the surface or material upon which the image is produced.

The aim has been to consolidate in one volume all the most useful techniques, processes, concepts, and methods required in the graphic arts professions. Clearly, restraint has had to be exercised to hold the book within reasonable bounds; the process has been more one of selection and elimination than of compilation.

Much is said in these pages that has never been said before. The author's intention has been to view the subject matter in the light of actual working experience rather than to parrot catalog descriptions that usually present only ideal or "typical" situations. Moreover, he has felt free to present not only the "what" but the "why" and the "how." A purposeful book is an instructive book.

Because conceptual understanding has been the foundation of the working descriptions, the *Encyclopedia* should be especially useful to beginners, to students at the secondary and college levels, and to those working on the fringes of the graphic arts or attempting to use a method or a process for the first time.

The assistance of the many manufacturers who provided photographs and literature about their products strongly contributed to this volume. Without their cooperation and worthwhile contributions the work would have been severely handicapped. The author regrets that not all manufacturers could be represented in this edition. Omission of a product or a service is no reflection on its quality. Inclusion of all manufacturers of graphic arts products and materials was virtually impossible.

The author is extremely indebted to the staff of consultants who gave unstintingly of their time and knowledge to the end that the *Encyclopedia* would be a reliable reference work. To single out any one consultant as being exceptional would be an injustice to the others, because all are exceptional. Their objective advice and comments have added greatly to the exactness of the contents.

It would be ungracious not to mention the illustrator, Clifford D. Lang, who deserves high praise for his work. The author is fortunate that Mr. Lang's experience, knowledge, and expertise have become a part of this work. He is outstanding as a technical illustrator and artist.

If the reader, student, or craftsman benefits from the *Encyclopedia* even in small measure, the author will be well rewarded for making the work possible. Suggestions and constructive criticism are invited, with the hope that they will be fruitful in leading to the next edition.

George A. Stevenson

The *Graphic Arts Encyclopedia* can be used for ready reference as one normally uses a reference book or for prolonged study of the many fields of interest in the graphic arts professions. It may therefore serve not only as a reference book but also as a textbook.

As a reference book. When the subject is known, refer to the main body of the text and find the topic heading, which appears in its alphabetical position.

When the topic heading is not known but a product or material can be assigned to a class or group, turn to the Product Index on page 430, find the classification or group to which the product or material belongs, and then find the product. The topic heading in the *See* column shows where the product or material may be found in the main body of the text. For example, if information concerning microfilm equipment is desired, a complete list of microfilm equipment is found under the classification "Microfilm equipment" in the Product Index. By selecting the particular equipment in the *Product* column and by checking the *See* column, the topic heading for the product or material can be found in the main body of the text.

When the name of a product or material is not known but the manufacturer's name is known, turn to the Manufacturers' Index on page 440 and find the name of the manufacturer. The topic heading in the *See* column shows where the product or material may be found in the main body of the text. For example, assume that information concerning Itek's plate-making equipment is desired. Refer to the name "Itek Business Products" in the Manufacturers'

Index, and in the *See* column note that information on this equipment may be found under the topic heading CAMERA, PROCESS: PAPER PLATES.

As a textbook. Prolonged study implies specializing in a selected vocation. The chosen subjects can be studied in the classroom under supervision, or the *Encyclopedia* can be used as a home study course. Because topic headings indicate the various fields of interest to which they pertain, it is a simple matter for the reader or an instructor to select headings in a specific field. Any attempt to study the *Encyclopedia* in its A-to-Z format, with a view to gaining an overall knowledge of its contents, is not practicable. The range of subjects is so extensive that a good grasp of them is unlikely if this method of study is pursued.

It is suggested, instead, that the instructor, student, or practicing technician commence at the beginning of the book and make a list of topic headings pertinent to his specific field of interest. Another alternative is to make a list of topic headings from the alphabetical Index which starts on page 467. Once the list has been completed, it will serve as an outline for an excellent approach to a study. Or, the instructor making the list can arrange the topic headings in any desired sequence to conform to the curriculum. For example, if the field of interest is technical illustrating, the list would commence with these topic headings: ACETATE, ACETATE INK, ACETATE OVERLAY, AIRBRUSH, AIRBRUSHING, AMBERLITH, ANGLE OF VIEW, APRON, ART FILE NUMBER, ARTIST, ARTIST AID, ASSEMBLED VIEW, and so forth.

If the interest is in the field of process-camera work, the following topic headings would start the list: ACETATE, ACETATE FILM, ACETATE ORTHO LITHO FILM, ACETATE OVERLAY, ACTINIC LIGHT, ACTINIC TRANSMISSION, AMBERLITH, ARC LAMP, ASSEMBLED NEGATIVE, BACK UP, BACKGROUND, BASIC REPRODUCTION PAGE, BENDAY, and so forth.

A few other examples of fields of interest are plate making, films, paper, editorial functions, overhead projection, color separation, cold-composition copy, bookbinding, typography, copying machines, engineering drafting, microfilming, duplicating machines, hot-metal and cold-composition work, and the methods of printing: letterpress, gravure, letterset, planographic, stencil, and screen-process printing.

A list of Associations and Societies and a list of Trade Journals that are related to the graphic arts professions are included in the back matter.

contents

A

AA *See* AC.

abstract Brief statement in outline or summary form, often prefacing a report or proposal and presenting the complete subject matter. An abstract tells what the report or proposal is about and what conclusions have been reached. It should be to the point and contain no more than 150 words.

AC Abbreviation for author's correction. A similar abbreviation is AA for author's alteration.

acetate Transparent or translucent plastic material. It is available either clear or in colors and in smooth or matte finishes. Pyroxylin and cellulose acetate compose the base for some photographic films. It has been a practice in the graphic arts field to call any transparent or translucent material acetate. A thin transparent paper material, for example, may be called acetate. Acetate typewriter ribbons, however, are opaque. (*See also* FILMS AND PLATES.)

acetate film Sensitized film having an acetic acid base. It is used in photomechanical plate making.

acetate ink Ink with special adhering qualities intended for drawing or printing on such materials as films and acetates. It is employed specifically in making projecturals for overhead projection and in printing on foils. Available in black and in colors, acetate ink is used in making transparencies, slides, and color overlays, as well as with plastics, drafting films, and so forth.

Acetate Ortho Litho film Du Pont film that has an acetate base. It is designed especially for camera and contact applications which require intricate stripping, cracking, and scribing and in which dimensional stability is of secondary importance.

acetate overlay Thin sheet of transparent plastic mounted by flapping to artwork. Acetate overlays have many useful applications in artwork and process-camera photography. To protect a mounted photograph that is to be made into a halftone, a clear acetate overlay of sufficient dimensional stability is flapped over the photograph by means of tape fastened across the top. Instructions for reworking by airbrushing are indicated on the overlay with a wax pencil. This use of an overlay is common when another copy of the photograph is not available for marking. A register mark is drawn on the overlay, keying it to the photograph. Marking an acetate overlay does not affect the surface finish of the photograph, whereas pencil may pierce a tissue overlay and harm the photograph. Vellum paper should not be used as an overlay because of its oily nature.

An acetate overlay is mounted on a photograph or other artwork when nomenclature or callouts are required. The nomenclature, consisting of typeset preprints or paste-ups, is placed on the overlay in register with the photograph. Register marks similar to those shown in Figure A-1 should be used. The marks should be equidistant. If five marks are used, marks are positioned in the lower right- and left-hand corners and the bottom center mark is eliminated. Register marks must be placed outside the crop marks. The process photographer registers the work, photographing it through the acetate overlay. Screening nomenclature with the photograph does not degrade ordinary production work, for the nomenclature retains a good definition. If a second set of nomenclature is required for a photograph, a second overlay must be made with the new nomenclature and used with the photograph.

Acetate overlays can be employed for color separation of line and continuous-tone copy. As an example, the colors red, blue, and yellow are to be used in conjunction with the black plate. Register marks are applied to the black, or base, art as well as to all three color overlays. Four negatives are made, and from these

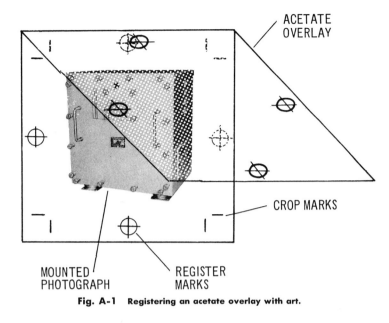

ACETATE
OVERLAY

CROP MARKS

MOUNTED
PHOTOGRAPH

REGISTER
MARKS

Fig. A-1   **Registering an acetate overlay with art.**

the process photographer separately photographs the black art and the three color overlays, all in register. Four plates from which the black and colors will be printed are made, and the color separation is complete. Caution must be exercised in using acetate overlays when close registration is required, for acetate is susceptible to expansion and retraction with changes in humidity. The cost of color separation is lowered and accurate registration is obtained in photomechanical work when color-separation negatives are produced by photographing the multicolored original successively through three color-separation filters and by using the black printer to add density to dark areas of the photograph or other artwork. (*See also* COLOR SEPARATION.)

Acetate overlays are also used for running heads or feet when headings, titles, or logotypes are repeated on each page of a publication or for pamphlets or booklets in which an image is repeated on each page. The overlays are hinged with masking tape and affixed to the copyboard. The copy is placed in register with the preprinted overlay, and the cameraman photographs the combination.

In addition, acetate overlays may be used to represent one or more configurations of like objects. The original represents one configuration, and an overlay represents another configuration on which undesirable images have been blocked out with white pressure-sensitive tape and new callouts added. A second overlay may be used to show an entirely different configuration.

acknowledgment   Author's statement expressing thanks and appreciation by listing the names of individuals or organizations that have contributed to his work. The acknowledgment may appear in the front matter, either as a dedication on a separate page or in the preface or foreword. It may also appear as a footnote.

actinic light   Light in the ultraviolet region of the spectrum that causes a chemical change in photosensitive materials, as in photography.

actinic opacity   Imperviousness to actinic light of specified spectral character, usually in the near-ultraviolet region of the spectrum.

actinic transmission   Transmission of actinic radiation by light-sensitive emulsions.

addendum   Something that supplements the main content of a book or other printed matter.

advance   Money paid by a publisher to an author and charged against his future royalties.

aerate   To introduce air between sheets of paper, either by riffling them manually or by employing a device in order to facilitate feeding in the printing press or to establish uniform thickness during bookbinding. Some printing and reproduction machines have small tubes from which streams of air are directed between the sheets to separate them. Aerating is also accomplished mechanically in some copying machines.

afterword   Composition at the end of a written work (usually of fiction) that comments on the history of the author and other aspects of the work. It may be written and added at any time after initial publication. The lapse of time between the first printing and the appearance of the afterword may be any number of years.

agate   Type size of $5\frac{1}{2}$ points.

agate line   Vertical measurement of advertising space equal to one-fourteenth of an inch.

air   Excess space in line or photographic art or in text matter. Too much "air" is indicative of poor planning and layout. However, space can be used to advantage to improve the eye appeal of an advertisement.

airbrush Atomizer that by compressed air discharges a spray of watercolor pigment on artwork.

airbrushing Act of using an airbrush to produce art or to improve the appearance of art. It is a graphic arts technique that stands by itself as a specialty. Airbrushing is used extensively in retouching photographs for fine reproduction. It is also used in the creation of art, particularly industrial art, where cutaway views are required for machinery, equipment, devices, etc. Line drawing is combined with airbrushing to produce the artwork. A small hand brush may be used to touch up details, but an airbrush is needed for larger areas, as in taking out or altering background, removing shadows, and coloring planes of an object with parallel or dissimilar tones. Highlights are added or deleted to produce varying effects. Glossy prints are recommended for best results.

Good photography eliminates the need for considerable retouching. Photographs should always be larger than the size intended for reproduction. The quality of artwork is normally improved when it is reduced, as small imperfections and fuzziness drop out, lines become firm, and tones stabilize. However, caution must be used to avoid loss of detail because fine light tones merge with surrounding heavier tones if the reduction is too great.

Sheets of thin transparent material called frisket paper are available for blocking out areas on art to protect the image from particles of spray. The frisket paper is pressed on the image and cut along areas and outlines of the image. The paper has a slightly adhesive quality which makes it stick to but not harm the print. The frisket paper is removed after airbrushing has been completed. A careful choice of colors (tones) is most important, as watercolors have a tendency to reflect different tones when dry and when spread in a mass. Test samples should be taken on a glossy sheet and tones compared for color density after drying.

album paper Paper used in photograph albums. Manufactured from mechanical or chemical wood pulp, it has an antique finish and is available in solid colors only. Black album paper is the most popular. Basic weights range from 80 to 110 pounds for 500 sheets of the standard size of 24 by 35 inches. The 80-pound weight is used extensively.

algebra symbols *See* TABLE 12.

alphabet length Length of the 26 lowercase letters of the alphabet as measured in points. The ideal measure for a line of printed text matter is considered to be $1\frac{1}{2}$ alphabets, or 39 characters.

alternate-position lines *See* PHANTOM LINES; *see also* LINE CONVENTIONS: ENGINEERING DRAWINGS.

Amberlith Hand-cut amber-colored masking and stripping film coated on a Mylar polyester film base. The film is milky in texture and photographs black. Amberlith films are companions to Rubylith (red) masking films; both Amberlith and Rubylith are trade names owned by Ulano. Amberlith cuts, peels, and performs in the same manner as Rubylith, except that it was developed specifically for overlays and camera-copy work because colors have a good show-through. It is not light-safe on lithographic plates but works on some chromate emulsions used in silk-screen processing. Amberlith is transferred to illustration boards and the like with thinned rubber cement. (*See also* RUBYLITH.)

Amberlith A3A is 0.003 inch thick, is coated on Mylar, and has the tackiest adhesive of all Amberlith films. It is recommended for camera copy, overlay work, and color separation and is available in rolls of 40 by 150 inches and 40 by 300 inches. Amberlith 3DA is a 0.003-inch-thick film on clear Mylar. Its adhesiveness is less tacky than that of A3A. It is available in rolls of 40 by 150 inches and in flat sheets (6, 12, or 24 sheets per package) in sizes of 20 by 25 inches, 22 by 28 inches, and 24 by 30 inches.

Plastic-Cut Amberlith No. 27 is 0.005 inch thick and is coated on vinyl backing. It is used for overlays and camera-copy work. After windows have been cut, work can be done with either crayon or brush because vinyl has image-adhering qualities.

ammonia-light process Dry diazo or whiteprint process. (*See* WHITEPRINT PROCESS.)

ammonia print Whiteprint copy produced by the dry diazo process. (*See* WHITEPRINT PROCESS.)

ampersand Symbol &, used in lieu of the word "and." The symbol is called a "short and." It should not be used in text copy unless it is part of the official name of an organization, but it is sometimes used in tables and illustrations when space does not permit spelling out "and."

angle bar (turning bar) In a web-fed printing press, a metal bar arranged between printing units at an angle to the direction of the press to turn the web (paper) as it feeds from unit to unit. Angle bars are often filled with air and perforated to reduce the heat caused by friction as the web travels through the press.

angle of view   Angle from which an object is viewed either in real life or in an illustration. In technical illustrations, the most appropriate angle of view is that which not only most adequately portrays the object in its normal configuration but shows the greatest number of parts or those surfaces which readily distinguish the article. In the fine arts, the most desirable angle of view is that which enhances the aesthetic value of the art.

anhydrous ammonia system   System used in the developing section of some whiteprint machines. Ammonia gas, stored in a high-pressure tank, is fed through a low-pressure line into the developing chamber. There it is mixed with water from a separate source and vaporized. The vapor then rises between and through perforated rollers to develop the material. This system makes possible the use of remote and multiple ammonia-supply facilities. In a remote installation, the storage tank and high-pressure lines are stored together in a separate room or building or in a sheltered area or shed outside the building that houses the machine. Only the low-pressure line to the machine enters the reproduction room. In a multiple installation, any number of interchangeable tanks can be connected to a single supply line to provide an uninterrupted flow of ammonia gas to any number of machines. The multiple installation is recommended especially for large departments.

aniline   Oillike liquid originally obtained from indigo but now prepared by the reduction of nitrobenzene and used as the basis for various inks and dyes.

animal sizing   Gelatin used for coating certain grades of paper. The gelatin is applied on the surface of the paper rather than made an ingredient of the pulp mixture from which the paper is manufactured.

animation   Effect of drawing pictures, such as cartoons, in time sequence so that when the assembled pictures are viewed in rapid succession the characters appear to be moving as in real life.

annex   Increment bound as part of a technical publication. It thus differs from an attachment, which is bound by itself. While an annex is related to the main body of the subject matter of which it is a part, its content is such that it can be more conveniently used by the reader as a separate entity within the publication.

annotate   To furnish explanatory notes which may or may not complement the subject matter of the text. Usually the notes are made in the margin.

antihalation backing   Protective coating on the back of films and plates (that is, opposite the emulsion side) that absorbs the image light and prevents the light from reflecting back into the emulsion. It is washed off during the developing process. (*See also* FILMS AND PLATES.)

antique finish   Rather rough finish of paper having low-bulk characteristics. It is designed to imitate the finish of handmade paper. The finish is not recommended for letterpress halftones but may be used for sheet-fed gravure halftone printing. Caution should be exercised in selecting an antique finish when halftones are to be used.

antique paper   Printing paper classified as an exotic type with a rough finish. It is especially suitable for printing type and line engravings by letterpress. Halftones may be printed by offset presses as well as by gravure presses on certain antique papers. Antique papers are used chiefly in booklets, books, folders, and brochures.

antique wove paper   Paper of low-finish characteristics. Laid lines or chain marks are not visible.

aperture card   Die-cut card containing an aperture for mounting a microfilm of text or illustrated matter. The image may be duplicated in a microfilm duplicator or enlarged on a screen for viewing on a reader, or a printout may be produced either on a reader-printer or on a printer alone. Figure A-2 is an example of an EAM (electrical-accounting-machine) tabulating aperture card with a

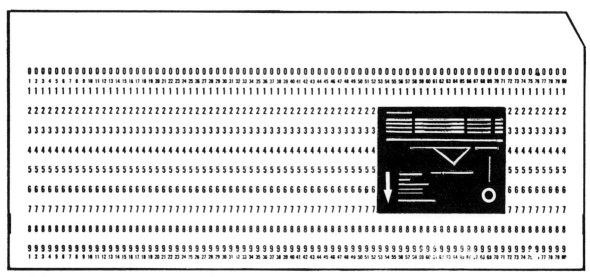

Fig. A-2   Tabulating card with mounted microfilm.

35-millimeter microfilm mounted in the aperture. Index information is provided at the top of the card for manual storage and retrieval. The card can also be retrieved with a sorting machine by using information punched in the card. (*See also* MICROFORM.)

appendix   Part following the final text page of a book, as distinguished from a supplement, which may be published separately. An appendix usually contains matter that is relevant but not essential to the body of the book and that would be awkward or distracting if it were presented in the main text.

apron   White space allocated at the margins of an engineering drawing for the protection of the drawing when rolled; also, additional white space allowed on a foldout page. When text matter or an illustration exceeds normal page dimensions, thus requiring a foldout, and the size is such that a convenient foldout cannot be made, an apron is left along the binding margin.

aqueous ammonia system   System employing a mixture of ammonia and water that is used in the developing section of some whiteprint machines. The mixture is supplied from a storage bottle, carboy, or drum through rubber tubing to the developing section. Liquid flow is controlled by a solenoid pump synchronized with the machine speed. The mixture is vaporized in the developing section. The ammonia vapor then rises between and through perforated rollers to reach the sensitized material, thus bringing out the latent image. Complete development is effected at all machine speeds.

arabic numerals   Figures 1, 2, 3, 4, 5, 6, 7, 8, 9, 0, as distinguished from roman numerals.

arc lamp   Electric lamp in which light is produced by an arc made when current leaps the space between two electrodes. Figure A-3 is a simple drawing illustrating the principle of "burning" an image with an arc lamp through a photolithographic negative onto a sensitized plate. The negative, produced by a process camera, has a translucent image and a black background. The negative is stripped into position on masking paper known as goldenrod with only the image showing. The whole is then mounted in a vacuum frame with the negative in front of a thin, flexible printing plate that bears a sensitized emulsion. The arc lamp burns the image through the translucent portion of the negative onto the plate. The latent image is then developed with a chemical wash, dried, and mounted on the printing press. Figure A-4 is a photograph of an arc lamp that is used for making exposures of copy in a wide range of sizes and applications.

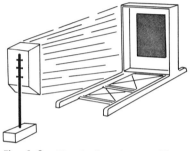

Fig. A-3   "Burning" an image with an arc lamp.

Fig. A-4   nuArc's H-35 Hi-Lite arc lamp.

architectural floor plan   Line drawing that shows the physical location of various elements and inside and outside perimeters of a house or other building structure (*see* Figure A-5). Floor plans are used in conjunction with elevation drawings of the structure. (*See also* ELEVATION DRAWING: ARCHITECTURE.)

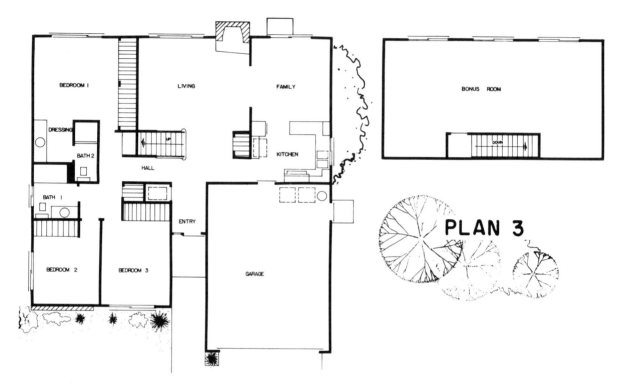

ELEVATION A

Fig. A-5   Architectural floor plan and elevation drawing.

architectural rendering   Perspective drawing of a house or other building structure as illustrated in the elevation drawing of Figure A-5. While renderings of this type are usually done in watercolors, other media such as oils, pencil, ink, charcoal or chalk, and airbrush are common. The renderings are used as sales drawings for real estate promotion. The oversize originals are displayed in the sales office, and the renderings are reduced for reproduction as illustrations in sales literature and newspaper or magazine advertising. Because tones vary through the range from white to black, the renderings are screened with a 133- to 150-line screen when they are reduced. Variations in exterior design are indicated by the designations "elevation A," "elevation B," etc., but floor plans remain the same.

arithmetic scale   Scale of lines equally spaced vertically and horizontally. It is thus distinguished from a logarithmic scale. A chart using an arithmetic scale has equidistant lines which represent equal values. (*See also* LOGARITHMIC SCALE.)

arithmetic symbols   *See* TABLE 12.

arrangement drawing   Engineering drawing which shows any projection or perspective of objects, with or without controlling dimensions, to indicate their relationship.

arrowhead   Indicator shaped like an arrowhead and used at the end of a lead line to direct attention to an object or a point of reference in conjunction with a callout number, letter, or other symbol. Caution should be exercised in using arrowheads. If an exploded view is congested with many callouts, only lead lines should be used. When practicable and when paste-ups or transfers are used, white lead lines and arrowheads are employed in dark areas. Black lead lines and arrowheads are used in white or highlighted areas. When a lead line crosses both white and black areas, a white-and-black lead line is used.

art   In the graphic arts field, any line drawing, photograph, or continuous-tone of halftone illustration. Only two kinds of art are considered for reproduction purposes: line and halftone. The term "art" is commonly used to mean any copy other than text.

art brushes   *See* BRUSHES, ART.

art file number   Key file number placed within the image area of each piece of original art. When an organization puts out publications in which numerous illustrations are used, an art filing system should be established to provide ready access to negatives and illustrations for future use or for rework. Filing all negatives or illustrations by groups is preferable to segregating the negatives and illustrations used in a particular publication or to filing according to product or article. Negatives should be filed with key numbers indicating (1) the type of art, (2) the equipment classification, and (3) the basic negative number within the classification.

The following suggested system may be enlarged or altered to satisfy individual requirements. The first symbol is a letter indicating the type of art:

E—Exploded view
S—Schematic (electrical, hydraulic, pneumatic)
T—Tool drawing
A—Assembled view (frontispiece)
B—Block diagram
P—Pictorial drawing
I—Inspection drawing
W—Wiring diagram

The second symbol is a number preceded and followed by a dash; it denotes the type of equipment and is assigned arbitrarily to a particular item or to similar items. The third symbol is the sequential number assigned to the illustration. For example, in the file number W-3-47, W indicates a wiring diagram, the numeral 3 indicates a particular class or type of equipment, and the numeral 47 represents the forty-seventh wiring diagram of the class or type that has been logged in. Care should be taken to avoid filing art negatives in groups by specific publications because it would then be necessary to trust to memory to find them. A logbook should be maintained to serve as an index and reference. In addition, reverse blueline copies can be made from each art negative and a file maintained by equipment classification for research and reference purposes. Reproduced type size for art file numbers should be no larger than 6 point. File numbers must be placed within the image area of the original art, adjacent to either the right or the left crop mark, in whichever location has the more open space. This system of filing negatives is advantageous in reworking art of the same family, since an enlarged print can be made from the art negative bearing the appropriate file number.

art-lined envelope   Envelope with an extra-fine paper lining. The lining paper may be plain or fancy.

art parchment *See* DIPLOMA PAPER.

artist Person engaged in fine, commercial, or industrial art. There are several types of artist: (1) the fine artist, whose work is motivated by values in which perception and taste govern the manual execution; (2) the commercial or industrial artist, who creates material used in advertising, magazine illustrations, labels, decorative packaging, displays, etc.; and (3) the technical illustrator, who is considered separately because his is the only work in which execution is based on technical knowledge of equipment or in which the objects depicted are of a technical nature.

Artist Aid Trademark of paste-ups and transfers. Artist Aid sheets include almost any character or symbol that can be printed (or drawn and then printed). Various letters, numbers, shadings, and symbols are printed on thin transparent or opaque acetate sheets having adhesive backs. These are termed "paste-ups." The desired design or character is cut out and burnished in position on the reproduction copy. With transfers, cutting is not required: the characters and symbols are affixed to the copy merely by burnishing.

artist's board *See* ILLUSTRATION BOARD.

ascender Portion of a lowercase letter which rises above the body of the letter, such as the upper part of the letters h and d. A descender is just the opposite, being that portion of a lowercase letter which descends below the body of the letter, as in p. (*See* Figure A-6.)

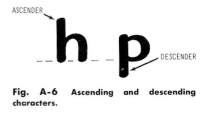

Fig. A-6 Ascending and descending characters.

assembled negative Photolithographic negative, consisting of line and halftone copy, from which a combination plate is made for printing. (*See* COMBINATION PLATE.)

assembled view Line drawing, halftone, or photograph of an object drawn or photographed to show the object assembled as one piece. The term is employed in technical publications. Assembled views may be used as frontispieces to give the reader a visual introduction to the equipment to be discussed, or they may appear in a box in an appropriate corner of an exploded view of the object in a parts list. While isometric projections are used more frequently in exploded views (because they are easier to execute than perspective drawings), assembled views should be drawn in perspective to eliminate distortion. Figure A-7 shows a line illustration of a modified van which serves as a frontispiece for visual introduction to the equip-

Fig. A-7   Assembled view.

ment. The symbols *A* through *D* indicate the physical location of various components and are keys to subsequent illustrations of the components. This method of showing a breakdown is used for equipment having several components, assemblies, or subassemblies.

assembly   In engineering and manufacturing, a multiple-piece item that can be disassembled into its component parts or units without destruction. An assembly does not independently perform or fulfill a specific or complete function but is essential for the completeness or proper operation of more complex equipment with which it is mechanically or electrically combined. When assemblies are part of a larger assembly, they may be referred to as "subassemblies."

asterisk   Symbol*, used to key text or tabular matter to a footnote. It is the first of a series of reference marks. (*See* REFERENCE MARKS.)

author's proof   Proof taken from set type, arranged in galley form, and printed as a strip. The galley is the first printing of the copy as it comes from the linecasting machine and is not page-numbered according to final page format. The copy is proofread by the printer, and typesetting errors are corrected. The author then proofreads and checks the proofs, using standard proofreader's marks. After all corrections have been made, the copy is arranged in pages, which include both text and illustrations. The author is usually required to check the copy again from page proofs. Great care should be used in making changes and corrections. While the publisher will make allowances for a reasonable number of corrections, excessive rewriting and changing by the author will be charged to him to defray the additional typesetting costs.

autogeneration   Duplication of an image on the same material.

automated drafting   *See* DRAFTING, AUTOMATED.

automatic linecasting control   *See* LINECASTING MACHINE.

automatic scanner   *See* ELECTRONIC ENGRAVING.

Autopositive materials   *See* KODAK AUTOPOSITIVE MATERIALS.

Autoscreen Ortho film   *See* KODALITH AUTOSCREEN ORTHO FILM.

autospacer   Automatic quadder mechanism in an Intertype automatic linecasting machine. It consists of space matrices used in conjunction with spacebands. The quadder mechanism in a Linotype machine is called a "self-quadder."

auxiliary roll stand   Additional roll stand for holding the web (paper roll) as it unwinds and feeds into the press. It may be mounted on top of another roll stand to permit one stand to be reloaded while the roll on the other stand is still unwinding. Unless such a dual roll stand is installed, only one web can be fed at a time.

auxiliary view   Engineering drawing showing the true shape of objects which have inclined faces or other features that are not parallel to any of the three principal planes of projection. The auxiliary view should be arranged as though the auxiliary plane were hinged to the plane to which it is perpendicular and had been revolved into the plane of the paper. (*See also* ORTHOGRAPHIC PROJECTION: ENGINEERING DRAWINGS.)

Avery   (colloquially called **sticky back**) White adhesive paper with a backing sheet, used in applying typed, printed, or drawn nomenclature. The nomenclature is cut out and pasted in position on line and halftone copy. The term is in common usage among illustrators and artists.

Avery is a product of the Avery Label Company. The company was founded by R. S. Avery, who, in 1935, perfected the first die-cutting machine that could cut through labels while leaving the backing paper intact. After being removed from their backing, the labels thus produced could be applied simply by touch, either by

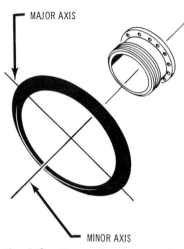

MAJOR AXIS

MINOR AXIS

Fig. A-8   Minor and major axes of an ellipse.

hand or with an automatic dispenser. This development, which made self-adhesive labels practical for manufacturing purposes, resulted in the founding of a new industry. Avery's self-adhesive labels and paper utilize chemical-release coatings which allow all types of adhesives to be removed from their protective backings. Avery industrial and consumer self-adhesive products include more than 100 combinations of materials and adhesives for self-adhesive labels. Among other products are labeling systems, dispensers, imprinters, and affixing equipment.

axis Imaginary line about which a body rotates; also a line around which structural parts are symmetrically arranged. An axis is any imaginary line which defines the position of planes of an object. An ellipse has two axes: a major and a minor axis. The major axis is that of an imaginary line extending through the center of the ellipse at its longest dimension; the minor axis is the imaginary line which extends through the ellipse at its shortest dimension. (*See* Figure A-8.)

axonometric projection Drawing that shows the inclined position of an object with respect to the planes of projection. There are three types of axonometric projection: isometric, dimetric, and trimetric.

1. Isometric projection is the projection of an object upon a plane equally inclined to the object's three principal axes. Parallel dimensions are shown in their true proportions. Isometric projection is the most common form of illustrating objects in an exploded-view format because drawing is faster and easier than in perspective projection. However, an isometric view distorts the object. For example, assume that two sides of an object are in exact parallel. The parallelism is reflected in the drawing, and the plane, represented by lines indicating the two sides, is in true proportion. Thus when the drawn object is viewed, parallel lines do not merge in a vanishing point as in perspective projection.

2. Dimetric projection is a tetragonal representation in which the three principal axes are at right angles to one another, two equal lateral axes having a different length from that of the opposite axes.

3. Trimetric projection is the representation of an object which has three unequal axes intersecting at right angles.

B

back cover Back outside surface of a case-bound or soft-cover book. The inside surface of the back cover is called the third cover for advertising purposes. (The inside surface of the front cover is called the second cover.) If a book has a self-cover, meaning that it is coverless, a blank page inserted at the end of the book is called a dust cover. (*See also* COVER PAPER.)

back matter Portion of a book or other publication that follows the main body of the text. Back matter includes such elements as exhibits, appendixes, a glossary of terms, the bibliography, and the index. It is generally folioed in sequence following the text.

back slant Inclination of a typeface, usually a display face, in which the characters slant backward, as opposed to italics or script, in which the characters slant forward.

back to back In printing, on both sides of a sheet.

back up To print or cause an impression to be made on the back of a sheet of orange or black carbon paper which is reversed in typing, thereby causing an impression to be made on the same sheet on which the material is typed. The resulting strong image offers resistance to light, and good reproduction is obtained when such copy is used for whiteprint reproduction. The term "back up" also means to print on the reverse side of a printed sheet. (*See also* ORANGE BACKING.)

backbone (shelfback; spine)   Portion of a book normally seen when the book is placed upright on a shelf or desk.

background   Portion of an image that is behind the principal object being illustrated or photographed.

backlining   Paper cemented to the backbone of a book, binding the signatures and allowing space between the backbone and the cover.

baking oven   Oven heated by incandescent lights to dry typed reproduction copy. It may have a series of mesh trays for holding separate pages and be lined in part with some heat-reflecting material, such as aluminum foil. The oven offers an advantage when ink rules are required, since a resin fixative is unnecessary. The term "baking" is also applied to drying the toner in xerographic copying and electrostatic printing.

balance   Arrangement of text illustrations in a manner pleasing to the eye. The copy should be balanced on a page or facing pages. Heavier elements should be placed at the bottom of the page and lighter elements at the top. A half-page illustration occupying the entire image width of the page should be placed at the bottom with text above it. The layout of two facing pages shows good judgment when the text and illustrations on both pages are in direct balance with each other. (*See also* LAYOUT.)

balloon   Rough circle or envelope used in cartoon strips and sometimes in advertising illustrations to encircle dialogue spoken by the characters. The term "balloon" also refers to any circle which encloses copy, such as index numbers or letters placed beside the bill of material on an engineering drawing and keyed to material on the face of the drawing. In technical illustrating a similar circle is commonly called a "bubble." (*See* BUBBLE.)

banner heading   Large caption placed across the top of a page.

bar chart   Graphic representation comparing numerical values by means of rectangles of equal width. The bars extend horizontally on the chart and usually represent quantity, as in Figure B-1. Time, distance, or some other value is shown on the other dimension of the chart. Shaded patterns may be used to construct a chart with

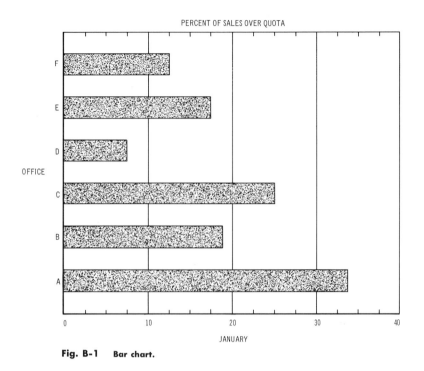

PERCENT OF SALES OVER QUOTA

Fig. B-1 **Bar chart.**

parallel double bars, divided bars, and symbols. A bar chart may also have a vertical baseline that divides the bars. Distances to the left of the baseline should show negative results, while those to the right should show favorable results. (*See also* COLUMN CHART; CURVE CHART; PIE CHART; SURFACE CHART.)

base Metal or wood structure on which printing plates are installed.

base art *See* BLACK ART.

base stock Foundation stock from which various papers are made.

basic Colloquial term for an original work, such as a technical manual, a planning document, or a commercial brochure, in which changes and revisions are made.

basic art *See* BLACK ART.

basic reproduction page Page containing camera-ready copy; also reproducible copy that is photographed and made into a page. (*See also* REPRODUCTION COPY.)

basic size   Predetermined size assigned to a class of paper. For example, the basic size of bond and writing papers is 17 by 22 inches. Although a basic size is a standard size, it should not be confused with the regular sizes into which paper is cut. While 17 by 22 inches is a basic size for bonds, bond paper may also be cut in sizes of 17 by 28, 19 by 24, 22 by 34 inches, etc., and all are considered standard or regular sizes. (*See also* TABLE 2.)

basis weight (basic weight)   Weight in pounds of 500 sheets of standard-size paper. Certain sizes for a given class of paper are accepted as standard; for example, the standard sizes for bond paper are 17 by 28, 19 by 24, 22 by 34 inches, etc. (*See also* TABLE 2.)

bas-relief   Form of low-relief sculpture in which the image is raised slightly above the background surface. The intent is to portray an illusion of a three-dimensional image on what amounts to a two-dimensional surface. The effect is obtained by emphasizing planes of the object in relation to their importance and magnitude. Foreground objects are given a deeper and more refined definition, whereas background objects are less clearly defined and are blended to suggest distance. The modern technique incorporates the use of a plastic powder and paint to make the relief. The image is first sketched or drawn with charcoal on a material such as masonite or plywood. Then the plastic powder is moistened to a working consistency and applied with a palette knife. When the relief is dry, the image is painted with oils and the bas-relief framed as desired.

bastard title   *See* HALF TITLE.

battered type   Type that has been damaged or broken or is otherwise defective.

bearer   In letterpress plate making, a piece of wood or metal used to hold and protect the type mass of foundry-proof pages. In electrotype and molding work, a bearer is any excessive metal retained on surrounding areas to confine the molding material.

bed   Surface of a flatbed printing press, either inclined or horizontal, on which the chase of composed type is secured for printing.

benday   Mechanical shading tint applied to a plate or artwork to give a variety of tones in line drawing. Originally the term was limited to the process named for its inventor, Benjamin Day.

Bible paper (india paper)   Light, thin, strong, opaque paper used for Bibles, dictionaries, sales manuals, and other purposes. Basic weights are 12, 20, 24, 30, 35, and 40 pounds for 500 sheets of the basic size of 25 by 38 inches.

bibliography   List of books, articles, or papers placed at the end of a chapter or in the back matter of a publication. It includes works from which the author has made excerpts or which he has used as reference material to substantiate a fact or theory, as well as works recommended for study. The name of the author, the title of the publication, report or reference numbers, the publisher, the place and date of publication, and any other information which will aid the reader in securing the cited material should be given.

billhead   Blank form used for posting billing charges. The name and address of the seller are at the top of the form.

bimetal plate   Printing plate composed of two metals. One metal rejects ink, while the other does not. Such plates are used in planographic printing (printing from a plane surface).

binder's board   Heavy paperboard that is covered with cloth and used for covering books.

binding, mechanical   Binding by means of metal clasps and prongs, rings, screw posts, or other metal fasteners, as distinguished from the standard methods discussed under BOOKBINDING. Mechanical binding also includes plastic methods of binding, sometimes called "comb binding." Plastic binding has gained in popularity, primarily because of low costs, attractive appearance, and the growing number of industrial brochures, booklets, and other publications bound on company premises. Companies have found it convenient and efficient to have the binding equipment available.

Plastic binding is available in a great variety of colors and is used for binding practically any sheets or pages into an assembly. All pages lie flat when the book is open, and binding margins are visible. Plastic binding is obtainable in diameters from $\frac{3}{16}$ to 2 inches. Depending on size, the back may be imprinted with a title or other descriptive material. Two operations are required for plastic binding: (1) the sheets are hole-punched on a punching machine, and (2) they are bound together with a binding machine. Figure B-2 illustrates an electric punch. This model punches a minimum of 20,000 sheets per hour, or approximately 55 sheets per lift under normal conditions. Mechanical binding machines that combine both the punching and the binding operations are also available. The machine may be manually or electrically operated.

In addition to plastic and loose-leaf binding, common forms of mechanical binding include post binding for loose-leaf publications,

Fig. B-2   Apeco's Model 30 electric punch.

SADDLE STITCHING · The term is derived from the method of sewing the cover and pages together. In this illustration, staples are used instead of binding thread.

POST BINDING. This method of binding employs three screw posts inserted through holes punched in the cover and pages of a publication.

SIDESTITCHING. This is a method of binding in which the cover is glued to the pages and the publication is then stapled through the side of its spine.

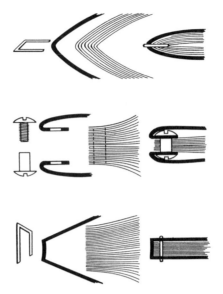

Fig. B-3   Types of mechanical binding.

saddle stitching, sidestitching, and spiral binding. In post binding, screw posts are placed in the margin of the book as illustrated in Figure B-3. This method of binding is used for publications which are subject to revision or for which it is desirable to add or remove sheets without difficulty. However, post-bound publications tend to close when used. If the reader is not required to hold the publication open, another form of binding should be selected. When post binding is used, ample space should be allowed at the binding margin. A minimum of 1 inch is recommended.

Saddle stitching (*see* Figure B-3) is a lasting method of binding short permanent publications. It should not be used for publications having more than 120 to 140 pages (60 to 70 sheets), for which this type of binding would not be durable. No less than $\frac{1}{2}$ inch should be used at the binding margin.

Sidestitching should be used for publications consisting of more than 140 pages. Publications with sidestitched binding also have a tendency to close when not held open, and a minimum binding margin of $\frac{3}{4}$ inch should be used.

Spiral binding consists of helical metal wire inserted through punched holes in the binding margin. This type of binding is used for thin publications and for those from which pages will not be removed.

Figure B-4 shows a Combo punching-binding unit. The machine can be set to punch sheets with 2 to 21 rings for booklets up to 12 inches in length at the binding margin. It accommodates 16 plastic-binding stock sizes from $\frac{3}{16}$ to 2 inches in diameter. A built-in unit is provided for binding.

Fig. B-4   General Binding Corporation's punching-binding unit.

Another automatic punch is shown in Figure B-5. A feeding hopper is adjusted to accommodate the sheet size and is then loaded with paper to be punched. A blade separates a lift of 15 to 25 sheets from the bottom of the stack, the lift is advanced, the stock is punched and ejected into a receiving tray, and the cycle is repeated. Speeds are adjustable to handle 30 to 70 lifts per minute, with an overall capability of 75,000 to 100,000 sheets per hour.

binding edge   Edge of a sheet or page that is nearest the saddle of the book. Right-hand pages are bound at the left side and left-hand pages at the right side. Ample space for binding should be allowed. If binding is such that the pages lie flat when the book is open, less binding edge is required. For small books, with a page size of 6 by 9 inches or less, an allowance of not less than $5/8$ inch should be made for pages that lie flat. The minimum binding edge for brochures, pamphlets, and booklets is 1 inch for a page size of $8\frac{1}{2}$ by 11 inches. In typing composition for printing, the edge of the left-hand page should have the same dimensions from edge to image as the right-hand page has from edge to image. Similarly, the binding margins of the two pages should have the same dimensions. If a page is printed horizontally, the margins should have the same width as on other pages. If possible, horizontal pages should be right-hand pages so that the copy may be read by turning the book clockwise.

black and white   *See* REPRODUCTION COPY; REPRODUCTION PROOF.

black art (also called **base art; basic art; key art**)   Basic art used in making process plates for illustrations of two or more colors. As the name implies, it is art that will be printed black and used in combination with color work.

black patch (also called **blackout; window**)   Black masking patch that is pasted or mortised into position in the exact size of a photograph on reproduction line copy. (A red patch serves the same purpose.) The photograph is screened and reduced if necessary, and the halftone negative is stripped into the window of the line negative, thus making a composite, or assembled, negative of line and halftone copy. If the photograph requires reduction—and it often does—the reduction must be in exact proportion to the window and the line negative left by the black patch.

black printer   Printer's term for the film (and subsequently the plate) that prints black in the color-separation process. The plate is also known as the key plate.

Fig. B-5 General Binding Corporation's automatic punch.

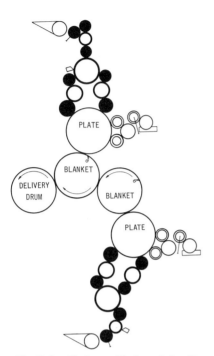

Fig. B-6   Blanket-to-blanket relationship of plates and blankets.

blackline   Black-lined copy, either text or artwork, produced by the whiteprint process. The only difference between blacklines and bluelines lies in the type of diazo-treated copy paper used.

blackout   *See* BLACK PATCH.

blanc fixe   White material used with china clay as a filler for coating and enameling book papers.

blank   Heavy paper used for advertising display purposes such as posters and window displays. Blanks are designated by ply, the ply indicating thickness.

blanket   Rubber sheet covering the cylinder of an offset press. The cylinder on which the blanket is mounted is called the blanket cylinder. The blanket receives the impression from the plate and transfers it to the paper. Since the image is right-reading on the master cylinder, the image on the blanket will be wrong-reading; thus a right-reading image is transferred to the paper.

blanket-to-blanket press (unit perfecting press)   Offset printing press in which the rolled web (paper) is fed between two blanket cylinders, each of which serves as an impression cylinder for the other. Figure B-6 illustrates the blanket-to-blanket relationship of cylinder plates and blankets. This system is employed in American Type Founders' Solna 24-inch perfector offset printing press. (*See also* PERFECTING PRESS.)

bleed   To extend to the edge or edges of a page, said of line or halftone work. The effect is produced by printing a fraction of an inch (usually $\frac{1}{8}$ to $\frac{1}{4}$ inch) of the image beyond the desired dimension and then trimming the sheet to obtain the bleed. Printers consider bleeding an additional cost factor.

blind copy   Typewritten carbon copy of a letter directed by the writer to an interested recipient without the recipient's name being listed on the original under the distribution notice. The recipient's name is listed only on the copy he receives and on the file copy.

blind embossing   Embossing without printing.

blind folio   Page number counted but not printed. It is sometimes necessary to identify a page as having an assigned number without printing the number. For example, to identify an inside title page with a printed page number is of no importance insofar as a point of reference is concerned. An inside title page therefore does not warrant this reference, and the page is counted but not printed with a page number. Pages in the body of a magazine are often counted but not numbered because an overprint of the page number on a colored bleed could not be distinguished if it were printed. However, during the manufacturing process it is imperative that individual pages be identified by number even if the number is not printed.

blind punching   In automatic linecasting control, perforating tape without producing decoded copy to be checked and edited. The copy must be proofed from the tape.

blind stamping   Pressing a design on a surface merely by using a die. Ink or other materials, such as gold leaf, that would give a more distinct image are not used.

blinding   In photomechanical plate making, a condition in which, despite a strong-looking image, a printing plate prints very weakly or not at all. Blinding may be caused by an excess of gum on the image, which therefore does not accept ink. The plate may be rubbed down with fountain solution to remove the excess gum. Some plates require going over with the developer. The manufacturer's directions should be followed in using the correct chemicals for final gumming. Blinding is also produced by glazed ink rollers or by a strong fountain solution that has worked into the ink, causing the ink to emulsify.

block diagram   Drawing in which blocks or rectangles are used to show the relationship between the components of an item or a piece of equipment. Lines and arrowheads indicate flow or sequence.

block in   To make the principal outline of an object during initial preparation by sketching blocks which are then usable as reference points.

block printing   Earliest-known form of printing, in which impressions were taken from wood. It followed the taking of rubbings. The material used in block printing was generally pearwood. The block was planed and squared to the desired page size, and the surface was rubbed with paste or sizing. The page was first written carefully on thin paper, which was made to adhere facedown on the block. The paper itself was then rubbed off, leaving the inked impression of the letters on the wood. The carver cut away the wood surrounding the characters, leaving them in relief. Actual printing was done by brushing ink on the block, laying a strip of paper on it, and then rubbing the paper with a dry brush. This method is still used in Asia today.

Origins. The Chinese consider block printing rather than the invention of movable type to be the real origin of printing. The exact date when true block printing began is not known, but scholars believe that the years 712 to 750 may be taken as approximate dates. While block printing undoubtedly originated in China, the earliest-known specimen of block printing, or of printing of any kind, is from Japan; it was produced between 764 and 770. It is of interest to note that the earliest-known work of printing and publishing was done during this period and is a most important event in the history of Japan and of the world. The empress Shōtoku, an ardent Buddhist, ordered the printing of 1 million charms, each to be enclosed in a little wooden pagoda and to be distributed among 10 Buddhist temples. The Japanese government has preserved a number of these pagodas and charms in the National Museum. According to the best information available, there are three of the original pagodas and charms in the British Museum, one in the Leipzig Museum, and at least two in the United States.

The first printed book known was produced by Chinese block printing. The book is the *Diamond Sūtra.* It was found in 1900 by a priest near the city of Tunhuang in northwestern China, where it had been preserved in a sealed cave, one of the Caves of the Thousand Buddhas. Now in the British Museum, the *Diamond Sūtra* is a landmark in cultural history. It is made up of six sheets of text, measuring about 1 foot high and 30 inches long, and a smaller sheet with an illustration. The seven sheets are pasted together to form a book roll. Toward the end of the text is a statement that it was printed on May 11, 868, by Wang Chieh, ". . . for free general distribution, in order in deep reverence to perpetuate the memory of his parents."

Linoleum-block printing. Block printing from linoleum is an old craft which is gaining in popularity among both adults and children, no doubt because of a strong desire for individual expression of creative ideas. It is one of the few forms of graphic expression in which the individual has complete control of his subject from creating the design to printing it.

A plain "battleship" linoleum block without pattern is used in block printing. Linoleum blocks are available either unmounted or mounted on plywood to make the printing block type-high. This height, 0.918 inch, is a standard dimension for the thickness of the printing block or form. Blocks with a white or gray surface are used for ease in transferring the design to the block. When the linoleum block is cold or old, it should be warmed to soften it for

MOUNTED AND UNMOUNTED LINOLEUM

CARVING THE LINOLEUM BLOCK

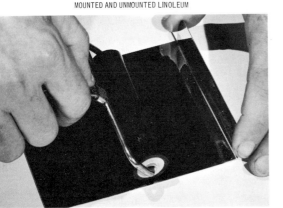

USING BRAYER AND INKING PLATE

ROLLING INK ON THE CARVED BLOCK

Fig. B-7 Instruments and techniques used in block printing. (*Courtesy of Hunt Manufacturing Co.*)

cutting. Figure B-7 shows some of the tools and techniques used in linoleum-block printing.

Other materials, including carbon paper for transferring the image, a triangle for squaring blocks, india ink, scotch tape, hard and soft pencils, paste, and art gum, are used from time to time. The printing paper should be soft and absorbent. Onionskin and newsprint are both excellent papers for proofing prints. Rice paper is ideal for finished work, although school sketching or drawing paper is suitable. Hard-surfaced, glossy, or enameled papers should not be used. For hand production of prints, small presses manufactured especially for block printing are available. Pressure is applied to the block on the paper with padding to ensure good printing. Industrial printing presses may be used for runs with relief printing plates, but the plates must have a reverse-reading image in order to produce a right-reading image. Inks for linoleum-block printing are made water-soluble for easy cleaning, as well as with an oil base. A full range of colors, including gold and silver, is available. Reducers and extenders for all conditions are also available.

Water-soluble ink is the most popular because the blocks can be cleaned easily with water. This kind of ink also blends well into light pastel colors and is excellent for school use. If a permanent color or black printing is desired, an oil-based ink is used. Oil solvents such as kerosine or benzine are employed for cleaning when oil-based inks are used. A roller called a "brayer" is used to roll the ink from an inking plate onto the printing surface. Any nonporous material such as tin may be used as an inking plate.

blocking out   Eliminating characters, portions of art, or any part of an image on reproduction copy or negatives by pasting them over, whiting them out with paint, or masking them. Blocking out can be used to great advantage in the whiteprint process.

blotting paper   Paper made especially to absorb ink or other liquids. It has a low finish and readily absorbs writing inks. Blotting papers are available in a wide range of colors and finishes and in 100- and 120-pound weights. Sheet sizes are 19 by 24 and 24 by 38 inches. (*See also* TABLE 6.)

blow up   To enlarge by photography an advertisement or pre-printed text for advertising and display purposes; also, to enlarge an illustration or a photograph for any purpose.

blowback   Act or result of making an enlarged print or copy, particularly from a microfilm such as 16-, 35-, 70-, or 105-millimeter film. The term is derived from "blow up" (to enlarge) and "back" and means reproduction back to a larger size.

blue-sensitive   Sensitive to blue and ultraviolet light, said of a plate or film which has little or no sensitivity to light of other colors.

blue streak   Streak of blue ink imposed along the margin and on the front page of some daily newspapers to indicate a specific edition when more than one daily edition is published. Ink is applied with a cylinder wheel mounted on the press. The device has its own ink supply.

blueline   Copy having blue lines with a white background. Bluelines are made from vellum, film positives, or any translucent or transparent original on which an image has been made and reproduced by the whiteprint process. Photolithographic negatives may produce what are commonly called "reverse bluelines" by utilizing the whiteprint process. Since these negatives have a translucent image and a black background, they produce a white image on a medium or dark blue background. (*See also* REVERSE BLUELINE.)

blueline print   Print in which the image is formed of blue lines. Such prints are durable and permanent, but the scale is only fair. They are made by contact with any negative on iron-sensitized paper or cloth by developing and washing. The paper has a rag content of 50 to 100 percent.

blueprint   Print in which white lines are produced on a blue background by the direct contact of pen or pencil positive originals with vellum or other translucent materials. When pencil is used, the original must be firmly defined and solidly delineated for fine reproduction. All blueprints are of contact size, as no enlargement or reduction can be obtained without a lens. Blueprint copies may be made 54 inches wide and in any length and are economical for a run of 1 to 100 copies. A portion of the original drawing can be used merely by placing the desired portion over the sensitized copy paper or other material. Blueprints are popular for production, construction, and architectural drawings. Because of their ability to stand hard usage, they are common in shops and in the field, where they may be exposed to direct sunlight. It is difficult to keep blueprints to exact scale, however, for the paper is subject to warping and shrinking because of the wet process of developing and washing. If the vellum or cloth original has been drawn with pencil, an ordinary pencil eraser will suffice to make corrections, but if ink has been used, an eradicator must be employed. (*See also* DARK-PRINT PROCESS; REPRODUCTION FLOW CHARTS.)

blueprint paper   Direct-copy–process paper manufactured with a good rag content to produce a smooth finish, wet strength, and good absorbency. To make the copy, the original or translucent master is placed in direct contact with the blueprint paper.

blueprint process   *See* DARK-PRINT PROCESS.

blurb   Copy slanted toward a sales angle, particularly copy on a book jacket. A blurb is usually written in brief paragraphs.

board   Any heavy board material, such as that used for mounting art or making displays. Also, heavier art stock may be called board, as in illustration board, canvas board, etc.

board art   Any artwork, especially original art, mounted on heavy board stock. Figure B-8 illustrates what may be done with original board art in sequence. It shows practices common to handling art for photo-offset printing, as well as some side steps that may be taken. Once an image has been produced, many processes and variations can be involved. The choice depends on what is required of the end product, the types of reproduction and printing equipment available or desired, the quality of the final publication, time limitations, and other factors.

In Figure B-8, the original board art *A* may be twice up or once and a half up in size. The art should be protected with a tissue overlay and mounted and flapped with kraft paper on rigid board stock. It should be identified with the figure number and title, the desired reduction size, and any other information consistent with art department policies and specifications. The art is photographed with a process camera, which produces the 8- by 10-inch art negative *B*. The negative is known technically as a photolithographic negative; it has a translucent image and an opaque background. From the negative is made a photoprint *C*, which may have a matte (dull) or a glossy finish. The photoprint is enlarged or reduced to match the size of the reproducible copy. The required dimensions for enlargement or reduction may be indicated on the negative by placing a strip of masking tape along the bottom (outside the crop marks) and writing the dimensions on the tape. A horizontal line, terminating at both ends in arrowheads to denote the dimension width, is drawn along the tape. The photoprint is then stripped in or pasted on the oversize basic reproduction page *D* and ruled or boxed in.

Before the art is stripped in, the basic reproduction page may be called a "skeleton," a "page frame," or a "page mask," usage varying with the organization. The figure number and such marginal information as the page content heading, running head, folio, or security classification are typed on the reproduction page. Whether it contains text or art, the page is known as "repro" or "camera-ready" copy.

The process camera is again employed, and a page negative *E* is produced from the basic reproduction page. The negative, which is reduced to page size, is a photolithographic negative having a translucent image and an opaque background. It may also be called a "base plate." The printer strips the page negative into orange masking paper containing grid lines to ensure exact positions, as in Figure B-8*F*.

The assembled masking paper and negative are now placed over a sensitive flexible printing plate, and the combination is positioned in a glass frame, where it is firmly held. A vacuum is em-

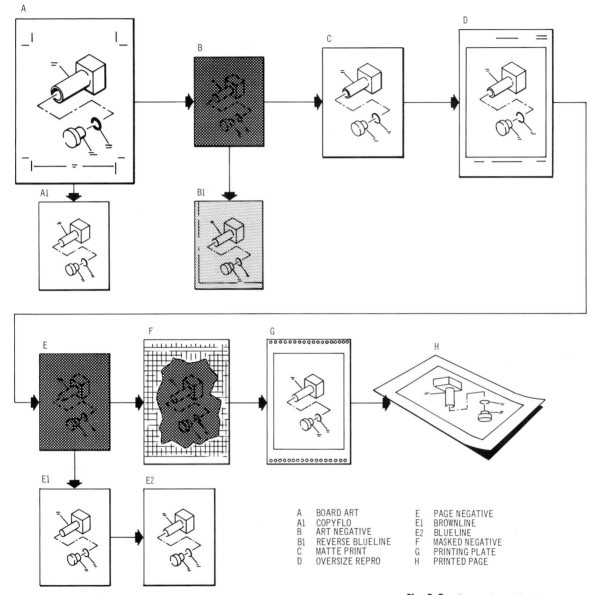

A	BOARD ART	E	PAGE NEGATIVE
A1	COPYFLO	E1	BROWNLINE
B	ART NEGATIVE	E2	BLUELINE
B1	REVERSE BLUELINE	F	MASKED NEGATIVE
C	MATTE PRINT	G	PRINTING PLATE
D	OVERSIZE REPRO	H	PRINTED PAGE

Fig. B-8 Generation of board art.

ployed to compress negative and plate within the frame. The negative and plate are subjected to strong arc lights which "burn" through the translucent image of the negative and activate the light-sensitive emulsion on the plate, leaving a latent image. The plate G is then developed by washing with a developer and water, and the page H is printed from the plate.

Many other steps may be taken with the materials produced, as indicated in Figure B-8. For example, if a piece of art similar to board art A is to be originated, the original art should not be reworked because it would then lose its identity. Instead, an enlarged matte or glossy print is reworked; when completed, it will have an identity of its own. For every piece of effective art, there should be an original piece of art with its own identity. When art must be submitted with manuscript copy for approval, the art negative B is used in making a reverse blueline $B1$ by means of a whiteprint machine. The negative is placed over the copy paper with the upper right-hand corners in register. The reverse blueline has a white image and a black or dark blue background. Since the negative measures 8 by 10 inches, the blueline will have a white binding margin on the left and a 1-inch white space at the bottom for figure number and title when $8\frac{1}{2}$- by 11-inch copy paper is used.

When an art negative is not available for the submittal of manuscript and art copy, Copyflo copies can be made and reduced to fit $8\frac{1}{2}$- by 11-inch bond paper. Copyflo is made by the xerographic process of reproduction on 35-millimeter film. The black image is suitable for reference or review copies.

Figure B-8 also illustrates a brownline $E1$ produced from the page negative E. When a government procurement agency orders technical manuals, it usually requires brownlines in addition to the reproducible copy and page negatives. Brownlines are made from sepia brownline paper of 100 percent rag content by running the negative and copy paper through the whiteprint machine. They are long-lived intermediates which may be filed as permanent copies. Bluelines, made from the translucent brownline as indicated in Figure B-8$E2$, have blue images with white backgrounds. Blueline copies are used for reference or as review copies.

body Piece of type on which a character is cast. The term also denotes a block of text copy, as well as the main part of a book or other publication exclusive of front and back matter.

body type (reading type; text type) Type of a size used for printing text material. Popular sizes range from 8 to 12 points, 9 and 10 points being quite common. (*See also* TYPE SPECIMENS.)

boiler plate Centrally prepared material of a stereotyped nature, supplied especially to small newspapers. The term "boiler plate" may also refer to artwork in common use, as well as to text copy that may require only slight alteration in context.

boldface Typeface that is heavier and darker than the body typeface, used especially for center and side headings to distinguish them from related text. The term is opposed to "lightface."

bond paper Paper used for ruling, printing, typewriting, and pen writing. Since bond paper is employed extensively for correspondence, which must be handled and filed, strength and permanence are paramount requirements. The surface characteristics of bond paper are therefore important. Three methods are used to size bond paper: engine, surface, and tub sizing. Engine sizing is accomplished by adding resin to the pulp while the pulp is in the beater. In surface sizing, the paper is sprayed with sizing solution on both sides before the web (paper) is advanced to the dryer rolls on the paper machine. Tub sizing is accomplished by immersing the paper in a solution of gelatin or starch. Better grades of paper are made with surface and tub sizing techniques.

Bond papers require an even finish, which is obtained by machine speeds that permit a "close" formation of fibers. There are two kinds of bond papers; one has a cotton or rag content, and the other is made from chemical wood pulp. All rag-content and 100 percent rag papers are sized by tub and surface processes. Practically all rag-content bonds are watermarked by the dandy roll; laid marks are obtained as desired. Rag-content bonds come in four grades, of 25, 50, 75, and 100 percent rag content, respectively. High-quality bleached wood bond paper is produced from various combinations of sulfate, sulfite, and soda pulp; all sizing is accomplished by the engine process in the beater. Most wood bonds are dried on the machine rollers. Several grades are made by each manufacturer, the better grades being watermarked. Standard weights of bond paper are 9, 13, 16, 20, and 24 pounds for 500 sheets of the basic size of 17 by 22 inches.

bond typewriter paper Boxed paper, or paper that has already been cut to the regular size of $8\frac{1}{2}$ by 11 inches or to legal sizes of $8\frac{1}{2}$ by 13 and $8\frac{1}{2}$ by 14 inches. Usually manufactured in white only, bond typewriter paper may have either a cockle or a smooth vellum finish. Standard weights are 9, 11, 13, 16, 20, and 24 pounds for 500 sheets of the basic size of 17 by 22 inches. (*See also* BOXED PAPER.)

book endpaper *See* ENDLEAF.

book face   Any typeface suitable for the text of a book. Book face is also an old term, used especially in technical publication circles, for a special kind of typeface known as IBM's Bold Face No. 1.

book-form drawing   In engineering drafting, an assemblage of drawings and related data pertaining to an item or a system under a single identifying drawing number and title. It is intended for special-purpose applications and employs combinations of printed or typewritten data and illustrations to show requirements. Book-form drawings should not be used to circumvent requirements for furnishing the individual drawings normally needed for items or for a system.

book lining   *See* ENDLEAF.

book makeup   Act of collating, arranging, and numbering pages of reproduction copy of a publication. It is the last function that prepares the publication for printing. A blank preprinted form showing individual pages may be used to assist makeup personnel and to direct the printer in the placement of each page. As many sheets of the form as are required are used to depict the pages of the complete publication. Page 1 of the body of the publication begins on a right-hand page. All matter preceding page 1 is front matter and can be laid out in reverse order from the last element to the cover page. Following are some elements which should receive consideration when organizing elements (not all the elements may be present in a given publication).

1. Front matter
   a. Front cover page
   b. Title page
   c. Copyright notice
   d. Foreword
   e. Preface
   f. Abstract
   g. Contents
   h. List of illustrations
   i. List of tables
2. Body
   a. Parts
   b. Chapters
   c. Sections
3. Back matter
   a. Exhibits.
   b. Appendixes
   c. Glossary of terms
   d. References

    e. Bibliography

    f. Alphabetical index

4. Pagination

    a. Front matter (lowercase roman numerals). Identify each element as to placement for a right- or a left-hand page.

    b. The first page of the first division of the body begins with a right-hand page and is assigned the arabic numeral 1. Succeeding pages are numbered in sequence.

    c. Consider that a part or a chapter in a particular publication may be designed to begin only on a right-hand page.

    d. Back matter is paginated either by continuing the numbering in sequence from the body (this practice is most popular) or by defining the element at the bottom of the page and beginning the first page with the arabic number 1. For example, Appendix A appears at the bottom left margin, for a right-hand page, with the numeral 1 at the right margin (for a left-hand page, Appendix A is placed at the right margin and the numeral 1 at the left margin).

5. Illustrations

    a. Define a foldout illustration by using the symbol F/O.

    b. Define a halftone page by using the symbol H/T.

    c. List the figure number of the illustration or the art file number, or both, for all illustrations.

    d. If an illustration consists of more than one page, show the figure number followed by "page 1 of 5," "page 2 of 5," etc.

6. Tables

    a. List all table numbers.

    b. Note that a particular table is a foldout by using the symbol F/O.

    c. If a table consists of more than one page, show the table number followed by "page 1 of 10," "page 2 of 10," etc.

book paper Classification of paper that includes various grades and many finishes. Among the grades are uncoated book paper, coated book paper, rotogravure paper, Bible paper, and offset paper. Book papers are used by printing establishments, publishers, manufacturers, educational institutions, and business, social, and other organizations. Most are manufactured from various combinations of sulfite, sulfate, and soda-bleached pulps. Some rag may be used. (*See also* separate articles on the various grades of paper.)

bookbinding Bookbinding as it is known today consists of a number of methods of holding pages together to form a book, booklet, magazine, or other multipage piece of visual material. Premodern bookbinding was an art invented out of the need to protect valuable manuscripts written on papyrus or parchment scrolls and lavishly decorated with designs and bookplates. The invention of the printing press gave great impetus to bookbinding. In modern hard-cover bookbinding, the binder receives two or four signatures consisting of 16 or 32 pages each, or quadruples of 16 pages each, which are bundled into convenient folded units. The signatures are arranged in page sequence. The books are then sewn by machines which pass threads through their spines. Air is driven between the pages to establish uniform thickness. After the book has been trimmed, the edges may be stained, marbled, or gilded. The back of the book is then treated with hot glue, and strong endleaf paper is affixed to hold the inside of the book and the cover together. Paste is applied to the outside of the endleaf, and the cover is encased. The book is pressed until the paste dries. It is then ready for marketing.

Figure B-9 shows a six-box inserter, stitcher, and five-knife trimmer that can produce 10,000 to 12,000 units per hour. Inserters are designed to feed signatures by a chain conveyor to a gang stitcher for saddle binding or to a delivery when inset but unstitched signatures are needed. A signal lamp, mounted above each pocket, flashes if a misfeed occurs. A book caliper, mounted between the inserters and the gang stitcher, detects the imperfect book and

Fig. B-9　Sheridan Company's Model FG 12,000-per-hour six-box inserter, stitcher, and five-knife trimmer.

Fig. B-10   Sheridan Company's four-box gatherer and stitcher.

routes it, unstitched, to the reject tray. The saddle stitcher can deliver books farmed out on a flat-belt delivery or can feed books directly to the trimmer. The trimmer accepts books from a feed-in table and trims and delivers them to a conveyor belt for delivery.

Figure B-10 is a photograph of a four-box gatherer and stitcher. Sheridan equipment is designed on the modular principle to permit connection not only to other Sheridan equipment but also to machines of other manufacturers.

The growth of industrial soft- and self-cover booklets, brochures, pamphlets, and similar matter has led to mechanical binding. Loose-leaf metal-ring binding, metal-prong binding, post binding, stapling, etc., are common in offices. Wire-spiral binding and plastic-comb binding are convenient and inexpensive methods. Since pages lie flat when the book is open, handling and reading are easy. (*See also* BINDING, MECHANICAL.)

booklet   Small book consisting of as much as, but not more than, 24 pages, yet having a sufficient number of pages not to be classified as a pamphlet. According to United States postal laws and regulations, for mailing purposes a book must have 24 pages or more (including the cover) in order to qualify for book mailing rates.

bottom out   Term used in page layout to indicate that a page of text closes near the bottom limitations of the page. Text or copy should be conveniently aligned within the prescribed vertical dimension of the page. Text should not ordinarily be set in type or typewritten as reproducible copy with the first line of a paragraph standing at the bottom of a page. It is preferable to leave the page short and begin the paragraph on the next page, for typewritten matter, or to take up the space with additional quadding or by adding space, as is done with proportional-spacing machines. Two lines of a paragraph may appear at the bottom of a page if the carry-over lines on the next page number two or more. A single word (orphan) or part of a sentence (widow) should never stand alone at the top of a page or column. The last word of a column or page should not be hyphenated, and a page should not end with a reference to a following list; instead, one or more items of the list should be placed at the bottom of the page. Care should be used to have no more than three broken words, requiring hyphens, at the right-hand margin of justified copy.

bounce   Effect of "bouncing" characters, produced by type, usually display type, set with a photographic typesetter.

bourgeois   Old type size. The nearest equivalent in the point system is 9 point.

Bourges   Trade name of the Bourges Color Corporation for a line of masking and stripping film and acetate sheets in 12 basic printing-ink colors that are compatible with the standard colors established by the printing industry. Each color covers tone values of 10, 30, 50, 70, and 100 percent. Color coatings are removed for highlights and clear areas by using a plastic stylus or a liquid color remover. Deeper tones and modeling can be added with Colotone liquid colors and modeling pencils.

The Bourges adhesive color sheets can be placed over pencil or pastel sketches for layouts and dummies and used for cutouts, overlapping, package design, and line separation color work. The sheets are cut out and affixed to dimensionally stable clear plastic. The 50, 70, and 100 percent tone values are recommended for line copy.

The Bourges overlay sheets, which have a workable coating but are not backed with adhesive, are designed with a special acetate that retains colors in separate layers to enable the artist to visualize, create, change, correct, or reproduce artwork. For color-separation work, the 50, 70, or 100 percent overlays, using the filters and films shown in Table B-1, are recommended. Only the 70 and 100 percent values should be used with line art containing fine detail. To obtain maximum line contrast, the overlay should be backed with brilliant white paper. For flat areas of lighter values, mechanical tints are used in combination with the line negative to reduce color.

Bourges overlays are continuous-tone sheets. All percentage values, including modeling and tonal gradations, can be produced as halftone copy with the filters and films shown in Table B-1. Any ruled or glass screen or gray film contact screen, of whatever ruling (60, 110, 150, etc.) the reproduction process requires, can be used. Magenta screens are not recommended because their color interferes with the color being reproduced. The screen or copy should be angled for the different colors: red, 75 degrees; yellow, 90 degrees; blue, 105 degrees; and black, 45 degrees.

T A B L E B-1 **Bourges Color-reproduction Chart for Eastman Kodak Wratten Filters**

Bourges color	Filter number	Color of filter	Film
Yellows: Process yellow, poster yellow, green, olive, emerald, ocher, lime, chartreuse	30	Rose bengal	High-contrast ortho
Reds: Process red, poster red, true red, orange, brown, terra-cotta, mauve, cerise	11	Light green	High-contrast ortho
Blues: Process blue, poster blue, purple, Air Force blue, teal blue	12, 16, or A	Yellow Red	High-contrast ortho Panchromatic film

For a "dropout," it is recommended that two negatives be used for halftone reproduction: (1) a halftone negative holding the full tonal range and (2) a highlight mask for the dropout. The mask is made immediately after the halftone, from the same copy, with the filters in position but without the halftone screen and with the lens wide open and a minimum exposure. Developing is stopped when tones begin to appear in areas other than the highlight. This line mask is then taped in register over the halftone and printed through both negatives. To duplicate the visual effect of the art, the colors are printed in the same sequence, usually yellow, red, and blue. Depending on the copy and the printing equipment used, the black may be printed first or last.

Bourges coated Solotone gray and white overlays are used to accent portions of an unretouched or retouched photograph while subduing other portions in a "phantom" effect. The coatings have values of 10, 30, 50, 70, and 100 percent. A selected overlay is placed over the photograph and attached to the top with masking tape. The coating on the overlay that covers the portion of the photograph to be accented is removed by scraping it with a stylus. (The coating on large areas is removed with a special color remover.) The removal of the coating exposes the accented image area, while the remainder appears in phantom.

An uncoated overlay can be used over artwork such as pencil, charcoal, and wash and watercolor drawings to add a degree of tone over the entire drawing. The desired tone value is merely placed over the drawing and the overlay reproduced as part of the original art.

Bourges adhesive-backed colors, Cutocolor and precut Cutotape, are used in audio-visual presentations, advertising art, industrial charts and systems, engineering design and graphics, technical illustrating, television-film artwork, and the like.

boxed paper (typewriter paper) Paper that has been cut and boxed (or wrapped), such as bond, onionskin, manifold, mimeograph, and duplicating paper. Cutting sizes are the letterhead size of $8\frac{1}{2}$ by 11 inches and the legal sizes of $8\frac{1}{2}$ by 13 and $8\frac{1}{2}$ by 14 inches. These are the utility sizes for offices, homes, libraries, schools, and almost any other place where a typewriter or an office duplicator machine is used. The government size for boxed paper is 8 by $10\frac{1}{2}$ inches.

SPECIAL TOOLS, FIXTURES, AND EQUIPMENT

A

PART NUMBER	MANUFACTURER'S DESIGNATION	APPLICATION
34321	Inner Section Tube Flattener	To flatten inner tubes of core assembly.
78909	Tube Tool Holder	To hold tube puller and bumping tips.
35678	Tube Puller	To remove broken or damaged tubes.
78645	Tube Tool Handle	Used with tube puller and tool holder to remove broken and damaged tubes.

B

Part Number	Manufacturer's Designation	Application
34321	Inner Section Tube Flattener	To flatten inner tubes of core assembly.
78909	Tube Tool Holder	To hold tube puller and bumping tips.
35678	Tube Puller	To remove broken or damaged tubes.
78645	Tube Tool Handle	Used with tube puller and tool holder to remove broken and damaged tubes

Table 1. Special Tools, Fixtures, and Equipment

Fig. B-11 Application of boxheads in technical publications.

boxhead Column heading in a table. All matter appearing directly under each heading is pertinent to that heading. If the table is ruled, a horizontal rule is drawn under the headings. Figure B-11 shows two forms of tables with boxheads for use in technical publications. The table in view *B* is generally preferred to that in view *A* for this usage.

boxing Enclosing an illustration or other material in a drawn or printed frame. When lines are drawn with ink, the proper weight must be used if the art is to be reduced.

B/P Symbol for blueprint.

brace Symbol or sign used to enclose, connect, and show relationships of text or illustrative matter. In technical illustrating, a brace encloses and identifies subassembly details of the main illustration of an exploded view. The brace indicates origin with respect to the main illustration. The word "bracket" is often used erroneously when "brace" is correct. (*See* Figure B-12.)

brayer Hand roller used to distribute ink over a printing plate. (*See* BLOCK PRINTING.)

break line Discrete line used on an orthographic engineering drawing. Long break lines are designated as "thin" lines; short breaks are indicated by solid freehand lines and are designated as "thick" lines. For long breaks, full ruled lines with freehand zigzags are used. Shafts, rods, tubes, etc., which have a portion of their length broken out are drawn as illustrated in LINE CONVENTIONS: ENGINEERING DRAWINGS.

brevier Old type size. The nearest equivalent in the point system is 8 point.

briefing chart (flip chart) Visual aid that graphically presents a story to an audience. The speaker or briefer uses the chart to monitor, illustrate, and emphasize pertinent points of his subject. Briefing charts are prepared with black or colored lettering and lines, as well as with pastels, and generally on a white stock sufficiently stable and rigid for mounting or standing. Sizes vary from the desk size of $10\frac{1}{4}$ by 13 inches for an audience not exceeding 10 persons to 30 by 40 inches for audiences from 10 to 40 persons and 42 by 52 inches for audiences from 40 to 70 persons. Copy on briefing charts should be confined to short descriptive phrases. Briefing-chart books may be prepared from the charts when a wider dissemination or a

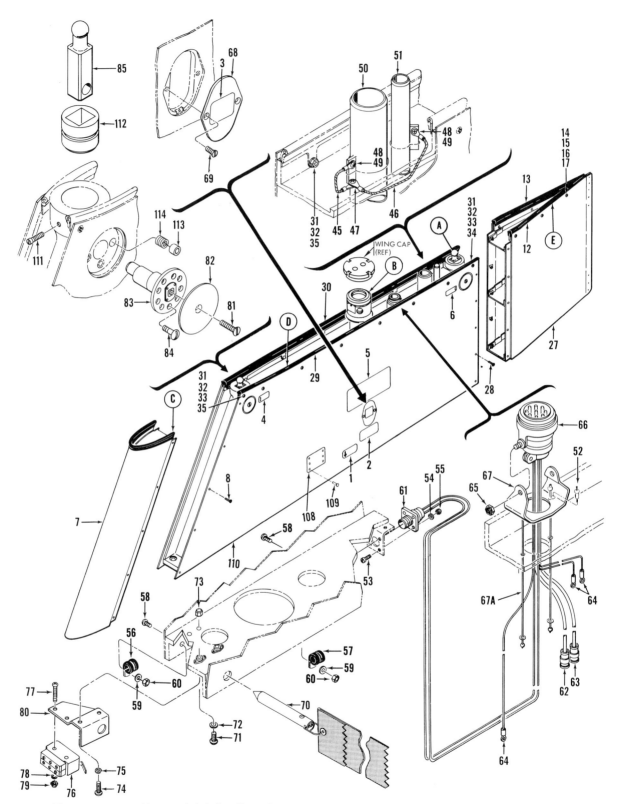

Fig. B-12 Using braces with an exploded-view illustration.

permanent record of the material is desired. The text on each chart should cover one major topic and not be congested.

brilliant   Old type size of $3\frac{1}{2}$ points. It is seldom used.

broad fold   Having the grain running along the short dimension, said of paper. It is the opposite of "long fold."

broadside   Advertising sheet, usually a self-mailer. The word is probably derived from the old practice of printing on only one side of a sheet and then folding as desired. Today a broadside may be printed on both sides or on portions of a single fold.

broadside page (horizontal page; landscape page)   Page that must be turned 90 degrees clockwise for right reading.

broken images   Unfavorable condition found in photomechanical plate making in which the image is absent in certain areas and fingerprints have developed on the plate. There are several causes for broken images. Tape or opaquing solution may be covering a portion of the image on the stripped flat, or tape or opaquing solution may have come off on the underside of the vacuum-frame glass. The plate may be underexposed, the image disappearing after a few revolutions of the press. Broken images may also be due to moisture on the plate prior to exposure. Plates should be handled by the edges only and fingerprinting avoided. They should be stored in lighttight containers away from moisture.

bromide print (silver print)   Print made from copy or photographic paper that has been treated with silver halides. The bromine halogen is compounded with silver halides to form the light-sensitive emulsion.

bronzing   Printing with a sizing ink and applying bronze powder that adheres to the paper and gives the effect of printing with a bronze metallic ink. The sizing in the bronzing ink has adhesive characteristics.

brownline print   Brownline image on a white background, sometimes called a silver print. It can be used as an intermediate or as a finished print. If printed on thin paper or transparentized film or paper, it can be used as both a reproducible and a finished print. If printed on thick paper, it is used for reference or display only. The process is wet, but a darkroom is not required. The print can be 54 inches wide by any length. Exposure is made by contact with any translucent original. (*See also* BROWNPRINT.)

brownprint   Whiteline image produced on a brown background. The brownprint process is a reversal process in which a negative is produced from a positive original. Prints so produced are usually intermediates. Brownlines and brownprints are made by the same process. Quite often, brownprints are made wrong-reading. This technique produces a sharper image than a right-reading image because of the emulsion-to-emulsion contact when printed. A brownprint is recommended for use as an intermediate in making positive blueline, brownline, wash-off, or photographic prints. The process is wet, but a darkroom is not required. The print can be 54 inches wide by any length. Exposure is made by contact with any translucent original. Brownprints and brownlines are made on the same material. The brownprint is a negative made from a positive; the brownline, a positive made from a negative.

brush pens   *See* PENS, TECHNICAL.

brushes, art   Brushes used for fine artwork as well as for such applications as show cards are divided by source into two categories, those manufactured from the red sable and the less costly grades whose hair is taken from squirrels, goats, fitches, other fur-bearing animals, and camels. The finest hair used commercially for brushes is taken from the thick center section of a sable's abdomen. The hair must be firmly rooted in the ferrule of the brush to a sizable depth for security and must have the maximum amount of snap to spring it back to normal shape. Moreover, the hair must have fine pointing qualities. Quality brushes are also distinguished by their seamless nickel or copper ferrules. Stroke brushes (brushes with square ends used for lettering or filling in solid areas) are of high quality when the hairs cling together and have a sharp, clear-cut definition at the brush edge. Sable or other brush hair that is set too shallowly in the ferrule has a tendency to pull out. Inferior brushes, such as those containing a mixture of dyed foreign soft hair with pure red sable, may be detected by an awkward thickness at the base of the brush at the ferrule, little or no ability to spring back to the original shape, and a tendency to bulk at the working end.

In the manufacturing process, art brushes must be cemented, oven-baked, crimped, and pressed. Not all fine brushes are made of red sable. Application and use may require other brushes. For example, white and black boar hairs, selected from spine bristles having tone and fiber, make excellent oil brushes. Each bristle has a natural curve and, in the manufacturing process, is "toed in," or interlocked, to produce a brush with a stroke that can be controlled. Brush size must be left to the discretion of the user

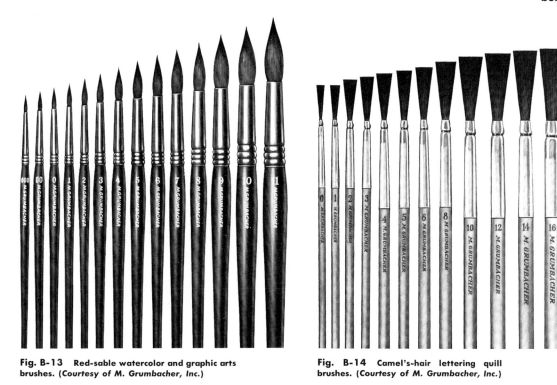

Fig. B-13   Red-sable watercolor and graphic arts brushes. (Courtesy of M. Grumbacher, Inc.)

Fig. B-14   Camel's-hair lettering quill brushes. (Courtesy of M. Grumbacher, Inc.)

because the choice of a given size depends on skill, the type of painting or lettering undertaken, the viscosity of the paint used, and, sometimes, the surface of the material to which the paint is applied. (*See* Figures B-13 and B-14.)

bubble   In technical illustrating, a circle enclosing a detailed drawing on a piece of art or on a second sheet. The drawing is drawn separately from the main illustration from which it originates (*see* Figure B-15.) The term "bubble" also refers to the formation of air beneath loosely mounted copy. This defect may be corrected by pricking the bubble with a pin.

buckram   Coarse cloth of linen, hemp, or, particularly, cotton, used in bookbinding as the exterior surface of a hard-cover book.

bug   Colloquialism for a letter scriber such as the Leroy or Wrico scribers. The term is also used colloquially to mean the union label of the printing industry, as well as a logotype of any kind.

bulk   Thickness of paper; also, the thickness of the total number of pages in a publication.

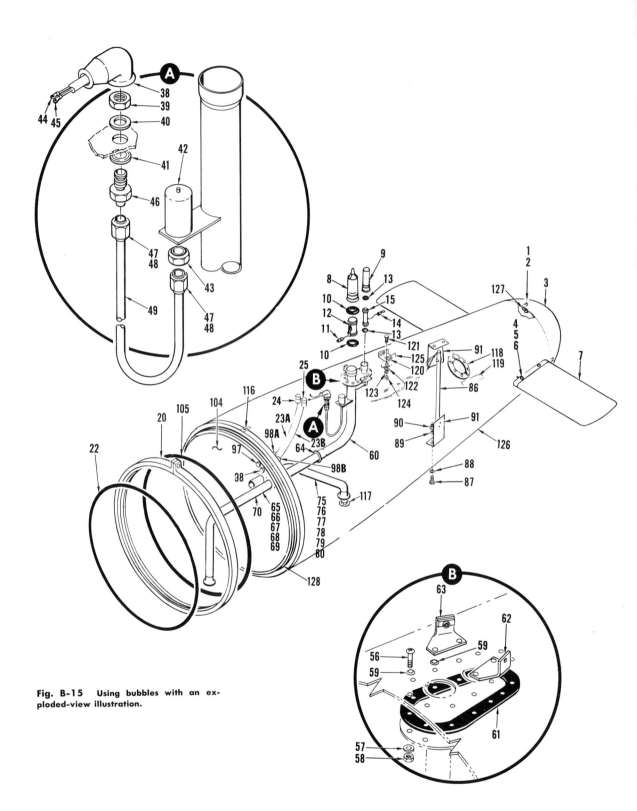

Fig. B-15 Using bubbles with an exploded-view illustration.

bullet Symbol •, used to preface listed items or a phrase, add emphasis, and generally embellish copy. It is sometimes called a "meatball." An example of the use of bullets follows:

- Quality control
- Reliability assurance
- Maintenance procedures

bundle Two reams of paper, or 1,000 sheets.

bundling Tying signatures of a book together during the binding process.

burnish To secure paste-up or mortised copy to the basic reproduction page or to material prepared for printing. A smooth burnishing bone, available in art and stationery stores, is most suitable. The copy is secured in place by heat from friction and pressure. A piece of clean paper or a tissue overlay should be placed over the copy while it is being burnished. However, if the table surface is clean, the copy may be turned over and burnished.

burnout In the whiteprint process or any other process in which light penetrates the original copy during exposure, the act or result of placing an opaque material, usually a sheet of paper, over the original copy to preserve space where new copy is to be added. After the first exposure, the opaque material is removed and the new copy is placed in position over the burned-out area, exposed, and developed.

burnout density Density remaining and read on a diazo material after exposure to sufficient actinic light to decompose the diazo salts and achievement of full development. The term is analogous to "fog" in photographic terminology.

burr Metal that protrudes above the printing surface when a routing machine has been used on a printing plate.

C

calculus symbols *See* TABLE 12.

calendered finish Degree of smoothness imparted to paper as a result of running it through the calenders of a papermaking machine. Smoothness varies with the number of times the paper is calendered.

California job case *See* CASE.

caliper In paper, a measurement of thickness expressed in thousandths of an inch; also, the instrument that measures the thickness.

call out In technical illustrating, to call attention to a part or item in an illustration by indexing it, i.e., by assigning it a number in the illustration (*see* Figure C-1). A lead line points, or "leads," to the part or item. The assigned number is found in an accompanying legend or parts list where other information concerning the particular part or item may be obtained. When an exploded view with callouts is keyed to a parts list, it is called an illustrated parts list, an illustrated parts breakdown, or a provisioning parts breakdown. To call out means also to refer to or discuss a thing in text.

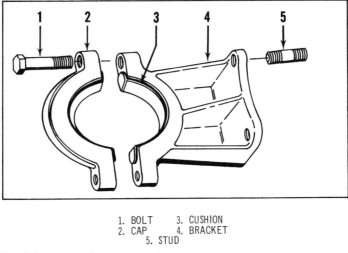

1. BOLT   3. CUSHION
2. CAP   4. BRACKET
       5. STUD

Fig. C-1   Using callouts on artwork.

calligraphy Beautiful handwriting or fine penmanship; in general, the art of writing or transcribing beautifully.

camera, horizontal Camera constructed to photograph copy or objects in the horizontal plane. The copy must be mounted vertically while the lens points horizontally.

camera, microfilm Camera designed to reproduce microfilm images of documents, newspapers, books, magazines, engineering drawings, reports, and any other information capable of being photographed. It is the microfilm camera that first photographs the document from which a microform is produced. "Microform" is a generic term for a reduced image made on film in sizes ranging from 16, 35, and 70 millimeters to 105 millimeters for roll microfilm or as a film unit cut and mounted for insertion in an aperture card. In addition, microfiches containing multiple images on a single microform are produced in microform sizes of 3 by 5, 4 by 6, and 5 by 8 inches. Related equipment for processing and handling microforms includes microfilm duplicators, readers, printers, reader-printers, processors, and retrieval systems.

The 3M Company's Model Filmsort 1000d microfilm processor-camera at one time converts as many as four $8\frac{1}{2}$- by 11-inch sheets or one 18- by 24-inch sheet to a 35-millimeter processed film mounted on a standard aperture tabulating card. The contents of the aperture card (and microfilm) are identified on the card with typed information as well as with punched holes. Thus the card can be retrieved by hand or by an automatic card sorter.

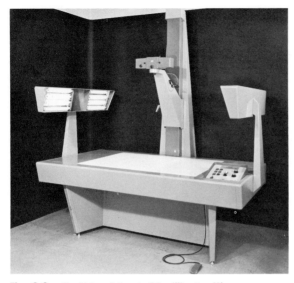

Fig. C-2   Keuffel and Esser's 35-millimeter Micromaster process camera.

Fig. C-3   Data Reproduction System's Model DRS8514 portable microfilm camera.

Figure C-2 illustrates the Micromaster 35-millimeter planetary camera, which has an automatic exposure control. The control is preset for each change of camera copy. Illumination from flourescent lamps remains constant with the exposure, which is instant and automatic. Actual exposure, however, is controlled by varying the shutter speed. The film size is 35 millimeters, unperforated, in 100-foot lengths. Frame size is adjustable from $1\frac{1}{2}$ by $1\frac{3}{4}$ inches to $1\frac{1}{4}$ by $\frac{3}{4}$ inches. The maximum copy size is $37\frac{1}{2}$ by $52\frac{1}{2}$ inches. An audible film-footage indicator gives a caution signal when 3 feet of film remain in the camera, and visual signals indicate shutter opening and film transport. Film advance is continuously variable from 2 inches to $\frac{1}{2}$ inch (the aperture size changes automatically with the film pulldown).

Figure C-3 shows a portable microfilm camera with an open book exposed beneath it. The unit, which is no larger than a typewriter, occupies an area of less than 17 by 24 inches and weighs 15 pounds. Microfilming of each document is controlled automatically with daylight loading of a 100-foot roll of 35-millimeter microfilm. Documents, bound pages, and ledgers up to $8\frac{1}{2}$ by 14 inches in size are microfilmed at the rate of 40 pages per minute. An exposure switch automatically adjusts light intensity, trips the shutter, and advances film for the next shot. A mechanical counter shows the number of exposures made, and a film-supply indicator shows the amount of unused film on the supply spool.

camera, Polaroid   *See* POLAROID MP-3 INDUSTRIAL-VIEW LAND CAMERA.

camera, process Photolithographic camera especially designed for process work, that is, for copying, making halftones, color separation, and the like. While some cameras are comparatively large, ruggedly constructed, and mounted to minimize vibration, other models are designed to supplement small printing departments by extending the application and utility of small offset duplicators. Large process cameras are mounted with their rear cases in darkrooms.

Photolithographic negatives are produced from which printing plates are made by offset printing. The image is "burned" through the translucent image area of the negative into the printing plate. The latent image on the plate is then developed and the plate mounted on the press for printing. A single page may be mounted in the copyboard, or, with cameras capable of handling large copyboards, pages may be photographed simultaneously in "groups" of 4, 8, 16, 32, and 64. The number of pages depends on the copyboard size and the capability of the printing press. Multiple-page photography is referred to as "gang shooting," and the original copy placed on or in the copyboard is called a "flat."

The Robertson Sprite horizontal process camera and the Meteorite planetary process camera (Figure C-4) are moderately small self-contained units. Both cameras are designed for the office, reproduc-

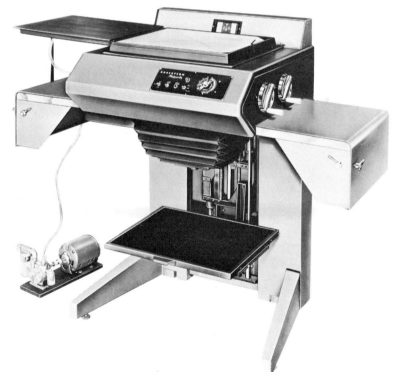

Fig. C-4 **Robertson Meteorite process camera.**

tion department, or shop. The film holder in the Sprite accommodates 14- by 17-inch film with a 15- by 18-inch contact screen. Enlargement is 200 percent of copy size and reduction 50 percent. The maximum copyboard size is 19 by 23 inches. The Meteorite has a film holder that accommodates 14- by 17-inch or 12- by 18-inch film with a contact screen measuring 15 by 18 inches. Enlargement is 300 percent of copy size and reduction 33⅓ percent. The maximum copyboard size is 18 by 23 inches.

The Model 320 process camera (Figure C-5) is adaptable for use by the majority of reproduction departments, commercial photographers, engineering departments, and photostat and blueprint concerns, and it may be used as a second camera by lithographers, photoengravers, silk-screen processors, and gravure houses. The copyboard and front case are mounted on a steel tube with guide rails. The 21- by 25-inch glass-covered copyboard accommodates opaque copy up to 1 inch thick. The copyboard rotates and locks in a horizontal position for easy loading. The vacuum film holder consists of a perforated vacuum plate mounted in a swinging door. The plate

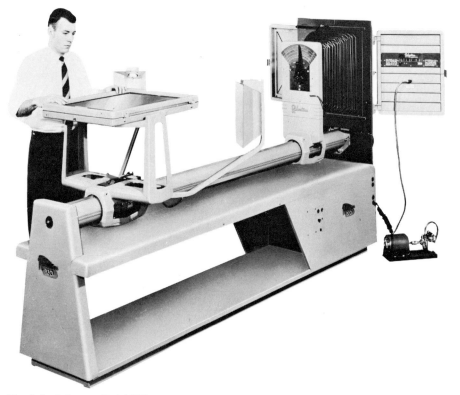

Fig. C-5   Robertson Model 320 process camera.

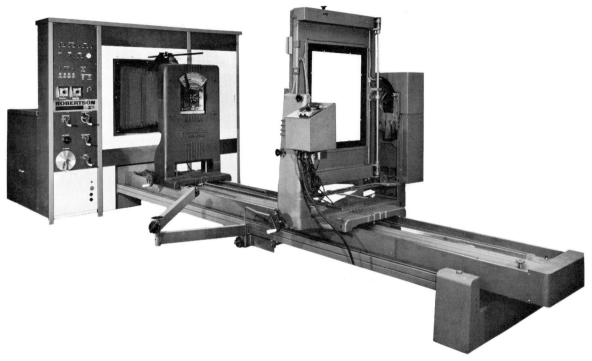

Fig. C-6 Robertson AC process camera.

is marked and zoned in the standard film and contact-screen sizes from 4 by 5 inches to 16 by 20 inches.

The Robertson Model 400 process camera is popular with small offset newspapers. The camera has a 19- by 23-inch film holder and a 30- by 40-inch glass-covered copyboard. Model 400R, a modification of the 400, permits the production of both normal and right-reading (laterally reversed) negatives from which most relief plates can be made directly.

It is claimed that 98 percent of darkroom operations are eliminated by the Robertson AC camera (Figure C-6). Such cycles as opening the vacuum film door, setting the vacuum zone, selecting the film size, loading the film, positioning the contact or glass screen, closing the door, and removing the exposed film are eliminated. Copy is loaded and unloaded while the darkroom operating cycle proceeds automatically. The camera handles standard cut sheet film or other sensitized materials in sizes from 4 by 5 inches to 20 by 24 inches. The copyboard is glass-covered, 30 by 40 inches in size, and of the tilting-rotating type.

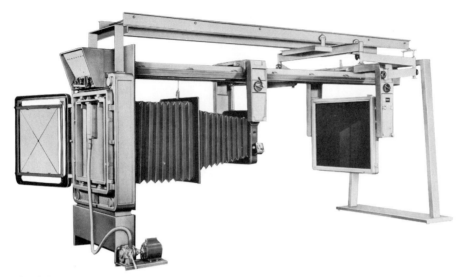

Fig. C-7   Robertson Jupiter process camera.

The Jupiter process camera (Figure C-7) is an overhead darkroom camera. The capacity of the vacuum film holder is 4 by 5 inches to 31 by 31 inches. The usable area of the copyboard is 44 by 34 inches; loading is horizontal.

Models SST-1418 and SST-2024 (Figure C-8) are nuArc Supersonic process cameras with film capacities of 14 by 18 inches and 20 by 24 inches respectively. The two models are similar in operation and construction. The copyboard has a spring latch and a copy platen of the pressure type with a plate-glass cover. The platen accommodates copy material ranging from thin typewritten pages

Fig. C-8   nuArc's Model SST-2024 process camera.

to paste-ups on thick board stock. To move the copyboard in a horizontal loading position, it is swung to a resting position on a stop plate. A locking pin then engages and locks the copyboard, and the glass frame rises and locks in position. The platen is rectangularly zoned for centering copy material on the copyboard. A quartz iodine cycle lighting system is used to illuminate the copyboard.

The operation of the lens shutter is solenoidal. A manual setting arm on the lens board is used to control the diaphragm opening by reference to a lens-diaphragm chart. Copy is scaled by direct percentage focusing. For example, if a line on the original measures 10 inches and is to be reduced to 5 inches, the negative is reduced to 50 percent of the size of the original.

When the master switch on the control panel of the exposure console is turned to the ON position, power is provided for all accessories. Two cranks on the control panel are moved to obtain the correct percentage of reduction or enlargement of the copy material. One crank operates the lens board and the other the copyboard. Corresponding tape viewers display the desired percentages, which are automatically focused.

When a toggle switch on the control panel is turned to FOCUS, the copy lights turn on and the lens shutter opens. Film size is determined by viewing the scale on the ground glass. The film is loaded on the back film holder (with a screen for continuous-tone copy) and is held in position by a vacuum that draws the film and screen tight to the film back.

Exposure time is based on the speed of the film, the intensity and distance of the light, the distance from the copyboard to the lens, and the distance from the lens to the film. All these factors, with the exception of film speed, have been compensated for in nuArc cameras with the lens-diaphragm and percentage setting systems. The exposure timer is numbered in seconds and has two hands, one green and one red. A black dial is turned to set the timer to the desired exposure time. Turning the dial moves both green and red hands from an exposure to a new setting. The red hand moves toward zero when the exposure button is pressed, while the green hand remains stationary for another exposure at the same setting. After exposure, the red hand on the timer returns to its position under the green hand, the lens shutter closes, and the copy lights turn off at the instant the exposure is completed.

The Lanston MH 40- by 48-inch overhead camera has a 60- by 80-inch transsuction copyboard. It is designed for airplane-template makers, cartographers, surveyors, and industrial engineers who require either small- or large-scale reproductions of such items as maps, charts, and printed circuitry. Cameras of this type are also produced in sizes of 24 by 24, 32 by 32, 40 by 40, 48 by 48, and 60 by 60 inches. Specifications for the MH 40- by 48-inch camera are: lens board, standard; wooden copyboard, 42 by 72 inches; tilting copyboard, 40 by 50 inches; diffuser for tilting copyboard; trans-suction copyboard, 40 by 60 inches or 60 by 80 inches; universal vacuum copyboard, 60 by 60 inches or 60 by 120 inches; vacuum back, 40 by 48 inches; ground glass, 40 by 48 inches; dry plates, 4 by 5 inches to 40 by 48 inches; film size, 4 by 5 inches to 40 by 48 inches; shutter, electric solenoid; overall height, 9 feet 6 inches; minimum darkroom-wall opening, 12 by 20 feet; and standard lens recommended, Goerz 42-inch Red Dot. The approximate gross weight is 6,930 pounds.

camera, process: paper plates   Several models of process cameras that produce paper plates are sold under the trade name Platemaster (*see* Figure C-9). They employ the silver-emulsion process, and plates are made without retouching for runs of as many as 10,000 copies or more, the number depending on the model. The plates are produced from a continuous roll at the rate of two per minute. Each model is fully automatic and is monitored through a control unit which contains an exposure button, a camera-cycle light, a camera on-off switch, a splice-indicator switch, a multiple-exposure switch, a plate counter, an exposure timer, and a plate-length selector. A microfilm enlarger is available as an attachment. Models are available to handle 16-millimeter roll film, 35-millimeter

Fig. C-9 Itek Business Products' Platemaster process camera.

Fig. C-10   Friden's Model S-R Compos-O-Line sequential-card camera.

roll film, roll film and aperture cards, and acetate jacketed and roll film. The enlarger includes (1) a special lens plate with solenoid and shutter and mirror assembly; (2) an image identification and positioning screen; and (3), as an addition to the control panel of the enlarger, an on-off switch and a rheostat for varying the intensity of the projection illumination. A repeat counter control that regulates the automatic production of as many as 80 repeat plates is available. A dial indicates the number of plates that have been made at a given time. Operational data and characteristics of the various models are shown in the accompanying table.

	Model 10.15RD	Model 11.17RD	Model 18.24R
Focusing scale, percent	50–110	50–110	50–110
Production rate, per min.	0–2	0–2	0–2
Plate size, in.	10 by 20	11 by 20	18 by 24
Minimum plate length, in.	8	10	
Maximum image area, in.	10 by 14	11 by 17	18 by 24
Maximum size of original, in.	20 by 28	22 by 34	36 by 48

camera, sequential-card Camera designed to reproduce listings such as telephone directories, catalogs, price lists, parts lists, and any other extensive lists that are ultimately referred to in readable form. Individually selected listings may be made by sorting cards that contain the listed items in image form. The listed item or image is photographed and, in final form, appears as printed matter in a publication. Most listings are repetitive and must be kept up to date. Sequential-card composition employs the mechanics of a printing device as the basis for composition and a card as a substitute for a slug of type. Each card represents an item on the final printed document. The file of cards is run through a sequential-card camera, which automatically photographs the desired information on a roll of film (*see* Figure C-10). After normal processing, the film is used to produce plates by offset printing. A system of this kind employs the following operating principles:

1. Basic source data are written, typed, or printed automatically in predetermined positions on the desired types of cards.

2. The completed cards are manually or mechanically arranged in the desired sequence.

3. The arranged deck of cards is placed in a device which subdivides it into page- or galley-length groups.

4. The cards are fed into the Compos-O-Line camera, where the data are photographically transferred to a roll of film or photographic paper.

5. The exposed film is developed and dried to produce continuous negatives.

6. The negatives are cut and stripped into page format according to job requirements.

7. The finished negatives are processed to produce printing plates for offset reproduction.

The Compos-O-Line subdivides cards into page or galley groups at a rate of as many as 18,000 cards per hour and photographs as many as 7,200 cards per hour. The camera can reduce images to one-half or enlarge them to twice the original type size. Both single-line and multiple-line composition are possible. The Model S-R Compos-O-Line camera can process any type of input card within a minimum range of 3 by 5 inches and a maximum range of 5 by 9 inches. A larger model can process cards as wide as 12 inches. Standard office file cards in sizes of 3 by 5 inches or 5 by 8 inches can be photographically processed. Standard-size tabulating cards ($3\frac{1}{4}$ by $7\frac{3}{8}$ inches) are compatible with the camera; aperture cards may also be used. These cards are die-cut to permit the mounting of microfilm images containing a page of text, engineering drawings, or other illustrative matter. Microfilm images may be enlarged and reproduced.

camera, vertical   Process or other camera placed in a position that permits photographing copy or objects in the vertical plane only. The copy must be mounted or lie flat on a horizontal surface.

camera, xerographic process   The xerographic process camera is unique because it uses electrostatic forces for reproduction rather than the conventional film-to-negative-to-plate method. Not only are different process steps required for making the printing plate, but a thin selenium-coated photoconductive plate is substituted for film. The Xerox Standard Equipment process camera (Figure C-11) will enlarge, reduce, or copy from the original in the same size on ordinary paper or on paper or metal offset duplicating masters. While the preparation of paper and metal offset duplicating masters is the most popular use, the camera will prepare transparencies, microfilm enlargements, and chemical-resist images. The xerographic process camera was originally developed to meet the demand for reducing engineering drawings from a 17- by 22-inch copyboard to an $8\frac{1}{2}$- by 13-inch xerographic plate. This camera is suitable as an adjunct to an offset duplicating department rather than for use as a rapid office copying machine. The latter service has been assumed by the Xerox 914, 813, and 2400 copiers. (*See* COPYING MACHINES.)

There are five reproduction steps in using the camera:

1. A photoconductive plate is electrically charged in the charging chamber of a processor.

2. After being charged, the plate is placed in the camera and the material to be copied is exposed directly to the charged plate.

3. The plate is then put in a tray assembly of the processor, and the latent image is developed.

4. After development, the image is transferred electrostatically from the plate to ordinary paper, vellum, or paper or metal offset duplicating plates.

5. The paper, vellum, or offset plate is then placed in a heat fuser and "baked," or fused, to make the image permanent.

(*See also* XEROGRAPHY.)

camera-ready copy   *See* REPRODUCTION COPY.

canvas board   Board or canvas panel manufactured especially for oil painting. A 35-ply board has the desired surface characteristics and construction. This board is available in sizes from 8 by 10 inches to 25 by 30 inches.

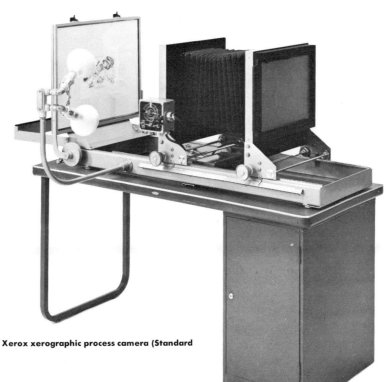

Fig. C-11   Xerox xerographic process camera (Standard Equipment).

cape   Complete set of engineering or other drawings for a piece of equipment or an installation.

caps   Common abbreviation for capitals.

caption   In general, any heading or title; more precisely, a descriptive title for an illustration or a table.

carbon paper   Paper used mainly to make duplicate typewritten copies. The name is derived from the carbon deposited on the paper, which is transferred to copies by percussion. A recent development is fluid-ink paper, from which ink is transferred instead of carbon. Paper used as typewriter carbons must be of good quality to withstand blows from keys. Typewriter carbon papers may have cut corners and an extended edge at the top for pulling them free from the copies. Standard typewriter carbon and fluid-ink papers are $8\frac{1}{2}$ by 11, $8\frac{1}{2}$ by 13, and $8\frac{1}{2}$ by 14 inches in size; they are sold in boxes of 100 sheets with 25 sheets to each folder. Colors are black, purple, red, blue, brown, and green.

carbro   Process of making color prints by using the negative of each of the printing colors, produced photographically, and developed with sensitized gelatin. The blue-filtered negative is printed on a paper backing with a light-sensitive emulsion that becomes a bromide print. The bromide print is then placed in contact with sensitized gelatin that has a tissue backing. A yellow pigment is contained in the gelatin, and a yellow image is produced after processing. The gelatin is transferred to a support and the tissue backing removed. The red and blue images, produced in the same way, are transferred in turn and the backing removed to register over the yellow image, thus completing the print.

card-to-card printout   Producing a duplicate microfilm aperture card from an original microfilm aperture card by using a microfilm duplicator. An up-to-date master file of cards can be maintained by providing duplicate copies on request.

card-to-paper printout   Producing paper copies of a microfilmed image from the aperture card on which the film is mounted. Depending on the copying machine, xerographic, diffusion-transfer-reversal, electrolytic, diazo, or stabilization processes of reproduction may be used. Copies can be made on plain bond paper, translucent stock for whiteprint reproduction, offset paper plates, or tracing paper suitable for reworking prints. Sizes vary with the machine.

cardboard Thick display material, not to be confused with the ordinary gray paperboard commonly known as cardboard. Cardboard is thick paper manufactured in a variety of colors and used for display, poster, and other advertising purposes. Finishes accept images applied by any medium, including printer's ink, crayon, watercolors, and pastels. The standard size is 28 by 24 inches in 8-ply and in 14-ply, the most popular thickness. A special board for illustrations may be obtained in either hot-pressed or cold-pressed form. The cold-pressed board is slightly toothier than the hot-pressed board. Novelty cardboards may be obtained in various colors.

caricature Representation of a person or thing that shows a deliberate exaggeration and distortion of features or mannerisms. Caricatures may be good-humored or bitterly satirical.

carry-over line Second or any succeeding line of a sentence, paragraph, or nonsentence list item. The carry-over line may be either flush left or indented in what is called a "hanging indention."

case Container having two drawers that are separated into compartments for holding individual pieces of type. The various pieces are hand-selected and placed on a composing stick to form a line of type. Capital letters are stored in the upper drawer, or case, and lowercase letters in the lower drawer, or case. (The terms "uppercase" and "lowercase" are derived from this storing method.) The California job case, however, has only one storage drawer for all characters, sorts, rules, and the like. Printing students must know the location of compartments and the particular types each contains. The term "case" also refers to a hard or stiff cover into which a sewn book is bound.

case-bound book (hard-cover book) Stiff-covered book. The cover is manufactured separately, and the sewn book is inserted and affixed to the cover. (*See also* BOOKBINDING.)

casein Phosphoprotein derived from milk and used to sensitize the surface of lithographic plates. Casein also serves as an excellent base in manufacturing glue and as an ingredient of artist's paints.

casein plate Sensitized plate. Casein is an ingredient of the sensitizing material.

cast-coated paper *See* COATED BOOK PAPER.

casting   Molten electrotype metal that backs the shell to a desired thickness.

casting box   Enclosed box made of metal that is used for casting stereotypes from molds called "mats" (abbreviation for matrices). Molding mats are made of papier-mâché.

catch line   Temporary heading used to identify a proof.

CB print   Print produced by a wash-off process that was pioneered and developed by the Charles Bruning Company, from which it gets its name. A CB print is made as follows:

1. Sensitized CB material is placed in close contact with a negative of the original.

2. This material and the negative are exposed to intense light. Light penetrates the translucent image area of the negative.

3. The unexposed sensitized coating on the material is washed off.

4. The material is then immersed in a developer, and the print is again washed to remove the developer.

A CB print is used to replace a poor original, to produce an ink-like substitute original, or to make a tracing-cloth revision of an original. Composite CB prints can be produced by combining negative intermediates made from several drawings or parts of drawings. A replacement facsimile of a lost or destroyed original can be produced by using a negative intermediate made from a whiteprint, a blueprint, or some other type of copy of an original.

cell   Typesetter's name for stock having no adhesive backing. The term "cell" is also used extensively in the production of animated cartoons. A cell consists of a sheet of clear acetate on which a cartoon image is drawn. The artist places one cell over the other and draws each cell to an advanced configuration. The series of cells is photographed, and when the completed film is projected rapidly on a screen, the result is one of animation.

cellulose   Fibrous residue remaining after the chemical treatment of base papermaking materials.

center fold   *See* CENTER SPREAD.

center heading   Caption or title that appears in the center of a page or column. Chapter titles are often center headings.

center line   Line used in orthographic engineering and mechanical drawings to indicate the axis of a depicted object. Center lines are

chart **63**

composed of alternating long and short dashes with a long dash at either end; they are designated as "thin" lines. Very short center lines, however, may be unbroken if they cannot be confused with other lines. Center lines are used to indicate the travel of a center. (*See also* LINE CONVENTIONS: ENGINEERING DRAWINGS.)

center spread Two center pages of a publication, used as a double spread (double truck) for advertising. In book work, the center spread is the center fold, where one printing plate may be used for both facing pages. The two pages are necessarily imposed in page-numbering sequence. There are as many center folds as there are signatures.

chain delivery Delivery of printed material as it emerges from the rollers on a conveyor that is driven by a link-chain and sprocket-wheel arrangement.

change bar In a revised technical publication, a vertical rule placed adjacent to text matter. The bar denotes a change in text and is extended to include the number of lines affected by the change. Change bars should be inserted to the left of the text for left-hand pages and to the right of the text for right-hand pages; they may be lost to view if they are placed in the binding margins. Such bars are useful because the reader can determine at a glance what text has been changed. A 3- or 4-point rule set out no more than $\frac{1}{4}$ inch from the text is recommended for a change bar.

character Any letter, number, punctuation mark, or space in printing matter. The average number of characters that can be set in 1 pica (there are about 6 picas to 1 inch) is known as characters per pica.

characteristic curve Curve drawn on a graph to represent the response of photographic material to varying amounts of light.

charcoal drawing Drawing made with fine artist's charcoal. The paper used should have a rib finish. The technique of rendering charcoal drawings is difficult to master. The drawing should be fixed with such a material as gum arabic dissolved in alcohol. Charcoal sketches are often used by commercial illustrators to outline an object before completing the work in oils or other media or to obtain client approval of a layout before finishing it.

chart Graphical representation showing values and quantities by means of bars, curves, columns, and symbols. (*See* BAR CHART; COLUMN CHART; CURVE CHART; PIE CHART; SURFACE CHART.)

chart, organization *See* ORGANIZATION CHART.

charting media Papers used by chartists to compose graphs and scale drawings. (*See* GRID.)

chartist One who has become proficient in the production of graphical representations.

Chart-Pak Trade name for preprinted pressure-sensitive adhesive-backed tapes and components made by Chart-Pak, Inc. These products are used as paste-ups for charts, graphs, map overlays, advertising layouts, newspaper borders, printed-circuitry configurations, and layouts of almost any design. Transparent tapes are available in colors or patterns for use on slides or transparent overhead projectors, for blueprint or whiteprint reproduction, and for occasions when the copy underneath must remain visible. Solid-color tapes with a glossy, matte, or fluorescent finish and pattern tapes or special printed tapes with an opaque white background are used for visual presentations, opaque overhead projectors, photographic reproduction, and

Fig. C-12   Chart-Pak tapes used for an architectural layout.

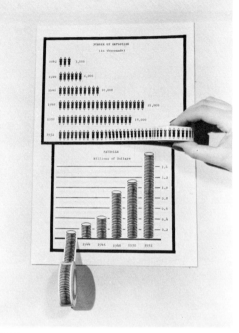

Fig. C-13 Trans-Pak die-cut symbols used for chart layouts.

Fig. C-14 Contak shading films and color tints used for art and projecturals.

contact prints. These tapes can be reproduced by the diazo process and with most office copying machines. Figures C-12, C-13, and C-14 illustrate the use of Chart-Pak tapes and components.

chase Rectangular metal frame in which composed type and printing plates are locked for printing. As a transitive verb, "chase" means to ornament metal by embossing or engraving.

check-out chart (also called **specification tree**) Chart form of presentation resembling a Christmas tree, a name by which it is sometimes known. It is used in technical publications as a kind of trouble-shooting chart to check the operating accuracy of a system in logically sequenced steps. (*See* Figure C-15.)

china clay Filler used with blanc fixe for coating book papers during the paper-manufacturing process.

chopper Device used in a web-fed printing press to make the chopper fold. The signature is conveyed from the first parallel fold in a horizontal plane, with the binding edge forward, until it passes under a reciprocating blade. The blade then forces it down between folding rollers to complete the fold.

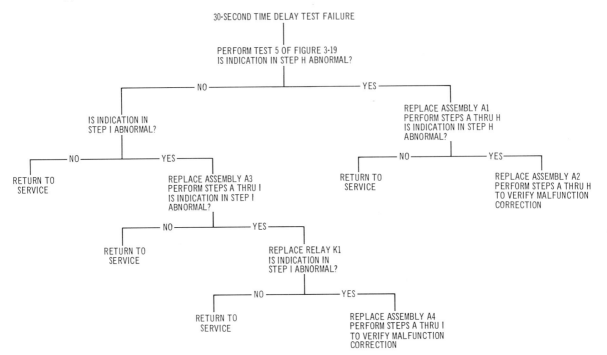

30-SECOND TIME DELAY TEST FAILURE

PERFORM TEST 5 OF FIGURE 3-19
IS INDICATION IN STEP H ABNORMAL?

NO — YES

IS INDICATION IN
STEP I ABNORMAL?

REPLACE ASSEMBLY A1
PERFORM STEPS A THRU H
IS INDICATION IN STEP H
ABNORMAL?

NO — YES

RETURN TO
SERVICE

REPLACE ASSEMBLY A3
PERFORM STEPS A THRU I
IS INDICATION IN STEP I
ABNORMAL?

RETURN TO
SERVICE

REPLACE ASSEMBLY A2
PERFORM STEPS A THRU H
TO VERIFY MALFUNCTION
CORRECTION

NO — YES

RETURN TO
SERVICE

REPLACE RELAY K1
IS INDICATION IN
STEP I ABNORMAL?

NO — YES

RETURN TO
SERVICE

REPLACE ASSEMBLY A4
PERFORM STEPS A THRU I
TO VERIFY MALFUNCTION
CORRECTION

Fig. C-15   Check-out chart.

chopper fold (cross-fold; right-angle fold) Fold made in a web-fed printing press after the first parallel fold and at right angles to it. Signatures are produced in 16-page multiples of the number of webs (rolled paper stock) in the press with one-fourth of the web width by one-half of the cutoff length.

Christmas tree *See* CHECK-OUT CHART.

chuck Device inserted in the core to support the paper roll on the roll stand in a web-fed printing press.

chute delivery Delivery of printed material from the press by forcing it between the cylinders into a chute.

circular Advertising piece in the form of a single sheet or a leaflet.

circular grid Grid used to form pie charts and plot data in polar coordinates. It is also employed in trigonometry, calculus, and analytic geometry. Circular grids are popular in light studies to plot flux determination in light beams and to show the relation of an illuminating source and points of illumination. In addition, they are well suited for plotting stadia survey notes. The center of the ordinates represents the station from which the stadic observations were taken.

Horizontal angles, distances, and elevations are plotted, and the appropriate points are then connected by contour lines.

classified ad   Advertisement composed of words only and sold by the line, as distinguished from a display advertisement, which is sold at a given rate per column inch. Word-line advertisements are set on linecasting machines.

Clearback Ortho Litho film   Lithographic film produced by Du Pont on a Cronar polyester film base. Fast, even exposures can be secured through the back of the film, thereby permitting reversing or "flopping" to obtain emulsion-to-plate image contact. The film is suitable for all line and halftone work but is particularly good for deep-etch lithography and photoengraving applications.

Clearbase film   Lithographic film produced by Du Pont on a Cronar polyester film base. The film has a special subcoating designed to hold opaques and blueline solutions without cracking or chipping. It is particularly suitable for stripping and lay-up.

coated book paper   Paper manufactured especially for printing fine-screen halftones. The base paper is the same as for English-finish book paper, but casein, starch, or glue and certain pigments are added. While coated book papers are usually glossy, some dull coated papers are manufactured. Coated papers are used when high printing quality is desired for color-separation work. They are divided into several classifications: coated-one-side, coated-two-sides, dull coated-two-sides, process- or machine-coated, and cast-coated.

Coated-one-side book paper is used for offset or letterpress printing of labels, posters, or any other type of application for which high-quality printing is required and for which one side may be adhesive-backed or pasted. Standard basic weights are 50, 60, 70, and 80 pounds.

Dull coated-two-sides book paper is used for illustrated booklets and books and for other applications in which glare must be avoided. This paper is suitable for halftone work of 120-line screen. Standard basic weights are 50, 60, 70, 80, 90, 100, and 120 pounds for 500 sheets of the basic size of 25 by 38 inches.

Coated-two-sides book paper is suitable for 133- to 150-line screens, but 120-line screen is recommended for fine reproduction of the highest quality. This paper is used extensively by printing establishments for catalogs, direct-mail pieces, brochures, pamphlets, and other applications for which quality printing is essential. The medium-priced, coated-two-sides paper is the paper most commonly used by printers. Standard basic weights are 50, 60, 70, 80, 90, 100, and 120 pounds for 500 sheets of the basic size of 25 by 38 inches.

Process- or machine-coated papers are made by applying coating on the surface of the paper as it passes through the drying end of the papermaking machine. The paper is then supercalendered, and the result is a high-quality coated paper of lighter weight. This paper is used for magazines, direct-mail pieces, catalogs, brochures, booklets, and other applications for which light weight and high-quality printing are desired. The basic weights are 45, 50, 60, 70, and 100 pounds for 500 sheets of the basic size of 25 by 38 inches.

Cast-coated papers have a high gloss and an exceptionally smooth surface. Advertising pieces, direct-mail pieces, fine wrapping papers, and labels are some of the applications to which the good appearance of this paper is well suited.

coated finish (enameled finish) High-gloss finish obtained in certain papers by adding pigments or ingredients such as satin white, china clay, or calcium carbonate. Coated finish is desirable in papers for fine color work and halftone reproduction. Direct-mail pieces, quality advertising sheets in catalogs, pages in magazines, and dust jackets for books are examples of coated-finish papers. Coated papers cause glare and are not good for solid text. They may, however, be used for text printed either by letterpress or by cold composition, because the hard finish results in good definition, bringing out serifs, and has excellent erasing characteristics when typewriter composition is employed. A good basic weight for typewriter composition or for running reproduction proofs by letterpress printing is 60 to 80 pounds.

coated-one-side paper Book paper coated on one side only. (*See* COATED BOOK PAPER.)

coated-two-sides paper Book paper coated on two sides. (*See* COATED BOOK PAPER.)

cocking roller (guide roller) Device used in a web-fed printing press to compensate for slight paper variations while the web (paper roll) is feeding. The "cocking" roller is located on the roll stand between the roll of paper and the "dancer" roll.

cockle finish Rough, wrinkled, irregular finish in paper.

cold composition (cold copy; cold type) Composition by machines such as typewriters and photocomposing machines or in any manner in which no molten metal is used to form the image. Apparently the term "cold composition" was derived as the opposite of "hot composition," which refers to casting slugs of type with molten metal on linecasting machines such as the Linotype and the Intertype. Movable type set by hand is referred to as "cold type" when it is contrasted with hot-metal type. Pressure-sensitive adhesives containing preprinted or photographically composed nomenclature, symbols, and the like are also called cold type.

The Justowriter (Figure C-16) is a good example of a cold-composition machine consisting of two units. It is an automatic tape-operated copy-setting machine that produces justified copy (that is, with even right-hand margins) for reproduction by printing. The two units are the recorder and the reproducer. The operator types the original unjustified copy on the recorder, which simultaneously records all the typing in the form of combinations of holes in a punched paper tape. This tape is then inserted in the reproducer, which automatically types reproduction proofs or direct-image plates (such as paper plates used with offset duplicators) at the rate of 100 words per minute. If desired, a motorized tape punch attached to the reproducer may simultaneously produce a punched tape. This tape may be inserted in the recorder to set justified copy in a different size and type style. Both the recorder and the reproducer have standard keyboards in addition to operating keys. A representative selection of type sizes and styles consists of 8-point Newstext, 10-point Booktype, 10-point Heritage, 10-point Modern, 12-point boldface, 12-point boldface italic, and 14-point Commercial. Two-column runarounds, justified tabular copy, centered copy, and, of course, single- and double-spaced lines are available.

Fig. C-16   Friden's Justowriter Model AA recorder (*left*) and Model JU reproducer (*right*).

Fig. C-17 **VariTyper cold-composition composing machine.**

The VariTyper (Figure C-17) is a cold-composition machine having a universal keyboard. The machine composes reproducible copy. Various models are available. Two different fonts may be used at one time by turning a control knob, so that matching italics, boldface type, etc., may be used in the same copy with text type. More than 300 typefaces and sizes, including the popular reading typefaces, are available.

The models may or may not be equipped with differential letterspacing, which means that the value of each letter depends on the area it occupies. For example, the letter M is set in a wider space than the narrower letters i or f. Once the line count is known, the VariTyper justifies copy automatically. A line of copy is first prejustified by typing it for an automatic line count. The carriage is then shifted and the line typed again to a preset measure opposite the prejustified line. Succeeding lines will then be justified, with even right-hand margins. Line measures are preset in the machine as desired. A selector provides leading (spacing) of 0 to 18 points between lines. Composing may be made on plates for offset duplicators or stencil work. A nonprint key is used to center or adjust a heading without a space count. By using the nonprint key, direct plate work copy may be prejustified, only the justified copy being permitted to register on the duplicating master.

A companion of the VariTyper is the Headliner. In addition, IBM's Executive series of typewriters is used to prepare cold-composition copy. (*See* TYPEWRITER; *see also* JUSTIFICATION.)

Figure C-18 is a photograph of the magnetic-tape Selectric typewriter (MT/ST). It may be used without the magnetic-tape console. A small interchangeable printing element eliminates the typebars and the moving carriage found on conventional typewriters. The Selectric is available in both carbon and ribbon models. Carbon ribbons are recommended for the preparation of reproduction copy. The MT/ST can produce error-free copy at a speed of as much as 180 words per minute. It mechanically stores typing production on magnetic-tape cartridges which are available for automatic retyping. Only changes are typed manually. The typist "instructs" the machine to "search" a magnetic tape on which the original typed material is stored for the point at which the change is to be made. The typist then "erases" the tape by typing over the unwanted material, at the same time storing the new copy for mass typing and future reference.

Information stored at two tape stations can be searched and combined, either through magnetic-tape instruction or through operator control. Line lengths are adjusted automatically when images are changed. Sentences and paragraphs can be respaced, and hyphens are dropped automatically. The MT/ST is designed for typing technical reports and manuals, legal briefs, statistical material, company telephone directories, insurance forms, and other documents that require periodic revision.

Fig. C-18   IBM's magnetic-tape Selectric typewriter.

Fig. C-19   Thomas 50-station Rotomatic collator and stitcher.

collating   Arranging proofs or sheets in order; hence, organizing, gathering, and assembling a book or other publication in page sequence. Hand collating for long runs is time-consuming and therefore expensive. Figure C-19 shows the 50-station Rotomatic collator and stitcher, which is designed especially for company-operated duplicating departments, medium- to large-sized printing establishments, and lettershops. The loading time is seven minutes for all 50 stations. Compensation is not required for various weights and finishes of stock. Each bin has a capacity of $1\frac{3}{4}$ inches of paper in sizes from $7\frac{1}{4}$ by 8 to 11 by 14 inches. The collator is programmed by a push-button device comprised of rows of color-coded buttons that control the delivery of paper in each of the stations. Stations can be activated or bypassed, and instructions for jogging or stitching are programmed automatically. Sheet combinations from 1 to 50 and set combinations from 2 to 25 are possible. Speed may be adjusted to a rate of as many as 25,000 sheets per hour. The collator detects a miss or a double sheet, and a five-digit counter keeps a running count of the total number of sets that have been collated and stitched.

The Thomas automatic A-10 high-speed collator operates at a rate of 30,000 sheets per running hour with 10 stations. Each of the 10 bins holds $1\frac{3}{4}$ inches of paper in weights from 13 to 110 pounds and can be loaded in ninety seconds. Adjustable-corner sheet separators on each bin minimize misses and double pages caused by perforated or punched sheets or by static electricity. A five-digit counter and an automatic angle stapler are other features of this collator.

Figure C-20 shows an eight-station automatic collator that can collate as many as 24,000 sheets per hour or can be slowed down to handle marginal papers that are normally unfitted for automatic collating. The machine can be continually reloaded while it is operating, and it can turn itself off when the paper at any of its stations is exhausted. In addition, a set of sheets can be punched with a variety of patterns, or the machine can be equipped with a single, double, or heavy-duty stapler. A jogging stacker is provided at the end of the production line.

collotype process *See* PHOTOGELATIN PROCESS.

colophon Brief technical description placed at the end of a book, giving information on the typeface and design, the paper used, production facts and printing techniques, or other physical aspects of the work. The term "colophon" refers also to an emblem or device identifying a printer or publisher; it may appear on the cover, title page, backbone, or jacket of a book.

color-blind emulsion Emulsion that is sensitive only to blue, violet, and ultraviolet light.

color coder Instrument used to compare the intensity of colors on printed samples and so permit faithful reproduction.

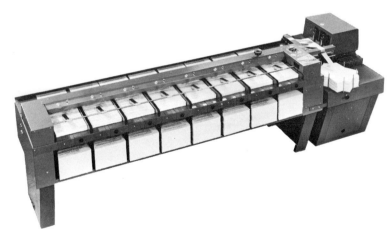

Fig. C-20 General Binding Corporation's eight-station automatic collator.

color correction Change made in reproduction work to correct the rendition of a color.

color identification Designation of the color of each process plate (acetate overlay) in illustration copy having two or more colors. The identification is marked outside the reproducible area on each overlay. When a color other than primary or secondary colors is required, a swatch should be provided to identify it.

color reproduction Any of several methods in which photographic masks are used to obtain better rendition of colors in the reproduction process.

color sensitivity *See* FILMS AND PLATES.

color separation Division of colors of a continuous-tone multicolored original or of line copy into basic portions, each of which is to be reproduced by a separate printing plate carrying a color. Usually three separations are made for continuous-tone work and any combination for line work. Basic methods of separating colors for printing are (1) using acetate overlays from which three black-and-white negatives are made to represent each primary color; and (2) employing different filters in the process camera, each of which allows some of the color in the multicolored original to be imposed on the negative, thus separating colors for reproduction by printing. Because acetate is subject to molecular change with changes in humidity, fine color registration is best achieved by using filters.

Acetate-overlay color separation involves the initial preparation of the black plate from which the black image is produced. A separate plate is used for each color. Primary-color plates should be on a matte-finish acetate film of sufficient body to withstand warping or shrinking. The color area to be printed from a plate appears in permanent black on the plate and is in perfect register with the other plates comprising the artwork. When secondary colors are required, they are obtained by overprinting the primary colors. Areas to be printed in secondary colors are also defined in permanent black on the appropriate primary-color overlays.

Each color plate should contain a minimum of four equidistant register marks, which appear outside the reproducible portion of the plate. The marks should be finely detailed and placed on the corresponding position of each overlay to ensure accurate register of each plate, thus producing perfect register of each color from the plates. The name of the color for each plate should be scratched on the plate outside the reproducible area. When a color other than primary or secondary colors is required, a swatch should be included with the printing instructions. Paste-ups and preprints should appear on the overlay containing the portion of art that is to be printed in the same color. When paste-ups and preprints are to be printed in a color that is not provided for by the art separation overlays, an additional overlay registered to the key, or black, art is used.

Color separation of multicolored originals by means of filters assures accurate registration and produces colors of the highest quality, all other factors being equal. The work is accomplished by the process cameraman. A filter transmits light of certain colors while it absorbs light of others. The most common filters are thin sheets or disks of gelatin or glass placed in front of the lens of the process camera or in a slot in the lens mounting. By using the proper filters, selected colors of light from a multicolored object are filtered out or reduced. A negative will then record only the colors transmitted through the filter. A filter never changes the color of light: it can only allow a part of some colors to pass through and stop other colors. In color-separation work, the colored original is photographed successively through three color-separation filters. The three black-and-white color-separation negatives thus produced are used in making the three printing plates which print the respective colors on paper. A fourth plate, called the "black printer," is usually made to add density to dark areas of the picture.

color separation, direct   *See* DIRECT COLOR SEPARATION.

color separation, indirect   *See* INDIRECT COLOR SEPARATION.

color-separation filters   *See* FILMS AND PLATES.

colors, primary   *See* PRIMARY COLORS.

colors, secondary   *See* SECONDARY COLORS.

columbian   Old type size. The nearest equivalent in the point system is 16 point.

column   One of the sections of text or other matter, such as display advertisements, that comprise a vertically divided page. It is measured horizontally and is usually justified. Each column of a page is established by a line measure for justified copy. The term "column" also refers to a vertical section of a table.

column chart (also called **vertical column chart**)   Graphic representation having juxtaposed vertical columns that usually denote a quantity, with the horizontal dimension representing time or some

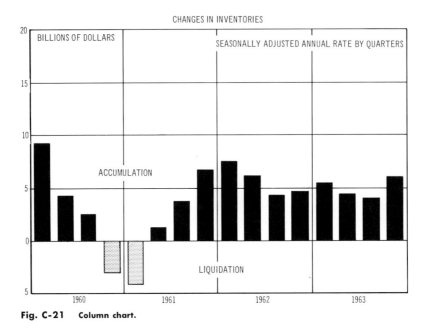

CHANGES IN INVENTORIES

BILLIONS OF DOLLARS

SEASONALLY ADJUSTED ANNUAL RATE BY QUARTERS

ACCUMULATION

LIQUIDATION

1960   1961   1962   1963

Fig. C-21   **Column chart.**

other value (*see* Figure C-21). An additional value can be represented by using double or divided columns or symbols such as a pig, cow, and sheep, interpreted to indicate pork, beef, and mutton. (*See also* BAR CHART; CURVE CHART; PIE CHART; SURFACE CHART.)

column inch   Space one column wide and 1 inch high, used to establish rates for display advertising. If, for example, a magazine has an established rate of $40 per column inch, the cost of an advertisement one column wide and 1 inch high would be $40. If the advertisement is one column wide and 2 inches high, the advertisement would cost $80. If the advertisement is two columns wide and 2 inches high, the cost would be $160.

columnar arrangement   Division of a page into two or more columns of display or text matter. Columns may be justified or run "ragged."

comb binding (plastic binding)   Form of mechanical binding with a plastic center strip from which curving prongs extend. The prongs are inserted in holes punched in the paper. Apparently the name is derived from the resulting comb effect. Plastic binding affords a solid spine on which the title of the book or other information may be printed. (*See also* BINDING, MECHANICAL.)

combination plate (also called **composite**) Plate containing both halftone and line copy. A black or red patch in the exact proportions of the halftone is mortised or pasted into the camera-ready reproduction copy in the position that the halftone will occupy. The halftone negative is stripped into position in the line negative, and the combination plate, containing both line and halftone copy, is made. Two negatives are necessary because halftone copy requires screening and line copy does not.

commercial Relating to any product manufactured and sold for commercial use or to any service so sold. Although a proposal may ultimately embrace a product or service purchased by the military, it is considered commercial if it is company-funded and if the company's style and format are used in the publication that supports the product or service. If, on the other hand, the publication is funded by the military and government specifications are required to prepare it, the publication is classed as military. A military publication, such as a handbook or a technical manual, has a publication number that is assigned to it by the cognizant agency.

commercial art Artwork of any kind that is prepared for predetermined commercial purposes such as advertising and general promotion. It is distinguished from fine art. Commercial art may be used by government agencies or by private industry.

commercial reproduction copy Reproduction copy which is not intended for government agencies or services and to which a publication number is not assigned.

Commercial S film Film using Du Pont's Cronar polyester film base to make continuous-tone negatives and positives, positive and canceling masks for color-separation techniques, and black-and-white film copies when red and green sensitivity are not needed. It is also well suited to the reproduction of artwork that combines continuous-tone and line material.

common-law copyright Legal right which protects an author or an artist for his unpublished work until the work has been first published. A common-law copyright takes effect at the moment the work is done, without any other action being necessary, and is recognizable in a court of law as long as the work remains unpublished. Unless the author or artist holds to certain practices, however, he may lose common-law–copyright protection by his own act.

Common-law copyright permits the originator to make restricted distribution for comment by others and for review by potential publishers. The originator reserves the right to restrain publication by others and the right to sell or assign his work to another person or persons. The common-law copyright can be destroyed (1) by publication and sale of copies for monetary gain by the originator or others; (2) by unrestricted distribution of copies without the statutory copyright notice, which implies dedicating the work to the public; and (3) by having the work published without a copyright notice in an uncopyrighted publication. (*See also* COPYRIGHT.)

comp   Abbreviation for compositor or for comprehensive. "Comp" is also used in art departments to mean to apply ("compose") nomenclature on artwork.

compensator   Adjustable roller used in a web-fed press to control the tension of the web (paper roll) and maintain paper smoothness.

complementary flat   Flat which contains material that is exposed in successive "burns" onto the same plate. This procedure is often necessary when several negatives must be pieced too closely together to be handled in a single flat, as is the case with halftones with close-fitting captions, or when halftones require longer exposure than line work.

composing stick (job stick)   Device for holding and arranging type while a line of type is being set by hand. It is made of metal and is adjustable so that a line can be set to the desired measure. The nicks (grooves) in the type are visible to aid in aligning it for right-reading printing. (*See* Figure C-22.)

Fig. C-22   Printer's composing stick.

composite   *See* COMBINATION PLATE.

composition   Material consisting of text in typewritten form for photo-offset reproduction or in typeset form for letterpress and other methods of printing. The material is better known as reproduction copy when it is composed on a cold-composition machine and as reproduction or etch proofs if it is in letterpress format. (*See* REPRODUCTION COPY; REPRODUCTION PROOF.)

compositor   One who sets type by hand or with an automatic typecasting machine.

Compos-O-Line   Trade name for a sequential-card camera manufactured by Friden, Inc. (*See* CAMERA, SEQUENTIAL-CARD.)

comprehensive   Layout of art and type, either in black or in colors, that is used as a presentation for advertising or other purposes. The comprehensive is neither a rough sketch nor a completed product but should be of sufficient quality and clarity to carry a message. The meaning and purpose of the theme should be readily understood. While the comprehensive should represent the end product as faithfully as possible, it need not be an exact facsimile. Several comprehensives covering the same subject may be produced for comparison.

computer graphics   Science of using computers to generate and interpret pictures.

condensed type   Type with a narrower face than that used in the same family of type.

construction drawing   Engineering drawing that illustrates the design of structures and surrounding areas, individually or in groups, and includes pertinent services, equipment, and other features required to establish all the interrelated elements of the design. Construction drawings, in general, present design information by pictorial plans, elevations, sections, and details. Maps (except those used in construction), sketches, presentation drawings, perspectives, and renderings are not considered construction drawings.

construction paper   Type of school paper manufactured from groundwood for use in the elementary grades for coloring, cutouts, pencil or charcoal drawings, etc. The basis weight is 80 pounds for 500 sheets of the standard size of 24 by 36 inches. Construction paper is manufactured in red, black, orange, yellow, green, dark blue, scarlet, light blue, light red, dark green, brown, white, gray, and light green.

contact print   Print or copy made in the same size as the original negative or master copy without the benefit of a reduced or enlarged print. It is made on sensitized paper by direct contact with the master or original.

contact screen   Halftone screen made on a film base with a graduated-dot pattern. The screen is placed in direct contact with the film or plate to obtain a halftone pattern from a continuous-tone original.

contact size   Size of a print or an image reproduced or copied in the same size as the original, without enlargement or reduction.

Contak   Trade name for shading films and color tints used in constructing art and projecturals. (*See* CHART-PAK.)

contents Portion of the front matter of a publication that lists the parts, chapters, sections, and sometimes the numbers and titles of paragraphs. A list of illustrations and a list of tables may also be included and follow in that order. The page on which each entry may be found is given opposite the entry. The single word "contents" is replacing the phrase "table of contents."

continuous form Series of perforated sheets attached in roll form. The sheets are fed into a printing press or other device, such as a computer printout, and are separated into individual sheets by tearing them apart along the lines of the perforations.

continuous-form press Printing press designed especially to print on continuous forms. Figure C-23 illustrates the Kluge web-flow continuous-form press, which is used both for printing custom business forms and for imprinting. Custom forms are usually prepared and printed to individual specifications. Imprints are stock forms that are rerun by the printer to add a heading or a vertical rule or a combination of captions and vertical and horizontal rules. Among the custom forms the Kluge press will produce are payroll registers, payroll checks, invoices, purchase orders, statements, insurance-premium notices, tax notices, earnings and withholding-tax statements, and bills of lading. Imprints include ledgers, cash and general journals, columnar forms and pads, visible binder forms, machine-bookkeeping forms, and data-processing forms. The maximum web width is 19 inches, and the minimum is $2\frac{1}{2}$ inches. The delivery-table and stock-table capacities are each 12 inches, and the speed is 3,500 impressions per hour.

Fig. C-23   Kluge web-flow continuous-form press.

continuous-tone art Photograph, wash drawing, or oil painting without a halftone-dot screen. Any image with a tonal gradation is a halftone[1] when screened and, in the graphic arts, is contrasted with line copy. After continuous-tone art has been screened, it becomes a halftone. A halftone is identified by examining the paper surface with a magnifying glass and noting the presence or absence of dot formations. (*See also* HALFTONE SCREENING.)

contour Form of an object drawn in outline. In map making, contour lines are lines that connect points of equal elevation.

[1]Because the meaning of words is based on general usage and acceptance, the definition of a halftone given here is used throughout the *Encyclopedia*. However, some authorities are of the opinion that screening continuous-tone copy does not cancel the full range of tones. Their preference is to call this copy full-tone instead of halftone. They contend that a halftone is actually continuous-tone copy altered to the extent that it is treated as line work when it is engraved for printing. (*See also* LINE CONVERSION.)

contrast In photography, the separation of tones; the range of differences from white through black; the density of certain areas of the image as compared with others. When tones are slightly defined, the image is said to be "low" in contrast, but when they are readily identified from white through black, it is said to be "high" in contrast.

controlling dimension Dimension, either horizontal or vertical, that determines the enlargement or reduction of an image.

conversion film process Product and process produced by Kalvar Corporation for Kal/Graphic, Inc., under the trade name Converkal. This process makes a reproduction negative directly on the shop proof press. The negative is then ready for offset plate making without processing. The film is dimensionally stable and has an opaque coating. When the film comes in contact with a heated metal typeform on a conventional printing press, the opacity clears to provide a negative reproduction of the image. The operation requires approximately three minutes, and no inking or special surface treatment of the type other than cleaning is required. Since Converkal is not light-sensitive, it can be handled and used in ordinary room illumination.

Form heating is produced as follows:

1. A type-high bearer (0.915 to 0.918 inch), 6 to 36 points, is placed away from each side of the form. Bearers should be short or be notched to provide air escape at the form corners.

2. The form is locked in the smallest convenient chase and is planed in the usual manner. String-tied forms may be used with channeled furniture.

3. Type-metal strip material should be used as lockup furniture. Wood or patent iron furniture should not be used.

4. The type surface of the form is cleaned thoroughly. All non-printing areas may be left unwashed since the darker color will absorb heat more rapidly and reduce warm-up time. A nonflammable solvent should be used for cleaning.

5. The typeform is then inserted in the Con-Rad 7, its approximate center being placed over the direct-contact heat control. The average heating time varies with the size, structure, and surface color (new or old) of the form but is about three minutes.

The reproduction negative is made as follows:

1. The form ink rollers are lifted or removed before the form is heated.

2. The Converkal film is placed in the press grippers.

3. Two pieces of 3-pica wood furniture are placed on the press

bed, one on the gripper end and the other along the side, so that the heated chase will fit solidly in a corner position.

4. The Con-Rad 7 lamps turn off when the typeform reaches the process-temperature level. The form is then placed on the press bed in the reproduction-negative position.

5. The reproduction negative is pulled within twenty seconds after removing the form from the Con-Rad 7 unit at a form surface temperature of 260 to 270°F.

cooling rollers   In a web-fed press, a roller installed immediately following the drying oven. It reduces the temperature of the web from oven temperature to the setting temperature of heat-set inks, which is approximately 80 to 90°F.

copy   Any matter, including photographs, rules, designs, and text, that is used in reproduction for printing in any manner.

Copy Block   Product of Craftint Manufacturing Company, consisting of preprinted blocks of copy in 10, 12, and 14 point to indicate the size of type and the area the copy will occupy. The material has an adhesive back and is pasted in place on a dummy layout to instruct the typesetter. Copy Block contains the normal leading (spacing between lines) applicable to text material.

copy card   Electrical-accounting-machine (EAM) tabulating card containing a frame of unexposed microfilm mounted in or over a rectangular aperture for subsequent exposure and development while still mounted in the card. Microfilm duplicators are used to make copies on copy cards from the original microfilm. (*See also* APERTURE CARD.)

copy casting   *See* COPYFITTING.

copy-dot reproduction   Photomechanical reproduction of halftone illustrations and associated line copy without rescreening of the illustrations. The halftone dots of the originals are copied as "line" material. Very careful photography is necessary to obtain good results.

copy paper   *See* DUPLICATOR PAPER.

copy scaling   *See* COPYFITTING.

copyboard   Frame that holds original copy while the copy is being photographed. It is called a "vacuum frame" when vacuum suction

Fig. C-24 Robertson's trans-suction copyboard.

is used in conjunction with the board. Without vacuum suction, the copy must be tacked or taped to the face of the board or inserted in a glass-faced frame in which it is secured by pressure. Vacuum copyboards are glass-covered and can be tilted and rotated for easy loading. Figure C-24 shows a trans-suction copyboard with the curtain raised for loading. A spring-loaded insert holds copy as thick as $\frac{1}{4}$ inch. Vacuum-blanket inserts may be used to keep thin copy, such as tracing, flat within a copyboard. The inserts are mounted in the board, and a vacuum pump and meter are supplied to create the vacuum. Open-faced copyboards (without glass) are available to hold large drawings or sensitized materials for the production of photo templates.

copyfitting (copy casting; copy scaling) In letterpress printing, arranging original copy by type and line measurements so that it will fit the available space. Each letter, space, and punctuation mark is counted as a character. Characters on an elite typewriter measure 12 to the inch and pica characters 10 to the inch. Leading is the space between lines of type. The most accurate system of typing copy to fit space is based on the character count. By multiplying the average number of characters per line by the number of lines of copy, the total number of characters can be found. For example, assume that the copy has an average of 40 characters to a line and that there are 50 lines; Multiply 40 by 50; the total is 2,000 characters. To find out how much space the copy will occupy when set in type, determine the measure, which is the width of the line of type in picas, in the typeface and point size desired. This information may be taken from a sample catalog furnished by the printer. The characters in the given typeface and size are counted in the amount equal to the measure, e.g., 30 characters per line, 40 characters per line, etc. Assume that the copy is to be set in 8 point to a measure of 20 picas and that the selected typeface is found to average 67 characters to the measure. Then, by dividing 67 into 2,000, it is seen that the copy will make 30 lines of type. For convenient assistance to the printer, copy may be typed so that each line will approximate the measure in picas. Refer to Table 7, where the conversion of 20 picas to inches is noted. The table shows that 21 picas are approximately $3\frac{1}{2}$ inches in length.

To establish the depth of copy required, the foregoing calculation is used to arrive at 30 lines of type set in 8 point. If the type is to be set 8 on 8, indicating no leading (extra spacing), 30 is multiplied by 8 and a total of 240 points is the depth. The total number of points is divided by 12 (the number of points in a pica), and the total depth is found to be 20 picas. If the 8-point type is to be set on a 9-point body (1 point of leading), expressed as 8 on 9, or on a 10-point body (2 points of leading), expressed as 8 on 10, the point or points of leading are multiplied to obtain the depth in points and divided by 12. To find the depth in inches, divide by 72, which is the number of points in 1 inch, or refer to Table 7.

It has been established that the ideal line of type should be about 39 characters in any type size set in lowercase letters. Lines of more than 50 or less than 30 characters should be avoided.

Copyflo Microform copying process and a registered trade name owned by Xerox Corporation. (*See* PRINTER.)

copyholder Person who holds and reads aloud the original copy during proofreading while the proofreader marks the proof (in the case of hot composition) or the reproducible camera-ready copy (in the case of cold composition). The term "copyholder" also denotes a frame for holding copy.

copying machines Machines normally used to reproduce copy in offices, company-operated reproduction departments, and printing and duplicating establishments. Included are the larger whiteprint copying machines employed not only in manufacturing plants but in commercial blueprinting and printing shops. Several of the smaller types of copying machines are known as photocopying machines. These produce copies from opaque as well as transparent and translucent originals. The larger copying machines, with which diazo salts are used as a sensitized emulsion on the copy paper and which can make copies only from transparent and translucent originals, are more properly referred to as whiteprint machines.

The copy paper used in copying machines may or may not be sensitized. With some processes it is necessary to produce a master from the original and then make additional copies from the master. The xerographic process copies from an original or a copy onto nonsensitized stock without the use of masters or intermediates. For the whiteprint process, the original must be on a translucent or transparent material that can be penetrated by light during exposure, and the copy paper must be capable of being developed because of light-sensitive characteristics. While most copying machines will reproduce color from originals, it is, of course, impossible to reproduce and impress a color on the copy without the use of colored ink. Copies are black regardless of the color of the original.

Copying machines are not classed as duplicators, although the copies they produce may be correctly termed "duplicate copies." Duplicating machines are those that employ a metal plate, a paper-plate master, or a stencil master as the form from which the image is transferred to stock. Offset duplicators, which use paper and flexible metal plates as the image source, are in fact small printing presses. Other types of duplicators are those that employ stencils in mimeographing, such as the mimeograph, and those that use masters to transfer dye images to stock in the spirit duplicating process, such as the Ditto duplicator.

Apeco's Systematic copying machine is a compact unit 21 inches wide, 13 inches deep, and 6 inches high and has a break-resistant plastic housing. It uses the diffusion-transfer-reversal process of making copies, combining one-step operation with provision of the developer in a plastic cartridge. The original positive and negative are fed into the unit in one step. Used solution is discarded by removing the cartridge, and a new cartridge is inserted to provide fresh developer. When the unit is turned on, the solution is pumped electrically from the cartridge into the developer at the proper level during use. The Systematic copies from opaque, transparent, or translucent originals and also copies color.

Fig. C-25 Apeco's Dial-A-Copy copying machine.

Fig. C-26 Bruning's Model 255 automatic-feed copying machine.

Dial-A-Copy, shown in Figure C-25, enables the operator to dial the number of copies needed. The machine uses the electrostatic method of making copies. It has a self-contained roll of copy paper sufficient to produce 500 letter-sized copies ($8\frac{1}{2}$ by 11 inches). The machine copies from written, printed, typed, drawn, or photographed originals and produces a copy every ten seconds. The copies themselves can be used to make offset masters capable of producing 200 copies on an offset duplicator.

Figure C-26 shows an automatic-feed diazo (whiteprint) copying machine. The copy-selector dial is set to produce 1 to 80 copies. The original to be copied is placed in a plastic carrier and inserted in the feed section. It is then magnetically retained in the exposure section and makes as many passes as are set on the selector dial. With each pass, a sheet of sensitized copy paper from a preloaded stack is automatically fed into the machine, matched to the original, and exposed. Multiple copies of letter-size originals or small engineering drawings are produced at a rate of more than 30 per minute. As many as 80 copies of originals measuring as large as 11 by 17 inches can be dialed. Larger originals up to a width of 18 inches by any reasonable length can be produced manually as with any diazo copier.

The Bruning Model 675 uses the Copyflex process of reproduction: after exposure to a mercury arc lamp, the copy is developed by passing it between rollers which apply a thin film of metered developer. The machine takes sheets or rolled stock up to a width of 42 inches by any length. The speed is 75 linear feet per minute.

The electrostatic copier shown in Figure C-27 produces copies from an original to fixed reductions of 20, 30, or 35 percent. For example, an 11- by 17-inch original can be reduced to $8\frac{1}{2}$ by 11 inches. The printing rate with the automatic feeder is fourteen $8\frac{1}{2}$ by 11-inch copies per minute. The operational sequence includes four steps: (1) a uniform electrostatic charge is placed on the paper; (2) an optical system scans the original, and the image is then projected from the original to the copy paper; (3) toner, automatically brushed over the surface of the copy paper, adheres to the image area; and (4) the toner is fused to the paper, thus forming a permanent black image. Copies emerge dry.

Bruning's Revolute Star is a whiteprint machine that employs ammonia-vapor fumes as the developing agent. A prime feature is the developing chamber, which contains four stainless-steel perforated rollers that guide the paper over the tank. The maximum printing and developing width is 45 inches on the 42-inch size and 57 inches on the 54-inch size. The maximum speed is 74 feet per minute.

Figure C-28 shows a photocopying machine that employs the diffusion-transfer-reversal method of reproduction. The machine's flatbed exposure section allows copying from single-sheet originals as well as from bound pages of books and magazines. Offset plates can be made by feeding the produced negative and special aluminum offset plate into the developer section. A timer controls light automatically by dial selection during an exposure range of $\frac{1}{2}$ second to 12 seconds.

Fig. C-28   A. B. Dick Company's Model 120 photo-copying machine.

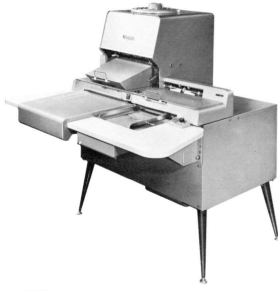

Fig. C-27   Bruning's Model 2000R electrostatic copier.

The Masterfax copying machine (Figure C-29) will do four things: make spirit masters, make offset masters, make facsimile copies, and laminate. In making direct spirit masters, carbon is not required. The copy to be duplicated is typed, written, or drawn on a clean white Masterfax sheet and then inserted in the machine with Masterfax carbon to make a direct-process (liquid-process) master. In making offset masters, a paper mat is included with the original and carbon, and the assembly is placed in the machine. In fifteen seconds the master is ready for use on the offset duplicator. Direct-process masters can also be made from original copy that has not been prepared on Masterfax paper. Masters may be made from newspaper clippings, correspondence, reports, and other material. Facsimile copies having a black image may also be made and produced on any weight of paper, including card stock, gummed labels, and cloth. The Masterfax also laminates office papers, documents, and other material with a plastic coating to protect them against heat, aging, moisture, and chemicals.

Verifax copiers are products of the Eastman Kodak Company. These desk-top machines (*see* Figure C-30) are used to copy a wide variety of originals of any color and from any paper. Opaque or two-sides material, coarse-screen halftones, and pen, pencil, and crayon writing can be copied. Bound volumes can be copied with some models, or a book-copying accessory can be used with any model. Copies are made on bond paper, have a high degree of permanency, and can be made on two sides of a sheet or as a four-page folder.

Fig. C-29 Ditto's Masterfax copying machine.

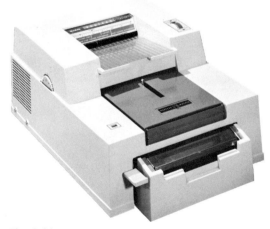

Fig. C-30 Verifax Cavalcade copier.

Fig. C-31 Kodak Readyprint copier.

Fig. C-32   Xerox Model 914 copier.

Also available are translucent stock, useful as an intermediate for printing on whiteprint or blueprint machines, and transparent sheeting for use with overhead projectors or as a heavy-duty intermediate.

Of special interest is the ability of the Verifax process to create offset masters by two methods. Masters can be created directly by transfer to suitable offset masters, such as the Kodak E-V master, or by the use of a Fine-Line Matrix as a negative to burn in presensitized plates.

Verifax copiers are operated by placing an original to be copied and a sheet of Verifax matrix paper in the exposure section. The matrix is then processed by placing it in an activator. After a few seconds, the matrix is withdrawn from the activator in contact with a sheet of copy paper (with successive sheets of copy paper if multiple copies are desired). Copies are dry and ready for use. Some Verifax models are largely automatic. The Readyprint copier (Figure C-31), which is similar to Verifax, can produce high-quality single copies in twenty-five seconds. Readyprint negatives can also be used to burn in offset plates.

The Xerox 914 copier (Figure C-32) utilizes xerography to produce facsimile copies of anything printed, written, typed, or drawn.

Operation is automatic, with production of as many as seven copies per minute. Figure C-33 illustrates how the 914 operates. The machine is recommended for use when 2,000 or more copies per month are required. Copy papers of standard 20-pound minimum weight, bond paper, manila, office stationery, card stock not more than 0.006 inch thick, and selected paper offset masters are recommended. The original, which may even be a three-dimensional object, is placed facedown on a scanning glass, and a scanning light passes under the glass. The image is projected to a selenium-coated photoconductive drum, thereby forming a pattern of electrically charged and discharged areas corresponding to the image and non-image areas of the original. The surface of the drum is positively

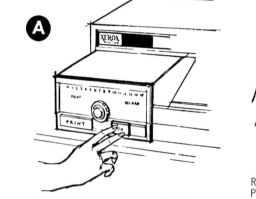

TO START COPIER PUSH ON BUTTON

RAISE COVER
PLACE MATERIAL TO BE COPIED (ORIGINAL)
FACEDOWN ON COPY GLASS

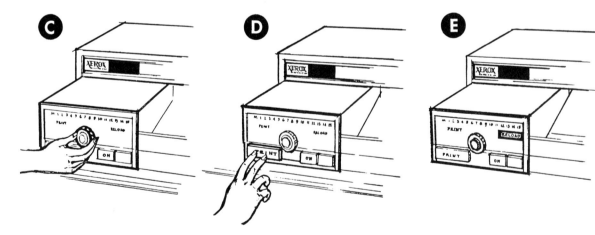

DIAL NUMBER OF COPIES TO BE MADE
BY TURNING PRINT – SELECTOR KNOB

IF MORE THAN 15 COPIES ARE NEEDED
DIAL M (MULTIPLE)

PRESS PRINT BUTTON

WHEN RELOAD SIGNAL APPEARS
914 COPIER IS READY FOR NEW
ORIGINAL

Fig. C-33   Panel operation of Xerox Model 914 copier.

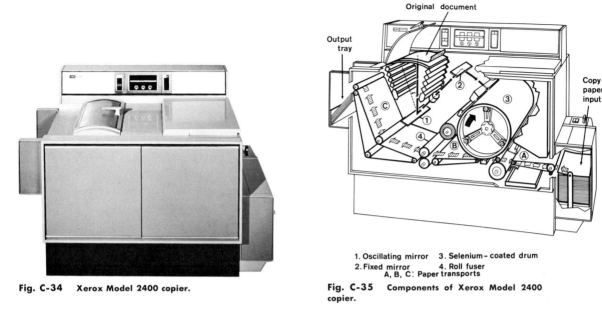

Fig. C-34   Xerox Model 2400 copier.

1. Oscillating mirror   3. Selenium – coated drum
2. Fixed mirror   4. Roll fuser
      A, B, C: Paper transports

Fig. C-35   Components of Xerox Model 2400 copier.

charged as the drum rotates clockwise. The latent electrostatic image is developed by a cascade of powder over the drum. The powdered image is transferred electrostatically from drum to stock. The image is then permanently fused by heat.

The smaller Xerox 813 copier uses the same process of xerographic reproduction as the 914 copier and is automatic in operation. The maximum image area is $8\frac{1}{2}$ by 13 inches, and copies are 6 percent smaller than the original. The 813 will not copy from three-dimensional objects.

Figure C-34 shows the Xerox Model 2400 copying machine, and Figure C-35 is a schematic illustration of its components. The machine is called the "2400" because it can produce 2,400 copies per hour. The 2400 uses the xerographic method of reproduction. Its operational sequence is as follows:

1. The original document is placed on the curved glass plate with the image facedown. A bank of fluorescent lights illuminates the image from below. The oscillating mirror scans the document and reflects the image, sending it along the optical path through a lens to a fixed mirror and onto the selenium-coated drum.

2. The paper on which copies are to be produced is brought up to feeder level by an automatic elevator. It is then fed into the machine and transported along belts, to which it is held by a vacuum system.

3. After a sheet of paper has been aligned properly at the first roll, it moves to the drum where the image is transferred to it, and then to a heated roll fuser, which permanently fixes the image on the paper surface.

4. From that point, the paper is carried along another transport to the output tray, where copies are stacked.

The xerographic-reproduction principle of operation is advantageous in that the toner, a fine powder composed of microscopic particles, can be applied to ordinary paper. Sensitized or diazotype copy papers are not needed. The number of copies desired is dialed in ranges from 1 to 499. Copies emerge dry. The 2400 copies from originals with any minimum size; maximum paper size is $8\frac{7}{8}$ by $14\frac{7}{16}$ inches, and maximum image size is $8\frac{1}{2}$ by 13 inches. Minimum copy-paper size is 8 by 10 inches, and maximum size is $8\frac{1}{2}$ by 13 inches. Recommended copy-paper weights are 16- or 20-pound stock. While the xerographic process utilizes electrostatic forces in transferring the image to the drum, the process differs from electrostatic printing in that the material to be copied on does not come in contact with a selenium-coated drum and the toner image is not transferred to a drum.

copyright   A number of types of material are copyrightable.

Books. Three steps must be taken to obtain the protection of the laws concerning copyright in books: (1) produce copies of the book with the copyright notice, (2) publish the work, and (3) register the copyright claim.

STEP 1. The work must first be produced in copies by printing or other means of reproduction. It is essential that the copies bear a copyright notice in the required form and position. The notice must contain three elements: (*a*) the word "Copyright," or the abbreviation "Copr," or the symbol "©"; (*b*) the year date of publication; and (*c*) the name of the copyright owner. The use of the symbol © may result in securing copyright in some countries outside the United States under the provisions of the Universal Copyright Convention, which protection might not be secured by use of either of the alternative forms of notice. The year date of publication is the year in which copies of the work were first placed on sale, sold, or publicly distributed by the copyright owner or under his authority. The name of the copyright owner must appear. The copyright notice will therefore take three forms, as follows:

© John Doe 1967

The copyright notice must appear on the title page or the page immediately following. The "page immediately following" usually means the reverse of the title page, since a "page" is regarded as one side of a leaf. (Books submitted for copyright to the Library of Congress have been rejected because this requirement had not been met.)

STEP 2. This step involves publishing the work bearing the copyright notice. "Publication" for copyright purposes is generally regarded as the placing on sale, sale, or public distribution of copies. The Copyright Law defines the "date of publication" as ". . . the earliest date when copies of the first authorized edition were placed on sale, sold, or publicly distributed by the proprietor of the copyright or under his authority. . . ." It is the act of publication with notice that actually secures copyright protection. If copies are published without the required notice, the right to secure copyright is lost and cannot be restored. If all copies are published with the required notice, the work is copyrighted. This premise may be modified by the proposed revision of the Copyright Law.

STEP 3. This third step consists in registering the copyright claim. Such registration or lack of registration does not affect the copyright but merely gives the copyright owner the remedies of the United States Copyright Law against an infringer. Immediately after publication two copies of the work, as published with the copyright notice, must be mailed to the Register of Copyrights, Library of Congress, Washington, D.C. 20540, together with an application on Form A properly completed and notarized and a small fee for registration. The term "books" refers to literary or textual publications with or without illustrations, such as fiction and nonfiction, poetry, collections, directories, catalogs, and information in tabular form. It includes not only material published in book form but also pamphlets, leaflets, cards, and single pages containing text.

Maps (Class F). This class includes all published cartographic representations of areas, such as terrestrial maps and atlases, marine charts, celestial maps, and such three-dimensional works as globes and relief models.

Works of art (Class G). This class includes published or unpublished works of artistic craftsmanship, insofar as their form but not their mechanical or utilitarian aspects are concerned, such as artistic jewelry, enamels, glassware, and tapestries, as well as works belonging to the fine arts, such as paintings, drawings, and sculpture. In order to be acceptable as a work of art, the work must embody some creative authorship in its delineation or form. The registrability of a work of art is not affected by the intention of the author as to the use of the work, the number of copies reproduced, or the fact that it appears on a textile material or textile product. The potential availability of protection under the Design Patent Law will not affect the registrability of a work of art, but a copyright claim in a patented design or in the drawings or photographs in a patent application will not be registered after the patent has been issued. If the sole intrinsic function of an article is its utility, the fact that the article is unique and attractively shaped will not qualify it as a work of art. However, if the shape of a utilitarian article incorporates features, such as artistic sculpture, carving, or a pictorial representation, which can be identified separately and are capable of existing independently as a work of art, such features are eligible for registration.

Reproductions of works of art (Class H). This class includes published reproductions of existing works of art in the same or a different medium, such as a lithograph, photoengraving, etching, or drawing of a painting, sculpture, or other work of art.

Drawings or plastic works of a scientific or technical character (Class I). This class includes published or unpublished two-dimensional drawings and three-dimensional plastic works which have been designed for a scientific or technical use and which contain copyrightable graphic, pictorial, or sculptured material. Works registrable in Class I include diagrams or models illustrating scientific or technical information in linear or plastic form such as, for example, a mechanical drawing, an astronomical chart, an architect's blueprint, an anatomical model, or an engineering diagram. A work is not eligible for registration as a "plastic" work in Class I merely because it is formed from one of the commonly known synthetic chemical derivatives such as styrenes, vinyl compounds, or acrylic resins. The term "plastic work," as used in this context, refers to a three-dimensional work giving the effect of that which is molded or sculptured. Examples of such works include statues of animals or plants used for scientific or educational purposes and engineers' scale models. A claim to copyright in a scientific or technical drawing, otherwise registrable in Class I, will not be refused registration solely because it is known to form a part of a pending patent application. Where the patent has been issued, however, the claim to copyright in the drawing will be denied copyright registration.

Photographs (Class J). This class includes published and unpublished photographic prints and filmstrips, slide films, and individual slides. Photoengravings and other photomechanical reproductions of photographs are registered in Class K, on Form K.

Prints, pictorial illustrations, and commercial prints or labels (Class K). This class includes prints or pictorial illustrations, greeting cards, picture postcards and similar prints produced by means of lithography, photoengraving, or other methods of reproduction. These works when published are registered on Form K. A print or label (not a trademark) containing copyrightable pictorial matter or text and published in connection with the sale or advertisement of an article or articles of merchandise is also registered in this class, on Form KK. In the case of a print that is published in a periodical, Form KK is submitted if the print is used in connection with the sale or advertisement of an article of merchandise; Form BB, if it is not. Multiple works are more appropriately placed in Class A than in Class K.

A claim to copyright cannot be registered in a print or label consisting solely of trademark subject matter and lacking copyrightable matter. While the Copyright Office will not investigate whether the matter has been or can be registered at the Patent Office, it will register a properly filed copyright claim in a print or label that contains the requisite qualifications for copyright even though there is a trademark on it. However, registration of a claim to copyright does not give the claimant rights available by trademark registrations at the Patent Office.

Titles, names, and short phrases. Names, titles, and other short phrases or expressions are not copyrightable. The Copyright Office cannot therefore register claims to exclusive rights in the names of products or organizations, pen names, stage names, titles, catchwords, slogans, advertising phrases, mottoes, and the like. This is true even if the name, title, phrase, or expression is novel or distinctive or lends itself to a play on words. In order to be copyrightable, a work must contain at least a certain minimum amount of authorship in the form of original literary, artistic, or musical expression. When a work is registered in the Copyright Office, it must be given a distinguishing title for purposes of identification. However, the fact that registrations are indexed by title does not mean that the titles themselves are protected by copyright. For this reason search is not undertaken to determine whether titles or names are original, for the records reveal many different works that are identified by the same or similar titles. Some brand names, trade names, slogans, phrases, and labels may be entitled to protection under the general rules of law relating to unfair competition or to registration under the provision of the trademark laws. The Copyright Office has no authority in these matters. Inquiries concerning protection under the trademark laws should be addressed to the Patent Office, U.S. Department of Commerce, Washington, D.C. 20231.[1] (*See also* COMMON-LAW COPYRIGHT; TRADEMARK.)

copywriting   Writing advertising copy and literature.

core   Paper or metal shaft around which the paper (web) is wound. It may be either returnable or disposable.

cornerer   Device equipped with a semicircular die that is used to cut round corners on printing stock.

correction overlay   Additional tissue overlay affixed to a board art for making corrections. Before the corrections can be made, the over-

---

[1] The information in this article is presented to assist the reader in an understanding of current laws with respect to copyright. Because laws change, it is recommended that competent authority be consulted concerning these matters.

lay must be registered to the art by drawing crop marks. A wax pencil should be used when marking an overlay attached to a photograph. Once corrections have been made, the overlay is replaced and returned with the art so that the corrections may be checked.

correction tape Tape employed to make corrections on masters used with spirit-process duplicators. The tape is mounted on an adhesive backing with $\frac{1}{6}$-inch widths for single-spaced copy and $\frac{1}{3}$-inch widths for double-spaced copy. To make a correction, the tape is removed from its backing and cut to the exact length of the error. The tape is pressed over the error on the back of the master. A clean strip of dye-carbon paper is then placed over the error, and the correction is typed over the error on the face of the master.

courtesy copy In business correspondence, a tissue copy (manifold or onionskin) that accompanies a signed original. It may be routed to interested persons while the original is held by the recipient for reference or action.

courtesy line (credit line) Line of text placed at the bottom of an illustration or in a parenthetical phrase following the figure title, in which credit is given to the person or organization supplying the illustration. The courtesy line may read, for example, "Courtesy of John Doe Art Studies." The type should be no smaller than 6 point. Credit should be given at all times, but in lieu of a courtesy line a product may be identified in the figure title. Examples of such identification are "Robertson's Model E process camera" and "The Model E process camera manufactured by Robertson."

cover flap *See* MOUNTING AND FLAPPING.

cover paper Paper used as covering to protect the contents of advertising brochures, pamphlets, books, booklets, etc. It may be obtained with finishes such as ripple, smooth, linen, fabric, corduroy, and antique. Antique is the most popular finish, followed by smooth and ripple. Base stock ranges from mechanical wood pulp to sulfite, sulfate, soda-pulp, and rag papers. Various coated cover papers, including plain heavy, plastic-coated, cast-coated, metallic, and cloth-lined papers, can be obtained. These coats and finishes meet almost every requirement of good appearance and durability.

Basic weights range from 40 to 100 pounds, 40, 50, 60, 65, and 85 pounds being the most popular. Some cover papers that are exceptionally heavily coated or are pasted in double thickness are sold in weights by points (10, 16, and 20 points). The basic size for all cover papers is 20 by 26 inches, in 500 sheets, except for weights sold by points. (*See also* TABLE 4.)

Craft-Color Trade name for thin colored self-adhering acetate sheets manufactured by Craftint. The sheets are available in a glossy finish for display as well as in a matte finish for pencil and ink work. Thirty-five or more colors are available. The sheets are used for multicolor layouts, dummy packages, displays, color reproduction, charts, maps, graphs, etc. The vermilion color photographs black and may be used through its transparency for accurate layout register. The colors are available in specific degrees of transparency or opacity, designated as T for transparent, ST for semitransparent, and O for opaque.

Craf-Tech Trade name for paste-ups by Craftint that include common pieces of hardware reproduced in various isometric views. These are especially useful in technical illustrating. (*See* Figure C-36.)

Craftint Trade name for paste-up and direct-transfer products of the Craftint Manufacturing Company. The products are used in newspaper advertising, direct-mail pieces, catalogs, sales manuals,

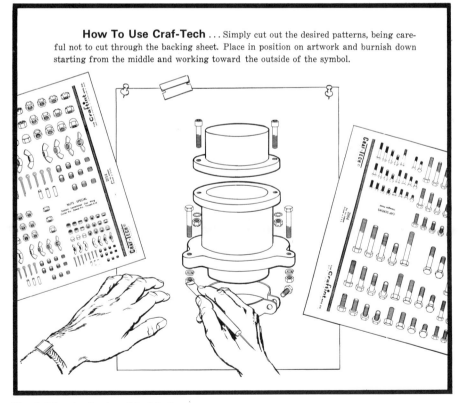

How To Use Craf-Tech ... Simply cut out the desired patterns, being careful not to cut through the backing sheet. Place in position on artwork and burnish down starting from the middle and working toward the outside of the symbol.

Fig. C-36 **Application of Craf-Tech patterns.**

1020

1022

1023

1025

1026

1027 BW

1028 BW

1100

1303

3014

3014A

1	TO	10	4000
1	TO	20	4001
1	TO	50	4004
1	TO	100	4006
1	TO	10	4010
1	TO	20	4011
1	TO	50	4014
1	TO	10	4020
1	TO	20	4021
1	TO	50	4024
1	TO	100	4026
1	TO	150	4027
1	TO	10	4030
1	TO	20	4031
1	TO	150	4037

A TO ZZ   A TO ZZ
A TO ZZ   4048
A TO ZZ   A TO ZZ

1 2 3 4 5 6 7 8 9 0
4049

Fig. C-37 Craft-Symbols.

Fig. C-38 Craf-Type (not actual size).

maps, graphs, cutaway drawings, architectural drawings, television and motion-picture titles, and other applications. Craftint categorizes its products as follows: Craf-Tech (line drawings of common hardware), Craf-Tone (shading mediums), Craf-Type (typefaces, symbols, sorts, etc.), and Letter-Set (dry-transfer sheets of alphabetical characters). (For a discussion of these products, see CRAFT-TECH; CRAF-TYPE; SHADING MEDIUMS; TRANSFER SHEET.)

Craft-Symbols Symbols manufactured by Craftint. They provide the artist with a library of symbols, from arrows to stars, to be used on layouts, finished art, and sign or presentation jobs. (*See* Figure C-37.)

Craf-Type Assembly of standard wax-backed acetate sheets of various typefaces and type sizes, symbols, characters, sorts, and designs by Craftint. A great variety of faces and sizes of type are obtainable (*see* Figure C-38). The range of sizes, which extends to a height of $1\frac{1}{4}$ inches, permits pasting up for layouts of all kinds. The sheets are available in 35 colors for convenient use on direct chart presentations. Thermo sheets, which have an especially prepared heat-resistant back, are obtainable for processes that involve heat during exposure, such as whiteprinting.

crash finish Linenlike paper finish. Its appearance is generally considered one of good taste.

creasing Making a partial fold in paper or board. Creasing by printing machines improves the endurance of sheets that must be folded, such as ledgers and heavy stock for cartons that are shipped "knocked down" and later assembled and formed for use.

credit line *See* COURTESY LINE.

crimping Creasing paper, especially at a binding edge where pages fold, so that the pages will be exposed and the book will open easily. (*See also* SCORING.)

Cronaflex drafting film Du Pont film having a standard thickness of 0.004 inch and a matte-finish drawing surface on one or both sides. It has a Cronar polyester base and accepts an extremely wide range of hard and soft pencil leads. The translucency of Cronaflex permits fast printing on blueprint or whiteprint reproduction machines. Cronaflex UC drafting film has a standard thickness of 0.004 inch and a heavy thickness of 0.007 inch. It is designed for high-quality ink as well as pencil drawings; emphasis is placed on minimizing pen wear.

Cronapress conversion film Nonphotographic pressure-clarifiable film used for producing one-to-one conversions to photomechanical plates from type, engravings, electrotypes, and other kinds of relief plates. The film is composed of a cellular pressure-sensitive coating on one side of a 0.002-inch sheet of clear Cronar polyester film base. The thin coating is opaque or milky white in appearance. It is not light-sensitive and can, therefore, be handled under normal illumination. (*See also* CRONAPRESS CONVERSION SYSTEM.)

Cronapress conversion system Du Pont system for making high-fidelity conversions from metal forms to photomechanical plates. It requires neither proof press nor camera; hence ink squeeze-out, density variations, lens distortion, and optical flare are eliminated. The metal relief form to be converted to film is placed on the vibration platform of a clarifying machine (Figure C-39), and a sheet of Cronapress conversion film is placed emulsion side down on the

Fig. C-39 **Du Pont's No. 100 clarifier.**

metal form. Next, a frame containing more than 10,000 tiny lead balls is locked in position over the conversion film and metal form. A vacuum is then created to bring the film and form into intimate contact.

Vibration created by the clarifier's motor and eccentric cams, sets the balls in motion. The bouncing balls strike the conversion-film surface at random; before conversion is complete, usually in six to eight minutes, there have been millions of impacts. As these impacts occur, the balls collapse the cellular coating of the conversion film where the film is in contact with a relief character or a halftone dot, thus producing a transparent, or clarified, image. The conversion film covering the nonprinting areas of the relief form remains opaque, or unclarified. The final result is a high-fidelity reproduction of the relief areas of the metal form with a transparent image and a milky-white background.

As the clarified or converted image is pulled from the relief form, it is a low-density right-reading negative. To increase the background density for contact printing, a black dye is applied to the coated side of the film. The cells of the unclarified areas of the converted film, which are still white and opaque, absorb the dye, thereby increasing the film's maximum density to more than 3.0. The transparent image areas remain clear because no cellular structure is left to absorb the black dye. Dyeing takes forty-five to sixty seconds on a production basis. The converted film is immersed in a stabilizing solution for twenty seconds to make the dye water insoluble. It is then momentarily rinsed in water, swabbed to remove residual dye from its surface, and dried. The dry conversion-film negative can be knife-etched, opaqued, stripped, and stored in the same manner as any lithographic film negative. The densified negative is now ready for contact printing to make the final negative or positive for offset plates, Dycril photopolymer printing plates (either letterpress or letterset), or gravure printing.

Cronar Registered trademark of Du Pont's polyester photographic film base. A fundamental study of polymer chemistry was made by Du Pont as long ago as 1928. In chemistry, polymerization is a reaction in which two or more molecules are combined to form larger molecules. In 1951, Du Pont produced experimental quantities of Cronar polyester photographic film base. This production demonstrated the feasibility of extruding a thick narrow web of polyester material and continually stretching and treating it to lock in the strength, durability, stability, and flexibility that are required in an ideal support for photographic emulsions. In January, 1957, the first polyester-based photographic product was made commercially available. The 0.004-inch Cronar film base was designed for applications in which flexibility and tear strength are essential. Shortly thereafter Du Pont was able to supply a complete line of color-separation, color masking, and lithographic films on a common support, thereby eliminating the problem of trying to get different materials, such as glass and acetate, to register to each other. Polyester films are flexible, are only slightly affected by changes in relative humidity and temperature, and will not crack or break in normal use. They are extremely resistant to tearing, lie flat, have excellent optical characteristics for assuring maximum image sharpness, and will not become brittle or change size with age.

Du Pont manufactures 21 graphic arts products for offset lithography, letterpress, letterset (modernized dry offset), gravure, and silk-screen use. All but 3 are on a Cronar polyester photographic film base. (*See also* ACETATE ORTHO LITHO FILM; CLEARBACK ORTHO LITHO FILM; CLEARBASE FILM; COMMERCIAL S FILM; CRONAPRESS CONVERSION FILM; DIRECT POSITIVE CLEAR FILM; DIRECT POSITIVE D FILM; HIGH CONTRAST PAN FILM; LITHO T PHOTOGRAPHIC PAPER; LOW CONTRAST PAN FILM; LOW GAMMA PAN FILM; MASKING (BLUE-SENSITIVE) FILM; MEDIUM CONTRAST PAN FILM; ORTHO A FILM; ORTHO D FILM; ORTHO M FILM; ORTHO S FILM; PAN LITHO FILM; PAN MASKING FILM; ROTOFILM; SCREEN-PROCESS FILM.)

crop mark   Mark used to define the limit of the reproduction area of an illustration and to establish the portion of the image that is to appear in the reproduction (*see* Figure C-40). Crop marks determine the size the image will take. They should appear on all illustrations at each of the four corners, marking the vertical and horizontal dimensions of the image area. Crop marks should be definite, be drawn with black ink, and extend no closer than $\frac{1}{4}$ inch to the outside of the reproduction area. The area designated by the crop marks should be a true rectangle. Though crop marks do not appear on final reproduction copy, they may be retained on the negative as evidence of the dimensions of the art.

cropping   Defining the reproduction-image area of line and continuous-tone art by drawing crop marks or of continuous-tone art by producing windows in negatives by means of dropout masks. Figure C-41 illustrates one method of cropping continuous-tone art. It includes the following steps:

1. Use a ruby- or amber-colored opaque stripping film slightly larger than the desired reproduction area of the photograph.

2. Secure the film with a strip of masking or other pressure-sensitive tape to the right of the mounted photograph along the vertical dimension. The tape serves as a hinge. Its left side must be straight and aligned to serve as the right edge of the masking window.

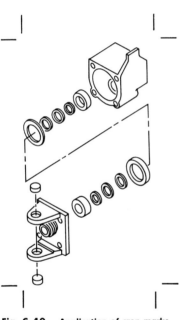

Fig. C-40   **Application of crop marks.**

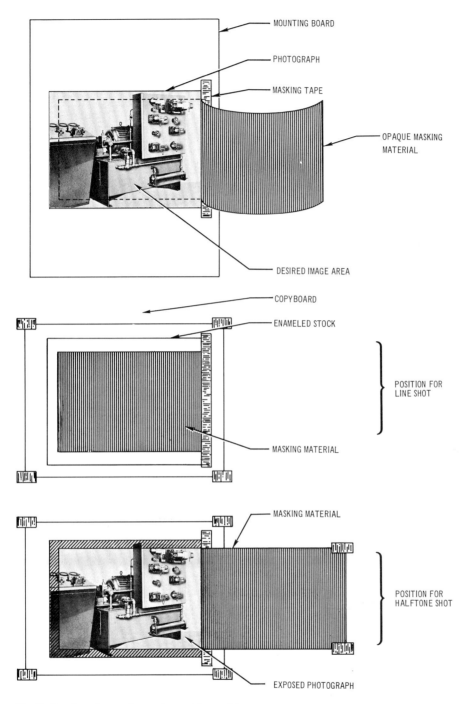

MOUNTING BOARD

PHOTOGRAPH

MASKING TAPE

OPAQUE MASKING MATERIAL

DESIRED IMAGE AREA

COPYBOARD

ENAMELED STOCK

POSITION FOR LINE SHOT

MASKING MATERIAL

MASKING MATERIAL

POSITION FOR HALFTONE SHOT

EXPOSED PHOTOGRAPH

Fig. C-41   Cropping continuous-tone art by masking.

3. Place a piece of mounting stock beneath the mask to avoid cutting through to the photograph.

4. Use a frisket knife and cut the film in a true rectangle on the three remaining sides to form the reproducible area of the photograph.

5. Peel and strip away excess masking outside the rectangle.

6. Tape the whole to the camera copyboard.

7. Tape a sheet of white enameled paper between the photograph and the mask, making certain that the mask is correctly aligned.

8. Photograph a line negative of the mask and leave the negative in the camera.

9. Remove the enameled paper. Swing the mask on its taped hinge and tape it flush against the copyboard, exposing the photograph.

10. Make a normal screened-halftone exposure of the photograph.

The line shot photographs only the mask and entirely eliminates the image of the photograph. The negative is still light-sensitive where covered by the opaque mask and will accept the halftone image. Any instructions pertaining to the size, title, or classification of the photograph may be written on the mask with a black grease pencil. This technique can be varied by cutting the mask into the shape of a heart, letter, numeral, or any other configuration or symbol desired.

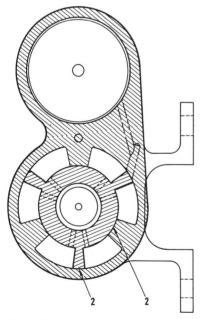

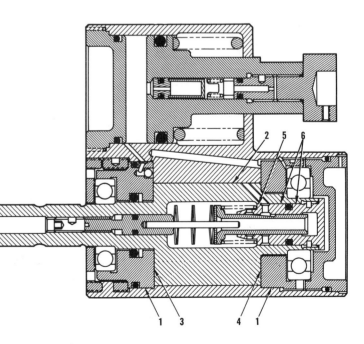

Fig. C-42   **Cross-section view.**

This use of a line shot and a screened shot should not be confused with cropping continuous-tone copy with line copy in a combination plate. In the latter technique, the line copy and continuous-tone copy are photographed by using two distinct negatives. The halftone is stripped into the line negative. (*See also* COMBINATION PLATE.)

Color blocks are fashioned by using various tints and shadings, as well as an opaque material (screened by the camera) that may be overprinted.

cross perforations   In web-press work, perforations made across the web, at right angles to the direction of web travel, to prevent signatures from bursting during folding. The perforations emit air trapped between the sheets and relieve sheet tension.

cross-fold   *See* CHOPPER FOLD.

cross-reference   Direction to a reader to refer to related matter in another part of a publication.

cross-section grid   *See* SQUARE GRID.

cross-section view   Technical illustration of an object in which all or part of the object is cut away to show the shape and construction of the cutting plane and the relationship of adjacent parts. In Figure C-42, parts of an object are designated by numbers keyed to a legend (not shown) describing them. This type of view is used in technical manuals to illustrate maintenance instructions for the overhaul of equipment and repair of parts when the interior construction or hidden features of an object cannot be shown clearly by other views.

crow quill   Very fine writing and drawing pen. The name is derived from the quill of the crow's wing, which was formerly cut to a fine point and used for writing with inks.

cumulative supplement   Supplement that includes all information contained in the preceding supplements of a publication and therefore supersedes them.

curve chart   Graphical representation that uses curves to reflect values such as time, distance, or any other condition desired (*see* Figure C-43). For example, the base of a chart may show a time value in years, months, weeks, or days, and the vertical dimension may reflect quantities. The curve chart is probably the most popular type of chart. (*See also* BAR CHART; COLUMN CHART; PIE CHART; SURFACE CHART.)

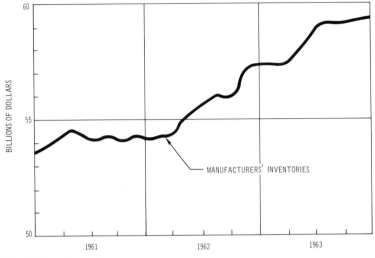

BILLIONS OF DOLLARS

MANUFACTURERS' INVENTORIES

1961   1962   1963

Fig. C-43   **Curve chart.**

curved plate   Printing plate, commonly a stereotype or electrotype plate, that is curved to fit the plate cylinder of a rotary printing press.

cut   Metal plate of an image from which the image is printed. The cut is prepared by photoengraving and has a relief (raised) surface. It is in reverse reading. When the image is imposed on stock, a right, or positive, reading results.

cut dummy   Cut proofs of illustrations arranged in sequence to facilitate page makeup.

cut-in initial   *See* INITIAL.

cutline   Placing of a caption in an illustration. In addition, the meaning of the term has been broadened to include instruction to the printer to insert an illustration during makeup. An example is "CUTLINE: Fig. 1. Rate-control mechanism."

cutoff   Paper dimension fixed by the size of the press cylinder, which limits the cutoff at right angles to the travel of the web. The opposing dimension is the width of the web; this can be varied. Common dimensions for a web-fed press are 36 inches in width by a $22\frac{3}{4}$-inch cutoff.

cutout   Piece cut out of stock by a steel die. A rectangle may be cut out of the cover of a soft-cover booklet to expose the title or other pertinent information printed on an inside page.

cutting chart *See* TABLE 3; TABLE 4; TABLE 6.

cutting-plane line   In engineering and mechanical drawings, a line indicating a plane in which a section is taken. It is designated as an "extra-thick" line. The line, together with arrows and letters, forms the cutting-line indication. The arrows, which are placed at the end of the cutting plane, indicate the direction from which the sections are viewed. The cutting plane may be a single continuous plane, or it may be bent or offset if details can thus be shown to better advantage. (*See also* LINE CONVENTIONS: ENGINEERING DRAWINGS.)

cylinder press, flatbed   Printing press in which the printing form remains on a flatbed and the paper, which receives the impression, is held by grippers and revolves on a cylinder. The pressure applied between the cylinder and the form is controlled by packing the cylinder surface. A flatbed cylinder press is suitable for all kinds of work, from printing on heavy rough stock to producing delicate halftones and color reproductions. It may be used to print books, folders, broadsides, catalogs, printed forms, and brochures. With slight modifications, it may also be used as a cutting and creasing machine for heavy stock.

A two-color cylinder press has a single bed on which the plates for two colors are installed. Two fountains of different-colored inks are used, and each color has its own impression cylinder and ink-distributing system. When the first color has been printed from its impression cylinder, a transfer cylinder receives and transfers the paper to the second color-impression cylinder and prints the second color. Thus two colors are printed on one side of a sheet in one trip of the paper through the press.

cylindrical casting   Stereotype cast into a curved mat for use on a rotary press. It is employed only in letterpress printing.

D

dagger The symbol †, used to key text or tabular matter to a footnote. It is the second of a series of reference marks. (*See* REFERENCE MARKS.)

daguerreotype Early type of photograph or the process of producing such a photograph. The name is derived from the French inventor Daguerre. Daguerrotypes were produced on silver plates or silver-covered copper plates.

damping Moistening the printing plate of an offset press. Lithography is based on the principle that grease and water do not mix. When ink rollers come in contact with the printing plate, its surface must be kept moist enough to prevent the ink from adhering to the part of the plate that has no image. The water solution is carried from the water pan to the plate by a roller partially immersed in the pan and then to damping rollers, which moisten the plate. Considerable skill and experience are required to maintain the proper proportion of ink and water.

dancer roll Name given to the rider roller in a web press. (*See* RIDER ROLLER.)

dandy roll   In paper manufacturing, the roller that contains the design, trademark, name, etc., and impresses these on the paper to form the watermark image.

dark-print process   Wet process used to make the common blueprint. It was the first method of reproducing large drawings in quantity. In the dark-print process, copies are made from right-reading translucent originals. The image is white on a medium or dark blue background of contact size. Copies are made by exposure to light and development in an aqueous solution. The copies are then dried, either in the blueprint machine or by exposure to air.

The dark-print process is the opposite of the whiteprint process. In the dark-print process, what was black is made white and what was white is made black; in the whiteprint process, what is black stays black and what is white stays white.

The copy paper used in making blueprints is called blueprint paper. It is iron-sensitized (by impregnated ferric compounds), whereas in the whiteprint process material coated with diazo compounds is used for copy paper. Formerly, the translucent original drawing used in making a blueprint was placed in an ordinary glass frame on top of what was then called litmus paper. The exposure was made by holding the frame to the sunlight for a few seconds. Light penetrated the nonimage area, where it destroyed the dye in the litmus paper. The image protected the image area of the paper from the sunlight. The paper was then submerged in water and washed. The result was a blueprint, which was hung up to dry. The principle is the same today, but the method of production has changed from hand to machine. The blueprint machine operates by ultraviolet-light exposure, and the print is developed, washed, and dried in the machine. It is also possible to make blueprints in a whiteprint machine by using only the exposure unit and bypassing the development stage. Blueprint paper must be used. The prints are then washed and air-dried.

Blueprints can stand hard usage because the copy paper contains a good percentage of rag, and they hold up well in shop and field. As blueprints are made by a wet process, however, the linear scale is only fair.

data points   Symbols used for plotting events or other information on graphs and charts. Data points (Figure D-1) are used with straight lines or with curves. A legend or key explains the meaning of each point. As an example, data points may be used to chart a sequence of events as the events take place or a sequence of proposed steps for a project. When open-faced data points are used, an event can be shown as having occurred by filling in the relevant point.

DISTINCTIVE SHAPES MAY BE USED FOR DATA POINTS:

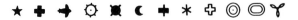

OR, MORE ARTISTIC SHAPES MAY BE USED:

AVOID SUBTLE DISTINCTIONS THAT MAY CAUSE DATA POINTS TO BE CONFUSED WITH THE ART:

Fig. D-1   Data points.

datum line   Line used in engineering and mechanical drawings to indicate the position of a datum plane. It is designated as a "thick" line and consists of one long and two short dashes evenly spaced. (*See also* LINE CONVENTIONS: ENGINEERING DRAWINGS.)

dead matter (killed matter)   In hot-metal composition, lead type masses, plates, cuts, etc., that are no longer required and may be melted down, or "killed," for reuse of the lead.

dead metal   Waste or unnecessary metal around or on a photoengraving. The metal is removed by cutting out, routing, or deburring.

dead time   *See* DOWNTIME.

deadline   Final time set for the completion of a task of any kind.

deaerate   In printing and reproduction work, to remove the air between sheets of stock, particularly as applied to "jogging" by the use of joggers.

decalcomania (abbreviated **decal**)   Art or process of transferring pictures and designs from specially prepared paper to china, glass, or other materials. Modern usage of decalcomania has been extended to include transferring images to almost any surface.

deckle edge (featheredge)   Natural uncut feathery edge of paper. The effect may be produced either by hand or by machine, usually in antique papers because of the decorative value it adds to booklet covers, brochures, and direct-mail pieces.

dedication Brief inscription in which an author dedicates a book, usually in personal terms, to someone of his family, kin, or acquaintance. The dedication appears on a separate page in the front matter.

deep-etch plate Special offset plate printed from a film positive instead of a film negative. The unexposed image is given a surface etch to provide "tooth" for the enamel. The portion of the enamel or bichromated coating left on the plate after burning in or developing, which protects the covered areas from the acid etch, is removed later. The deep etch provides a rugged image because the enamel is laid directly on the etched surface rather than on the bichromate.

delayed dwell In a platen press, the time delay necessary in quality foil-stamping and embossing work, for which a combination of heat, impressional strength, and dwell-on impression is required. The heat is needed to soften the binders and coatings in paper, board, and other materials. Once the fibers in the stock have been softened, they can be realigned and reshaped to permit a sharp embossment. Heat is also required for foil stamping, and the increased dwell allows time for the heat to penetrate from the embossing or stamping die to the foil and thence to the stock. The delayed dwell is necessary to obtain proper adhesion of the foil to the stock. (*See also* PLATEN PRESS.)

dele Proofreader's mark indicating that a letter, word, phrase, sentence, or paragraph is to be deleted.

delineate In the graphic arts, to give depth to line art by making certain outlines heavier. The word also means to describe in detail.

density In general terms, the relative darkness of an image area as seen by the eye; in technical usage, a measure of light-stopping ability or blackening of a photographic image as read on a densitometer.

density, burnout *See* BURNOUT DENSITY.

density, maximum Highest density obtainable with a particular photographic or sensitized material after complete development. When one looks at a negative or a positive, the maximum density is the highest density noted.

density, minimum Lowest density noted on a photographic or sensitized material. The term is used in contrast to maximum density.

density range (density scale) Measured difference between the minimum and maximum densities of a particular negative or positive.

depth Thickness, measured downward from the surface of an object. The term "depth" is used only with objects having a third dimension, never to describe a plane surface.

descender *See* ASCENDER.

detail assembly drawing In engineering drafting, an assembly drawing on which some items are shown in detail in lieu of preparing separate detail drawings.

detail drawing Engineering drawing that gives detailed information on an item. It includes the form, dimensions, material, finish, tolerances, and other requirements of the item. The term also denotes a drawing used to show parts of structures and the relationship of parts, their sizes, contour, and construction materials.

detail view In engineering drawing, a view which shows part of the principal view of an item, using the same plane and arrangement but in greater detail and on a larger scale. (*See also* ORTHOGRAPHIC PROJECTION: ENGINEERING DRAWINGS.)

diagram drawing Engineering drawing that uses symbols to show the features and relationships of items and systems.

diamond Old type size. The nearest equivalent in the point system is $4\frac{1}{2}$ point.

diazo compound Mixture of diazo salts combined with an azo dyestuff component. The salts are sensitive to light, especially when ultraviolet light reflects on treated paper. The light destroys the salts, but the dye remains to reflect the image of the original. The whiteprint process of reproduction, as well as other methods of copying, uses paper, cloth, or film coated with diazo compounds. Diazo-treated film is employed extensively in microfilming.

diazo film Film used as a flexible transparent base and coated with emulsions of diazo salts and couplers.

diazo-generated reproduction Reproduction made from an image that has itself been reproduced by the whiteprint process or some other process in which a diazo compound is used as the emulsion-sensitive base.

diazo paper Paper treated with a diazo compound and an azo dyestuff component. Reproduction of the image depends on the light sensitivity of the dye. Development is achieved by destroying the diazo compound, the dye remaining to reflect the image. By varying the azo dye, black, red, blue, or sepia colors are produced to form the image. Reproduction is accomplished by utilizing ultraviolet light for exposure; therefore, all originals or masters must be on transparent or translucent material such as vellum, tracing cloth, or film. (*See also* WHITEPRINT PROCESS.)

diazo print Reproduction made by using the whiteprint process.

diazo process *See* WHITEPRINT PROCESS.

Diazochrome projecturals Diazo-sensitized films that produce colored-dye images on a transparent plastic base. Diazochrome is a trade name of the Technifax Corporation. The films are designed for use in overhead projectors and lend effectiveness to the $3\frac{1}{4}$- by 4-inch standard stereopticon. They are also used for displays, overlays, and novelties.

diazotype process *See* WHITEPRINT PROCESS.

die cutting Cutting cardboard, paper, card stock, or other material with regular or irregular designs formed into dies. Pressure is applied to the die press containing the die, and a lift of the material is cut. If the cut stock is to stay in the material, small pieces of cut material are left to hold the die-cut piece together until they can be punched out later, as is done during the assembly of a point-of-sale display box.

differential letterspacing *See* PROPORTIONAL SPACING.

diffraction Apparent deflection of light into the geometrical shadow of an obstacle. Light appears to bend slightly around the edges of opaque material.

diffusion-transfer process Successful and popular method of producing an image from an original by the diffusion of chemicals, in which the image is transferred from a negative to a material such as paper or a flexible printing plate. The original may be opaque

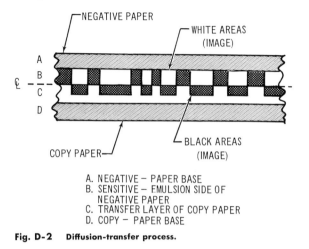

A. NEGATIVE – PAPER BASE
B. SENSITIVE – EMULSION SIDE OF
   NEGATIVE PAPER
C. TRANSFER LAYER OF COPY PAPER
D. COPY – PAPER BASE

Fig. D-2 **Diffusion-transfer process.**

or translucent or may have copy on both sides of the sheet. The process is used largely by manufacturers of photocopying machines. Though grossly exaggerated for clarity, Figure D-2 portrays the negative-paper and copy-paper relationship. The center line divides the two papers. The original has already been exposed to the negative. The sensitive-emulsion side *B* of the negative paper is composed of gelatin and grains of silver salts. Transfer layer *C* of the copy paper is composed of gelatin also, in addition to silver sulfide or colloidal silver.

After exposure and during development, the negative paper is pressed against the copy paper as illustrated, with the emulsion side *B* of the negative paper and the transfer layer *C* of the copy paper in close contact. During development, the grains of silver salts in the emulsion side *B* of the negative paper which have been exposed to light (have not been protected by the image) are converted into black metallic silver; that portion of the negative appears black. Where the silver salts have not been exposed to light (have been protected by the image), they remain intact and the negative paper remains white. Thus a black-and-white negative image is formed on the negative paper. The undeveloped silver salt grains, which now represent the image, pass by diffusion into transfer layer *C* of the copy paper or other material, where, by chemical action, the salts are converted into black metallic silver and form the image on layer *C*. Thus black areas on layer *C*, which represent the image, are formed under the white areas of layer *B* of the negative, and a positive image of the original appears on the copy paper.

dimension drawing (inspection drawing) Cross-sectional illustration used in overhaul and maintenance technical manuals to instruct personnel how to inspect, repair, and replace parts of equipment

so that the equipment may be kept within designed operating tolerances. In Figure D-3, supporting text instructs repairmen on the
disposition of parts that do not meet the requirements outlined in
the illustration.

dimension line In orthographic engineering and mechanical drawings, a line used to indicate the dimension between two points. It
is designated as a "thin" line. Dimension lines are unbroken except
where space is required to insert the dimension. (*See also* LINE
CONVENTIONS: ENGINEERING DRAWINGS.)

dimensioning *See* SCALING.

dimetric projection *See* AXONOMETRIC PROJECTION.

dinky In newspaper jargon, a half roll (web) of paper measured
along the width, not along the diameter. For a 14-page newspaper,
12 pages would be produced from three full rolls and a dinky roll
would be provided to print the remaining 2 pages. The four webs
(three full webs and one dinky) would then be joined at the former
section to produce the 14 pages.

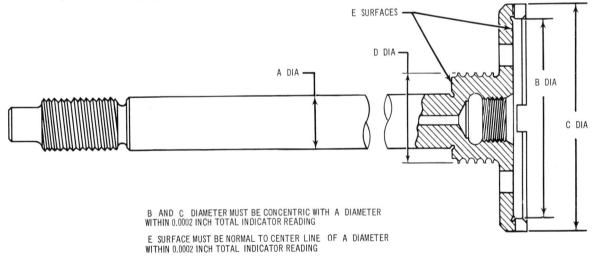

B AND C DIAMETER MUST BE CONCENTRIC WITH A DIAMETER
WITHIN 0.0002 INCH TOTAL INDICATOR READING

E SURFACE MUST BE NORMAL TO CENTER LINE OF A DIAMETER
WITHIN 0.0002 INCH TOTAL INDICATOR READING

A	B	C	D
0.3936 IN. MIN	1.4370 / 1.4372 IN.	1.62 / 1.64 IN.	0.6545 IN. MIN

Fig. D-3 **Dimension or inspection drawing.**

diploma paper (art parchment)   Fine printing paper manufactured especially for greeting cards, official documents, certificates, awards, diplomas, and the like. The paper may contain up to 100 percent rag; the basic size is 17 by 22 inches and the basic weight 50 pounds.

direct color separation   Color separation in which the various separation exposures are made through a halftone screen so that screened separation negatives may be obtained directly. (*See also* COLOR SEPARATION.)

direct-copy process   *See* WHITEPRINT PROCESS.

direct image   Image applied directly to a paper or printing plate. (*See* DIRECT PLATE MAKING.)

direct mail   Literature mailed by an advertiser directly to an addressee, usually to promote or sell a product or a service.

direct plate making   Any method of applying an image on the surface of a coated printing plate without intermediate steps (*see* Figure D-4). Direct plate making is particularly suitable for producing an image on paper plates. Intermediate steps are used for indirect plate making with a process camera, xerographic photocopying machines, and other processes. Any typewriter can be used for typing text on paper plates, although lines are ruled with ink or drawn with a special reproducing pencil. Corrections are marked on the plate with a nonreproducing pencil. The nonreproducing-pencil marks dissolve when washed off the plate by an aqueous solution during the first few revolutions of the master cylinder.

An image may also be applied directly to the plate by preprinting or with an ink pen, graphite or grease pencil, ballpoint pen, rubber stamp, brush, or crayon. Colors are produced by making separate color plates in register with the use of a light table.

The offset method of printing is based on the principle that grease and water do not mix. The master plate is placed on the master cylinder of the duplicator, and the aqueous solution is applied to the plate from a fountain. The solution is repelled by the grease-receptive image but is accepted by the nonimage area on the master. The ink adheres only to the grease-receptive image and is repelled from the wet nonimage area of the plate. As the master cylinder revolves, the various rollers continue to supply the solution and ink to the plate on the master cylinder. The image is transferred from the master plate to a cylinder containing a rubber blanket. An impression cylinder then brings paper in contact with the blanket cylinder, thus offsetting the image from blanket to paper.

Use of an offset duplicator makes it possible for an organization to control copy during all phases of production, thus enhancing both control of copy and speed of execution. Quality, costs, quantities, and time schedules are important factors to consider when offset duplication is compared with other methods of reproduction. (*See also* OFFSET DUPLICATOR.)

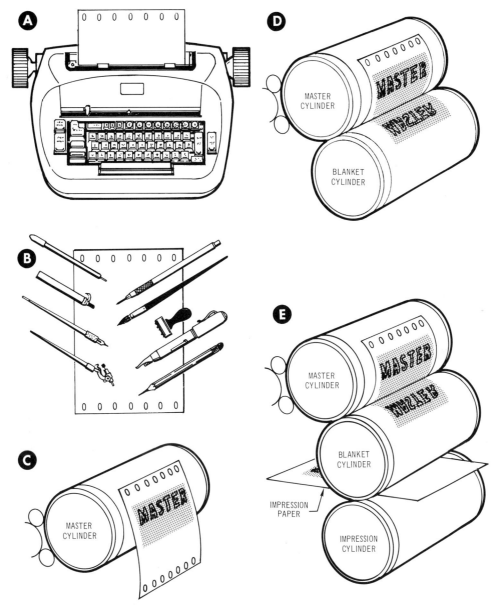

Fig. D-4 **Direct-image plate making.**

Direct Positive Clear film   Lithographic film produced by Du Pont on Cronar polyester film base. It is used to make duplicate line and halftone positives or negatives with single exposure and development steps. The film can also be employed for lateral reversals, combination line and halftone work, step-and-repeat work, transparent overlays, and the printing of combination images that are part negative and part positive. Exposure is normally made through yellow or orange sheeting.

Direct Positive D film   Lithographic film produced by Du Pont on Cronar polyester film base. It is a high-contrast, high-maximum-density, slow-contact speed film with treated surfaces to control Newton's rings, and facilitate critical contact for exposing Dycril photopolymer printing plates, smooth-surfaced presensitized offset plates, and screen tints. The film is capable of positive-to-positive and negative-to-negative reproduction with single exposure and development steps.

display ad   Advertisement that is not placed under a classified heading with word-line advertisements. It may include artwork in addition to text copy.

display blank   Paper manufactured especially for show cards, posters, outdoor advertising, etc. Standard sizes are 22 by 28 by 44 inches. Display blanks may range in thickness from 2-ply (0.012 inch) to 16-ply (0.056 inch). The most popular thicknesses are 6-ply (0.024 inch) and 8-ply (0.030 inch). Popular colors are velvet white, white, ivory buff, light tan, yellow, light green, light blue, pink, oyster gray, black, imperial blue, scarlet, orange, and shamrock green.

display board   Heavy blank board used for display advertising. The standard size is 40 by 60 inches. Some boards are coated and colored on both sides with the same color; coats are usually dull. The popular thicknesses are 14-ply, 28-ply, and 43-ply. Colors are ivory, canary, ultramarine, blue, shamrock green, black, cardinal, and snow white. The surfaces have a good tooth for crayon, charcoal, ink and paint.

display type   Large type used for magazine and newspaper headings, posters, etc. The type is distinguished from body, or text, type used for text material. Display type is used also for display advertising. (*See also* TYPE SPECIMENS.)

display type writer   *See* TYPE WRITER, DISPLAY.

display typesetters   *See* TYPESETTERS, PHOTOGRAPHIC.

distemper *See* TEMPERA.

divider *See* INDEX GUIDE.

document, engineering *See* ENGINEERING DOCUMENT.

dodger Small handbill. (*See* HANDBILL.).

dodging Method used in printing photographs to create greater contrast between light and dark areas. The effect is obtained by moving a light screen between the light-exposure source and the photographic paper. Dodging is used in the aerospace industry to improve photographs photographed from outer space.

dogleg Colloquial term for a bent lead line. A lead line is drawn off in one direction and turned at an angle to point to or indicate an item or to call out an item or part on an illustration. The first part of the lead line is horizontal. The line then "doglegs" to point out the object and, in most cases, terminates in an arrowhead.

dot area Halftone pattern consisting of dots and the clear spaces between them. The percentage of the area that is occupied by the dots (which may consist of developed silver, printing ink, etc.) is known as the percentage of dot area. In a checkerboard pattern the percentage of dot area is 50 percent.

dot etching Changing tone values by chemically reducing the size of, or "etching," halftone dots. This method is used in lithography when tone values or color strength must be changed during the photographic steps rather than on the printing plate.

dot leaders *See* LEADERS.

double-burn To "burn" images in register on a sensitized plate from two or more different negatives.

double-coated paper Heavily coated paper. It is not necessarily coated on two sides but may be double-coated on one side only. Requirements for coated-two-sides, double-coated-one-side, or double-coated-two-sides paper should be stated specifically.

double image Two impressions of an entire image or of a portion of an image. A double image is, of course, undesirable. In printing, a double image may be caused by pages' touching each other during the pressrun while the ink is still wet. In the process of making plates, negatives, or projection or contact prints, a double image may be caused by a movement of the copy, plate, or negative during exposure.

double-imprint unit In a web-fed press, a unit with two sets of cylinders that permits an imprint to be changed while the press is running at full speed.

double spread (double truck) *See* CENTER SPREAD.

Doubletone Sheet of high-grade board stock manufactured by the Craftint Manufacturing Company. It is processed with two invisible shading screens, one of a light tone and the other of a dark tone. The artist applies one of two different developers to bring out the tone desired on the drawing. (*See also* SHADING MEDIUMS.)

downtime (dead time) Lost time due to malfunction of equipment, such as a breakdown during a pressrun, or loss of time when the time is chargeable to a job. The term also denotes a period of time when personnel are not working and are charging time against an assignment or a work-order number.

draft To compose a drawing or an illustration, usually with the intention of adding refinements after examination; also, to sketch an object. As a noun, the term denotes a preliminary version, such as a rough draft or first draft of a manuscript. A final draft, however, is the copy to be printed, duplicated, or reproduced.

drafting, automated Method of producing an image by means of a computer, the graphic information being transposed into digital form and the digital data converted into a graphic display. Originally, automated drafting was confined primarily to engineering design and drafting work. Now art pieces, such as electrical and mechanical schematics, flow diagrams, and charts as well as other line drawings, are made with the aid of computers. Isometric, perspective, trimetric, and dimetric illustrations are all possible. Automatic drafting equipment is complex and sophisticated, and a complete explanation of its operation cannot be presented here. The following discussion is intended to show technological advances and trends in automated drafting.

There are four general procedures for producing images with automated equipment:

1. The designer makes a layout of the object and designates reference points with dimension values, which the computer interprets as connecting lines.

2. The reference points are converted to numerical values, and

these values are inserted in electrical-accounting-machine (EAM) cards as punched holes.

3. An individual called a programmer sorts the cards in a succession of desired drawing steps according to the value expressed by the punched holes.

4. A magnetic tape is produced by the computer from the deck of punched cards. The tape operates in conjunction with a device called a "plotter," which contains the inking pen that forms the image on paper.

One automated drafting system involves the use of digital computers and punched tape. Small wires, or "fingers," ride on top of the tape as it moves along a directed path. When the wires are exposed to the holes in the moving tape, they "drop down" through the holes and make a connection that establishes electrical continuity. The continuity thus established stops and starts small electric motors. The motor shafts are geared to operate the inking pen at the time and in the direction commanded by the holes in the punched tape.

Figure D-5 shows the Gerber Series 1000 automated drafting system with control console and drafting table. It will scribe, draw, or print lines, curves, and symbols at a single digital command. The all-digital design includes a magnetic core memory. The system is capable of infinitely variable decimal scaling and also provides absolute zero offset. The Series 1000 computer control system may be integrated with a variety of drafting-table designs to meet requirements ranging from ultrahigh-accuracy printed-circuit work and high-speed designing to the lofting of aerospace configurations.

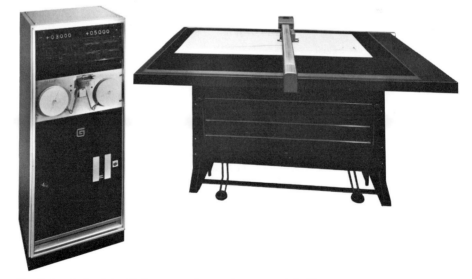

Fig. D-5 **Gerber Scientific Instrument Company's automated drafting system.**

An input is received from a photoelectric punched-paper-tape reader at a rate of about three hundred characters per second, from a manual keyboard, or directly from computer-punched cards or magnetic tape. The system operates in two distinct switch-selected modes: (1) absolute coordinate position data are accepted for drafting operations, and (2) incremental data are accepted in a variety of machine-tool numerical-control formats for tape verification without postprocessing. The magnetic core memory, available in 1,024-, 2,048-, or 4,096-word lengths, stores input data as well as commands for symbol generation. Decimal scaling, infinitely variable from 0.000001 to 9.999999 times size, is controlled by thumb-well switches. Similar switches allow zero offset, thereby making it possible to shift the plotting origin to any point on or off the drawing surface. In addition to those for zero offset and decimal scaling, manual controls are provided for mirror-image drawings, selection of any two of five axes, single or continuous plotting, and 20 to 100 percent of maximum speed. Position indicators display decimal information from on-line or off-line inputs.

The control console is composed of digital logic modules that are functionally grouped, color-coded, and keyed for interchangeability and ease of maintenance. Compact digital step motors are used throughout the drive system, thereby eliminating the need for servo controls. Each digitally driven step of the motor is an instant high-torque start-and-stop pulse that is made without slippage. The special-purpose control system computes the proper acceleration and deceleration rates for optimum traversing speed. The commands for symbol generation, which are stored in the magnetic core memory, are recalled at a single command to draw or scribe any symbol. The drawing head plots circular as well as linear interpolation at one command, thereby reducing program-preparation time and increasing the flexibility of the system. Absolute position feedback encoders further guarantee the highest possible accuracy.

The absolute position or incremental distance data are translated to graphic presentation on standard drawing surfaces, metal, coated Mylar, optical comparator material, or sensitized film. A solenoid-controlled vacuum hold-down system may be applied to specific zones or to the entire plotting surface. A 72-symbol printer for speed in annotating or a six-position turret-type drawing head for drafting flexibility may be manually or automatically controlled.

A display of graphs, curves, design data, verification of numerical machine-tool tapes, and map and chart reading require a high-speed drafting system. High accuracy is necessary for printed- and integrated-circuit applications, as well as for comparator chart scribing and pattern and template production. The complete range of table sizes can meet the requirements of small drafting work or of lofting, as in the aircraft, marine, and automotive industries. Drafting tables can operate in either a horizontal or a vertical position. Pinions at each end of a torsionally rigid tube in the X carriage mesh with precision racks. The Y carriage is driven by a ball screw in the X carriage. Drawing speeds of 60 to 240 inches per minute are attained.[1]

drafting and tracing materials Paper, cloth, or film may be used for drafting and tracing. These materials are characterized by their stability, tear strength, erasability, translucency, permanency, and ability to accept pencil and ink. Drafting papers must be translucent for whiteprint reproduction, be sufficiently translucent for tracing, and have good erasing characteristics. Erasability is of major importance. The weight, transparency, and strength of tracing papers vary with their manufacture. The greater the rag content, the greater the strength; but transparency may thus be sacrificed. Natural tracing paper should be used for sketching only when permanency is desired. Prepared tracing papers, which are treated with synthetic resins for translucency and drawing finish, combine strength and transparency.

Drafting cloth combines the advantages of transparency, strength, surface finish, and permanency. It will withstand repeated erasures without major surface deterioration, and aging does not affect its drawing or reproduction capability. Although drafting cloth is erroneously referred to as linen, it consists of cotton fibers treated with starch in the manufacturing process so that they will accept ink or pencil. Unless the cloth is resistant to moisture, however, white spots will appear because starch is water-soluble. If the cloth is exposed to excessive moisture, it will shrink and lose stability and the surface finish will be destroyed.

Drafting film is a somewhat recent innovation as a drawing material. It has great tear strength, dimensional stability, high transparency, and resistance to aging, heat, and dissolution. Moreover, it is waterproof. Mylar polyester film, a Du Pont product, is a popular base for drawing films on which surfaces and coatings are applied.

drafting machine Machine (*see* Figure D-6) that combines the functions of a T square or straightedge, a triangle, scales, and a protractor in one unit. Since it is controlled entirely by one hand, the other hand is left free for drawing. In operation, the scale assembly moves parallelly only. Thus, when the machine is set so that one scale is horizontal and the other vertical, the operator has a T square horizontally and a triangle vertically. When a triangle angle is required, the operator can instantly shift and snap the scale assembly into place at any unit multiple of 15 degrees. By releasing

[1]courtesy of Gerber Scientific Instrument Company.

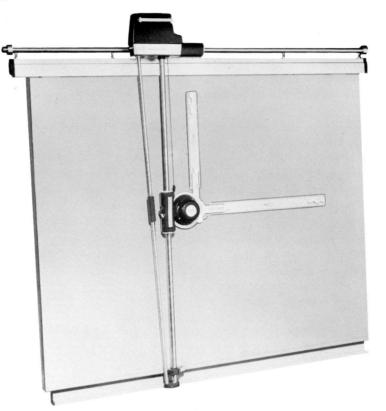

Fig. D-6 Keuffel and Esser's Paragon Auto-Flow drafting machine. (*Courtesy of Keuffel and Esser Co.*)

a lever, he can shift the scale assembly without changing the zero setting of the protractor. This adjustment is used to align the scales to the base of a new drawing. Since the adjustment has a range of 180 degrees, the scales can be set to operate from any oblique base with a zero setting of the protractor. Scales are available in a wide variety of graduations suitable for any type of work. They are adjustable and interchangeable.

drilling Using a rotating die or drill to make holes in sheets of stock or binding. It is preferable to employ the term "drilling" when this method is used and "punching" when ordinary paper punches are used.

drop folio Page number appearing at the foot of a page.

drop shadow Shadow of an image appearing behind the image, produced in such a manner that it is subordinate to the image. Drop shadows are common in logotypes and display advertising.

dropout Halftone negative, print, or plate from which certain areas present in the original have been removed by masking or opaquing. A silhouette dropout is one in which the entire background has been removed to emphasize the central image. The term "dropout" is also widely used to describe the blocking or masking out of any undesirable or unwanted image area.

dry diazo process Whiteprint process that employs ammonia vapor in the developing stage to reproduce contact-size copies from transparent or translucent originals. The development of this process dates to World War I, when a substitute reproduction process was needed to relieve the shortage of critical photographic papers. In Germany, a Benedictine lay brother named Koegel knew that certain combinations of diazo chemicals were sensitive to light. Believing that these chemicals could be applied to paper and other materials, he got in touch with a dye manufacturer, who provided him with chemicals for experiment. The result of his success, combined with the many improvements that have been made in the process, is evident. Figure D-7 illustrates how colored image lines are formed by the chemical reaction of two substances in the coating, one a light-

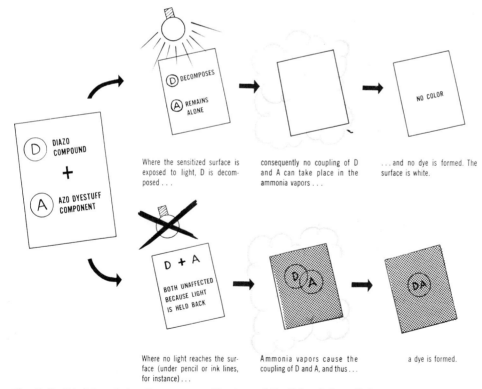

Fig. D-7 Principles of dry diazo process. (Courtesy of Keuffel and Esser Co.)

sensitive diazo compound and the other an azo dyestuff component, which produces the color when the component couples with the diazo compound. Coupling takes place when the coating is subjected to ammonia vapor.

dry finish   High finish obtained in paper without the use of moisture while the paper is being processed through calender rolls during manufacture.

dry ink (also called **powder ink: toner**)   Very fine powder used to form the image in some copying processes and in electrostatic screen printing. In the electrostatic process, dry ink, when automatically brushed onto the surface of the copy paper, adheres to a defined area to form the image by electrostatic attraction. The xerographic method employs a selenium-coated drum to which the image is attracted by electrostatic forces. The image is transferred to copy paper by rotating the drum. Electrostatic screen printing involves the deposit of dry ink on the receiving substratum. In all cases, the ink must be fused by heat or chemical means to fix the image.

dry mat paper   *See* MATRIX PAPER.

dry mounting   Method of mounting photographs without paste or rubber cement. A light thin paper called mounting tissue is used in conjunction with heat to mount photographs, prints, or other materials. The tissue acts as an adhesive between the copy or print and the mounting board. The procedure is as follows: (1) the mounting tissue is tacked to the back of the print with a hot iron, leaving the corners free; (2) the tissue is trimmed to the same size as the print; (3) the tissue and the print are positioned on the mounting board; (4) the face of the print is covered with clean paper and placed in a hot mounting press at a temperature ranging from 200 to 250°F, and pressure is applied for about ten seconds or longer. The duration of the pressure, which depends on the thickness of the print, allows the print to adhere to the mounting board as the result of heat. An ordinary electric hand iron may be used if a mounting press is not available. Care should be taken to have the iron hot enough to render the adhesive, but not hot enough to scorch the print. When color prints are being mounted, a somewhat lower temperature should be used. An electric hand iron should not be employed because its lowest setting may be too hot for color prints.

dry offset   *See* LETTERSET PRINTING.

dry stripping   Removal of the stripping layer from a film after the film has been processed and dried.

dry-to-dry processing Method of operation of an automatic film processor. The processor is loaded with unexposed dry film; it processes the film automatically through the stages of feeding, developing, fixing, washing, and drying, and then deposits the dry processed negative in a receiving tray.

drybrush Rendering technique used to give a shaded or hatched effect to art. The drawing medium—ink, watercolors, oils—is laid on in excess while it is wet. Then a stiff dry or damp brush is used to spread and brush the medium to other areas of the drawing.

dryer In web-press work, an oven located after the last printing unit through which the web passes. The dryer heats the web roll to a temperature as high as 350°F to dry heat-set inks. Gas, electricity, or steam may be used as the heating medium. Air blasts are employed to disperse volatile gases.

Dryphoto *See* OZALID DRYPHOTO.

drypoint Engraving made by using a sharply pointed instrument or needle directly on a copperplate. Drypoint engraving is an etcher's art. As the needle scores the plate, a ridge of copper is thrown up in relief to form the image. Drypoint is also used in retouching etched plates.

DTR Abbreviation for diffusion-transfer-reversal, a method of reproduction used in office copying machines. (*See* DIFFUSION-TRANSFER PROCESS.)

dual roll stand In web-press work, a roll stand that supports two units, one mounted above the other, in order to feed two rolls through the press at the same time. Production is higher than if only one web were used at a time.

dull coated paper Paper that has a dull finish, although it is coated. Paper may have a dull finish on one side and a highly polished coat on the other. Such paper may be used for fine color work or halftones on the glossy side and text on the opposite side, where the dull finish eliminates glare for reading solid copy.

dull coated-two-sides paper Book paper having a dull finish but coated on both sides.

dull finish Matte paper finish without gloss or luster.

dull seal Typesetter's term for stock having an adhesive back.

dummy Rough draft or proposal of a piece of printing material, pasted or bound together in the exact reproduction size and showing the areas that illustrations and text will occupy. Rough sketches and copy are usually included. The term "dummy" also denotes a sample book made up to show bulk, size, binding, paper, etc. For example, a dummy book consisting of blank pages and cover can be used to determine the size of the jacket.

duotone Two-color halftone print made from a screened photograph when one color or hue is desired. Two identical plates are made. The first plate is run in the desired color, and the second plate is run in black. During exposure, the second screen is turned at an angle of 15 to 30 degrees to the first screen to prevent the screens from meshing. (Meshing causes an undesirable checkered pattern called "moiré.")

duplex paper Paper having a different color or finish on each side of the sheet.

duplicate Identical copy of an original. A duplicate must be identical in every respect to the original. It is not a duplicate unless it is an exact likeness, and the image must therefore be of the same size, although the paper may be of any size. An enlargement or a reduction is not a duplicate.

duplicating, offset *See* OFFSET DUPLICATOR; *see also* DIRECT PLATE MAKING.

duplicating, spirit *See* SPIRIT DUPLICATING.

duplicating, stencil-method *See* MIMEOGRAPH.

duplicator, microfilm *See* MICROFILM DUPLICATOR.

duplicator paper (copy paper) Paper designed specifically for use as a master paper with spirit, gelatin, and other office duplicators (but not offset duplicators). Duplicator papers are available in basis weights of 16 to 24 pounds for 500 sheets of the basic size of 17 by 22 inches. Most duplicator papers are boxed in cut sizes of $8\frac{1}{2}$ by 11, $8\frac{1}{2}$ by 13, and $8\frac{1}{2}$ by 14 inches.

Duplimat masters *See* MULTILITH DUPLIMAT MASTERS.

dust cover Blank page inserted at the end of a coverless book for the protection of the last page that contains copy; also, the jacket of a hard-cover book.

dwell-on impression   *See* DELAYED DWELL.

Dycril   Registered trade name of the Du Pont photopolymer printing plates used in the conversion of metal relief plates for photomechanical reproduction (*See also* CRONAPRESS CONVERSION SYSTEM.)

Dycril Type C printing plate   Printing plate for letterset use on a conventional offset press. The Type C plate consists of a layer of photosensitive plastic called "photopolymer" and is bonded to a backing of Cronar polyester film base. It is the first Dycril plate to have a nonmetal support. Most existing presses need not be undercut to take the plate.

The Type C plate is placed on a rotary exposure cylinder, and a negative is placed over it (*see* Figure D-8). After an exposure of four to five minutes and without preconditioning, the plate is ready for "washout" to yield a 0.008-inch relief printing image. The Type C plate has a total thickness of 0.017 inch. Washout takes $2\frac{1}{2}$ minutes (*see* Figure D-9), and the plate is ready for the press after a short drying time. Some Type C plate letterset pressruns have reached nearly 3 million impressions.

dye transfer   Absorption process for making color prints with gelatin relief matrices. The matrix film produces a relief image in the gelatin when it is exposed through a color-separation negative. The three matrices are soaked in appropriate dye solutions. First the yellow printer is placed in contact with a gelatin-coated paper, which absorbs the dye. The matrix is then removed, and the red and blue printers are applied in turn and in register to complete the color separation.

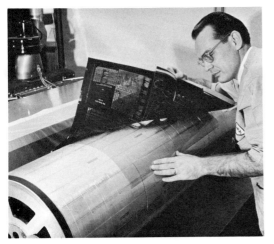

Fig. D-8   Exposing Dycril Type C plate.

Fig. D-9   Washout of Dycril Type C plate.

E

EAM Abbreviation for electrical accounting machine.

edge marks *See* HANGER MARKS.

edges, plate type *See* PLATE TYPE EDGES.

editing Preparation of a manuscript for publication. It may include revision, rewriting, and checking for accuracy, as well as what is usually termed "copy editing." Unless a copy editor is technically qualified, he should not make technical changes. Copy editing includes checking numerical sequence, marking for type, and making the style of the manuscript consistent. Spelling, punctuation, and grammar are corrected. Modified proofreader's marks are used in editing the manuscript. When possible, however, the corrections are written above the affected word or words rather than in the margin. Colored inks or colored pencils are generally used.

edition When a book is published for the first time, all copies are said to be the first, or original, edition. Reprintings of the first printing are called the second printing, third printing, etc. When an edition has been revised substantially, it is a second edition as well as the first revised edition; the first pressrun of this edition is the first printing of the second edition or of the first revised edition. These sequences keep recurring. A new edition requires a new copyright notice to protect rights to added material, but reprints from the original plates are protected under the provisions of the original copyright notice and date.

EF   Abbreviation for English finish.

eggshell finish   Finish similar to the texture of an eggshell, applied to book papers or boards.

electrical schematic   Diagram of the operational functions of an electrical or electronic system. The system's parts and components are represented by lines and symbols. When the electrical energy source is shown, it should originate at the left of the schematic, flow to the right, and then flow up or down, depending on the system. Adjacency of parts and components need not be depicted, but the system must function graphically. The schematic must be so drawn that the circuitry can be traced from component to component in the sequence of their respective functions, although no attempt is made to indicate the actual physical size and location of parts and components.

Electrofax paper   Sensitized copy paper used in copying machines in which electrostatic forces are utilized with toner (dry ink) to form an image. Bruning's 2000R electrostatic copier is an example of a copying machine that uses Electrofax paper. The process is as follows: (1) a uniform electrostatic charge is placed on the Electrofax copy paper; (2) an optical system scans the original, and the image is then projected from the original to the copy paper; and (3) toner is fused into the paper by heat, thus forming a permanent black image. Electrofax copies can be used as offset duplicator masters for limited runs.

electrolysis   Chemical decomposition of a compound by the passage of an electric current through an electrolyte. (*See* ELECTROTYPE PLATE.)

electrolytic engraving   Photoengraving process in which the non-image area on a relief printing plate is charged positively and then etched away. It is the reverse of electroplating.

electrolytic reproduction   Process of reproducing an image from film onto sensitized copy paper. The copy paper consists of a paper base, a thin layer of metal foil, and a coating of zinc oxide with resin as a binder. The coating is photoconductive and sensitive to light. In darkness, it is impervious to an electrical charge and has a high resistance. During exposure, light lowers the resistance of the translucent areas of the film that it penetrates, and a latent image is formed on the copy paper. Thus, a difference in resistance values is established between the image and nonimage areas. The image area has become an electrical conductor. After exposure, the copy paper is subjected to an electroplating solution, and direct current flows between the solution and the foil. The solution contains metal ions that are attracted to the image area (the area with the least resistance), and a metallic visible image is formed on the coating of the copy paper. The solution is applied to the surface of the paper as it passes over a moist sponge. Although the paper is thus moistened, it emerges comparatively dry. Electrolytic reproduction is used in some microfilm reader-printers, as the process takes only a few seconds.

electronic engraving Engraving printing plates by electronic means. The Vario-Klischograph (Figure E-1) is an automatic scanner that engraves from transparencies or reflection copy and produces screened separated positives in either enlarged or reduced sizes. The name is derived from "vario," meaning variable, "cliché,"

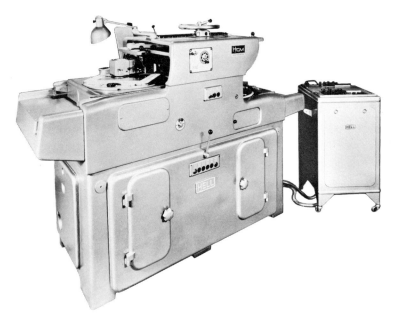

Fig. E-1   HCM Corporation's Vario-Klischograph electronic scanner and engraver.

meaning an oft-repeated phrase, and "graph," or writing; hence it is a changeable repeating plate-making machine. The lever, switch, and push buttons for controlling the mechanical action can be seen on the front of the machine in Figure E-1. The engraving table can be observed at the left beneath the light, and the picture table is at the opposite end. The hydraulic-drive mechanism is not visible. The electronic control cabinet is pictured on the right as a separate unit. Engraving and picture tables are connected to a vacuum pump so that both originals and blocks are held firmly in position by air pressure.

During engraving, the hydraulically driven engraving table moves to and fro so that the original moves beneath the scanning head. By means of a screw, the scanning head is driven step by step at right angles to the motion of the table. The copy is therefore scanned point by point and line by line. The electrical signals from the photocells, which correspond to the brightness and density of the copy, are fed to the engraving side through the electronic control cabinet. The amplified signals control the depth of the stylus in the engraving system. Like the scanning head, the stylus moves step by step across the table at right angles to the table motion.

The picture element seen by the scanning head is simultaneously engraved as a dot on the block. The scale can be varied from an enlargement four times the size of the original to a reduction to one-third of the size. The table drive and the cross-feed mechanism for the scanning and engraving heads are so constructed that their relative motions may be easily adjusted. Thus, during enlargement, the picture table moves more slowly than the engraving table, whereas during reduction the reverse is true.

The machine also makes it possible to enlarge or reduce portions of a picture. From nine screens, between 60- and 150-line, various combinations of four may be fitted to one machine and selected with a screen-selector lever. An engraving head adjusted to optimum electronic conditions is supplied for each screen. For line work, four cross-feeds of 183, 244, 366, and 488 lines per inch are built into the machine. One line engraving system is used for all feeds. The change from halftone to line engraving is made with a switch.

Two operations are required for line and halftone combinations. The halftone is engraved first and is then covered with a thin adhesive film. The line drawing or typed matter is engraved through this film. If screened positives are engraved, however, they can be copied to produce negatives and the line matter stripped in during the process.

Zinc, magnesium, copper, aluminum, stereometal, and plastic may be engraved in thicknesses between 0.02 and 0.08 inch. The machine is adapted to the various materials partly by electronic controls and partly by the use of different engraving styluses. By engraving on a special transparent plastic coated with an opaque dye, screened positives suitable for direct printing onto offset plates can be engraved. The special advantages of this technique are that the dots are sharp and have no fringes and that white areas can be engraved away. In the same manner, it is possible to produce screened positives that, after coming in contact with negatives, are suitable for production of "wraparound" plates.

The maximum size of black-and-white or colored reflection copy is 13.4 by 19 inches, and that of block from black-and-white or colored reflection copy is 12.2 by 17 inches. The maximum size of colored-transparency copy is 10 by 8 inches, and that of block from colored-transparency copy is 12.2 by 17 inches. Halftone screens are 60-, 65-, 75-, 80-, 85-, 100-, 120-, 137-, and 150-line. In all, 24 screen combinations, each involving four different screens, are available.

electronography   Printing process in which the ink (toner) is transferred by electrostatic attraction across a gap between the printing plate and the opposing surface, and the receiving material accepts the deposit of ink. (*See also* ELECTROSTATIC SCREEN PRINTING PROCESS.)

electrophotographic duplication   Process of making duplicate copies by utilizing electrostatic forces. It is unrelated to the electrostatic screen printing process.

electroplate   To cover with a coating by electrolytic means. (*See* ELECTROTYPE PLATE.)

electrostatic process   Copying or printing process in which an image is deposited on a material by means of electrostatic forces. Several methods of utilizing electrostatic forces have been developed. The methods themselves may be distinguished, and so may the purposes for which the equipment is designed. Is the equipment classified as a copying machine or as a printing press? The application of electrostatic forces is distinctive in each case. In one method, termed "xerography," the image is transferred by contact from a selenium-coated plate or drum to stock. This method is used in the Xerox 813, 914, and 2400 machines, which are classified as copying machines because copies are made from originals and reproduced on paper. A second type of machine, such as the Bruning Copytron 2000, transfers the image directly from the original to special Copytron paper. The fine powder, or toner, is automatically brushed on the paper and adheres to the image by electrostatic attraction. This machine is also classified as a copying machine because it makes copies from originals.

A third method of applying electrostatic forces is pressureless printing, known technically as the electrostatic screen printing process. Since this method uses a plate stencil through which toner is attracted to and deposited on almost any receiving surface, it can be classified as printing. The word "pressureless" is descriptive of the process because the printing plate does not touch the receiving substratum, as happens in conventional printing. In the electrostatic screen printing process, a charge is placed on the printing element and an opposite charge on the plate, thus creating a magnetic field. The receiving substratum or article imposed within that field intercepts the ink particles (toner) as they travel to the opposite charge. In the case of a conductive material, the material itself will take the charge and serve as a pole. Common to all electrostatic methods is the toner that is used to form the image instead of the wet or paste ink used with conventional printing presses. (*See also* DRY INK; ELECTROSTATIC SCREEN PRINTING PROCESS.)

electrostatic screen printing process (also known as **pressureless printing**)   Printing process developed by the Electrostatic Printing Corporation of America and therefore called the EPC process. A thin, flexible printing element, with finely screened openings defining the image to be printed, is used. An electric field is established between the image element and the surface to be printed. Finely divided "electroscopic" ink particles, metered through the image openings, are attracted to the printing surface, where they are firmly held by electrostatic forces until they have been fixed by heat or by chemical means. Since the image-forming element need not touch the image-receiving surface, quality is not dependent on the finish of the material. Rough textures and irregular surfaces take clear and legible images.

Full-color reproduction requires a series of printing elements representing the color separations. The material to be printed passes under a succession of these elements, and a multicolored-powder image ready for fixing is formed. The proper dry ink is available for each material to be printed.

The first applications of the EPC process were made in the packaging and the product-identification field. Apples, potatoes, avocados, melons, and other foods were marked with trademarks, brand names, or other information. Figure E-2 illustrates a two-lane Pure-Food-marker printing machine. Edible marks have been approved by the United States Food and Drug Administration. Equipment has also been developed for printing on such items as electronic components, lumber, plywood, sheet metal, sheet glass, metal parts, ceramics, corrugated boxes, and printed-circuit boards.

Fig. E-2 Unimark's Pure-Foodmarker pressureless printing machine (printing on avocados).

electrotype plate Duplicate printing plate produced by electrolysis. The image of the original plate is impressed under pressure into a mineral wax, a vinyl compound, sheet lead, or a wax-coated sheet of paper or metal to form the mold. Silver spray or a graphite coating is applied to the mold to make it electrically conductive, and the mold is then suspended from the negative pole of a direct-current circuit in an electrolytic bath. A bar of metal is suspended in the bath from a positive charge. The metal may be copper, nickel, iron, chromium, or a combination of these materials.

When current is applied, the metal decomposes and a thin film of it is deposited on the mold. The shell now contains an exact duplicate of the printing surface of the original plate. When backed with a low-melting alloy for strength, shaved for proper thickness, leveled, and trimmed, it becomes an electrotype printing plate.

Sheets of lead are often used instead of wax for molding halftones because halftones require fine work. When a vinyl compound such as plastic is used as the molding material, the plastic is lifted from the shell, but wax must be melted away. Sheets must be carefully stripped from the mold when lead is used. Chromium and nickel are used as plating materials for long runs because these metals are durable. Electrotype plates may be flat or curved to fit rotary cylinder printing presses.

Electrotypesetter   Operating unit for automatic linecasting control, manufactured by the Radio Corporation of America. It is controlled by punched tape. The reader is cable-connected to a slug-casting machine such as a Linotype or an Intertype. The keyboard of the casting machine is removed, and matrices are released by a solenoidal operation.

electrotypy   Art or process of producing electrotype plates. (*See* ELECTROTYPE PLATE.)

element   In advertising, any of the parts, such as display type, text copy, and line or continuous-tone art, that compose an advertisement; in book makeup, any of the components of the front matter, body, and back matter of a publication. (*See also* BOOK MAKEUP.)

elevation drawing: architecture   Rendering of design variations of different models of residences or commercial buildings, often used in conjunction with an architectural floor plan. Different models are indicated by "elevation A," "elevation B," etc. Elevation drawings are made in perspective. (*See also* ARCHITECTURAL FLOOR PLAN; ARCHITECTURAL RENDERING.)

elevation drawing: engineering   Drawing that depicts vertical projections of structures, inboard and outboard profiles of aircraft, automotive and marine equipment, or parts of such equipment. An elevation drawing shows the shapes and sizes of walls, bulkheads, openings, projections, or recesses, space allocation, compartments, the location and arrangement of machinery and fixed equipment, and the like. It may also indicate construction materials.

elite   Type size for typewriters approximating 10-point printing type. Elite type has 12 characters to the linear inch of copy and 6 lines to the vertical inch.

ellipse   Enclosed plane forming a regular oval. The shortest dimension through the center of an ellipse is called the minor axis; the longest dimension, the major axis. (*See also* AXIS.)

elliptical-dot screen   Contact screen that incorporates an elliptical-dot structure and produces an elliptical dot in the middle tones. This feature eliminates the sudden jump in density usually encountered in vignetted areas of the reproduction where the corners of square dots join at the same place in the tonal scale. Since only the diagonal corners of elliptical dots join at any one place in the tonal scale, a smoother reproduction is obtained and grain characteristics are minimized. The elliptical-dot screen is used for black-and-white reproduction in the same manner as a square-dot contact screen.

em   Type measure equal to the square of the type body. The name is derived from early type practices in which the letter M was cast on a square body. One-half of an em is known as an "en." The quadrat, which is used for horizontal spacing, is measured in ems or ens. (*See also* QUADRAT.)

em dash   Dash 1 em in length, as —. This is the regular dash used in punctuation.

embossing   Producing a raised design on paper or other material. A brass or bronze die contains the image to be embossed. When set in intaglio, it serves as a plate on the bed of the press. A soft, pliable material like papier-mâché is placed on the cylinder of the press. As the cylinder revolves, it presses the papier-mâché into the intalio image on the bed. The papier-mâché, with the relief design on it, is then dried, trimmed, and printed. In a second operation, the relief design on the cylinder forces the printed image facedown into the intaglio counterpart in the die on the bed. Thus a raised surface appears on the material.

embossing press   Printing press capable of embossing work as well as regular printing. Some platen presses have this advantage. (*See* PLATEN PRESS.)

emulsion   Coating of a photographic material that is sensitive to light. It is usually made of silver salts suspended in gelatin or of a diazo compound.

emulsion speed   Rate of response of a photographic emulsion to light, determined under standard conditions of exposure and subsequent development.

en   *See* EM.

en dash   Short dash, such as the dash used in ranges (e.g., 1900–1950) or to join two compound adjectives.

enameled finish   *See* COATED FINISH.

encaustic Method of preparing images by means of heat. An encaustic painting is made with wax to which color has been added; it is then fused with a hot iron, which fixes the color.

endleaf (book endpaper; book lining; flyleaf paper) Paper at the beginning or end of a book, half of which is pasted to the cover and half of which forms a flyleaf. It must have sufficient strength to hold the inside of the book and the cover together, and it must accept paste without crinkling.

engine sizing In paper manufacturing, application of emulsified resin in the beater. Almost all chemical wood papers are sized in this way.

engineering document Any specification, drawing, sketch, list, standard, pamphlet, report, or other written information on the design, procurement, manufacture, test, or inspection of equipment or services.

engineering drawing In standard usage, an orthographic drawing of a piece of equipment or an article or of its detailed parts, containing information and instructions sufficient to manufacture the equipment, article, or parts. Some engineering drawings are not orthographic, but give a perspective or an isometric view of an article. Such drawings, which are made for commercial reasons, are known as "sales drawings." Engineering drawings are made on tracing paper, linen, or film, all of which are translucent for the reproduction of copies, usually by the whiteprint process. Pencil is generally used. The use of perspective and isometric projection on engineering drawings intended for government services is discouraged. (*See also* ORTHOGRAPHIC PROJECTION: ENGINEERING DRAWINGS.)

english Old type size. The nearest equivalent in the point system is 14 point.

English finish Paper finish that is smoother than machine finish, but not so smooth as that of supercalendered stock. It is popular for magazines, brochures, and illustrated booklets for which halftone screening is employed and for which paper must be of reasonably good quality. (*See also* UNCOATED BOOK PAPER.)

engrave To incise designs or images on the surface of a material from which printing impressions can be made. (*See* PHOTOENGRAVING.)

engraver's proof Proof of a line cut or halftone engraving. The proof is inspected to determine whether the image has acceptable printing characteristics.

envelope drawing In engineering drafting, a drawing that shows an item in sufficient detail to identify it for procurement purposes. The drawing gives such information as mounting and mating dimensions, tolerances, weight limitations, finishes, and other physical requirements.

envelopes Figure E-3 shows a number of styles and sizes of envelopes for a variety of purposes. (The names suffixed with an ® are the United States Envelope Company's registered trade names.) An envelope must be uniform in die cut, size, folding, gumming, quality of paper stock, weight, surface characteristics, and color. Any lack of uniformity could cause delay and expense because of printing difficulties.

EPC Abbreviation for Electrostatic Printing Corporation of America and for the electrostatic screen printing process developed by this firm. (*See* ELECTROSTATIC SCREEN PRINTING PROCESS.)

epidiascope (optical lantern) Lantern that projects enlarged images on a screen from illustrations, text copy, or photographs imposed on a transparent material. In its simplest form, the epidiascope consists of a lantern body, a light source, and lenses that magnify the object. The light source may be a carbon arc lamp or a strong incandescent lamp. The epidiascope is useful in illustrating lectures.

equivalent weight In the paper industry, the weight of 500 sheets of paper in a size either larger or smaller than the basic size. (*See* BASIC SIZE.)

erasing and eradicating Errors may be removed from copy by applying an abrasive material or a chemical solvent. Successful erasing with rubber erasers and eradication by means of a fluid depend on such factors as the surface finish of the material, the grit content of the eraser, the strength and potency of the eradicating fluid, and the manner in which the erasing or eradicating is done. Proper erasing and eradicating are important to the appearance and reproduction quality of cold-compositon copy, engineering drawings, and technical artwork. High-grade tracing papers and linens are manufactured to withstand erasure pressure. Careful erasing on linen or tracing papers with a high rag content therefore presents no problems. In contrast, erasing on bond or paper stock manufactured from wood pulp with little or no rag content is extremely difficult. It is easy to erase on paper stock having a coated or enameled surface because the surface

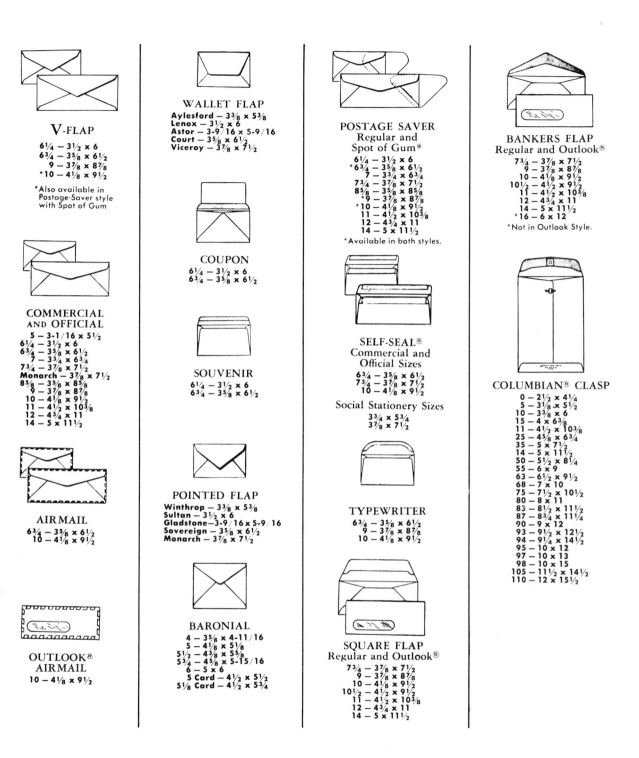

V-FLAP

6¼ — 3½ x 6
6¾ — 3⅝ x 6½
9 — 3⅞ x 8⅞
*10 — 4⅛ x 9½

*Also available in
Postage-Saver style
with Spot of Gum

**COMMERCIAL
AND OFFICIAL**

5 — 3-1/16 x 5½
6¼ — 3½ x 6
6¾ — 3⅝ x 6½
7 — 3¾ x 6¾
7¾ — 3⅞ x 7½
Monarch — 3⅞ x 7½
8⅝ — 3⅝ x 8⅝
9 — 3⅞ x 8⅞
10 — 4⅛ x 9½
11 — 4½ x 10⅜
12 — 4¾ x 11
14 — 5 x 11½

AIRMAIL

6¾ — 3⅝ x 6½
10 — 4⅛ x 9½

**OUTLOOK®
AIRMAIL**

10 — 4⅛ x 9½

WALLET FLAP

Aylesford — 3⅜ x 5⅜
Lenox — 3½ x 6
Astor — 3-9/16 x 5-9/16
Court — 3⅝ x 6½
Viceroy — 3⅞ x 7½

COUPON

6¼ — 3½ x 6
6¾ — 3⅝ x 6½

SOUVENIR

6¼ — 3½ x 6
6¾ — 3⅝ x 6½

POINTED FLAP

Winthrop — 3⅜ x 5⅜
Sultan — 3½ x 6
Gladstone—3-9/16 x 5-9/16
Sovereign — 3⅝ x 6½
Monarch — 3⅞ x 7½

BARONIAL

4 — 3⅝ x 4-11/16
5 — 4⅛ x 5⅛
5½ — 4⅜ x 5⅝
5¾ — 4⅝ x 5-15/16
6 — 5 x 6
5 Card — 4½ x 5½
5⅛ Card — 4½ x 5¾

POSTAGE SAVER
Regular and
Spot of Gum*

6¼ — 3½ x 6
*6¾ — 3⅝ x 6½
7 — 3¾ x 6¾
7¾ — 3⅞ x 7½
8⅝ — 3⅝ x 8⅝
*9 — 3⅞ x 8⅞
*10 — 4⅛ x 9½
11 — 4½ x 10⅜
12 — 4¾ x 11
14 — 5 x 11½

*Available in both styles.

SELF-SEAL®
Commercial and
Official Sizes

6¾ — 3⅝ x 6½
7¾ — 3⅞ x 7½
10 — 4⅛ x 9½

Social Stationery Sizes

3¾ x 5¾
3⅞ x 7½

TYPEWRITER

6¾ — 3⅝ x 6½
9 — 3⅞ x 8⅞
10 — 4⅛ x 9½

SQUARE FLAP
Regular and Outlook®

7¾ — 3⅞ x 7½
9 — 3⅞ x 8⅞
10 — 4⅛ x 9½
10½ — 4½ x 9½
11 — 4½ x 10⅜
12 — 4¾ x 11
14 — 5 x 11½

BANKERS FLAP
Regular and Outlook®

7¾ — 3⅞ x 7½
9 — 3⅞ x 8⅞
10 — 4⅛ x 9½
10½ — 4½ x 9½
11 — 4½ x 10⅜
12 — 4¾ x 11
14 — 5 x 11½
*16 — 6 x 12

*Not in Outlook Style.

COLUMBIAN® CLASP

0 — 2½ x 4¼
5 — 3⅛ x 5½
10 — 3⅜ x 6
15 — 4 x 6⅜
11 — 4½ x 10⅜
25 — 4⅝ x 6¾
35 — 5 x 7½
14 — 5 x 11½
50 — 5½ x 8¼
55 — 6 x 9
63 — 6½ x 9½
68 — 7 x 10
75 — 7½ x 10½
80 — 8 x 11
83 — 8½ x 11½
87 — 8¾ x 11¼
90 — 9 x 12
93 — 9½ x 12½
94 — 9¼ x 14½
95 — 10 x 12
97 — 10 x 13
98 — 10 x 15
105 — 11½ x 14½
110 — 12 x 15½

Fig. E-3 Envelopes and mailing pieces. (*United States Envelope Company.*)

itself is removed in erasing. Only high-quality coated or enameled stock having a glazed finish should be used for reproduction proofs or for camera-ready copy prepared on office composing machines. Supercalendered stock without a coated finish should not be used. Some paper stocks have the appearance of being coated because of their high luster and glossy finish. This appearance is obtained by passing the paper through the calender rolls many times during the manufacturing process. The degree of gloss and smoothness varies with the number of times the paper has been calendered. Such paper stocks should not be used for producing camera-ready cold-compositon copy because they are very poorly suited to erasing. The eradicating fluids recommended by the manufacturer of the material should be used for tracing paper, linen, and film.

erection drawing   Engineering drawing that shows the procedure and sequence for the erection or assembly of individual items or subassemblies of items.

erratum   Error in writing or printing; also, an acknowledgment of such an error. Errata sheets are often sent to recipients of technical books to correct technical, typographical, and other errors.

escapement   Mechanism in a linecasting machine that dislodges individual matrices from their respective magazines. The matrices thus dislodged are arranged to form a line from which slugs or lines of type are cast with molten metal. The term "escapement" also applies to a ratchet device on a typewriter. When a typewriter key is struck, the carriage moves, or "escapes," to the left and space is provided for typing the next character.

etch   To corrode with an acid or similar material; also, to make a design on a metal plate by employing a corrosive substance. The metal plate is coated with a varnishlike material. The design is made with a sharp instrument, which destroys the material and exposes the metal. Then acid is used to eat out the exposed metal, thus forming an image from which an impression can be made.

etch proof   *See* REPRODUCTION PROOF.

excelsior   Old 3-point type size, now seldom used.

Executive   Name of a series of proportional-spacing typewriters produced by IBM's Office Products Division. (*See* TYPEWRITER.)

expanded type (extended type)   Type with a wider face than that of usual type of the same family.

exploded view Line drawing or photograph of a piece of equipment, an article, or a component or part of an article in which the parts are drawn separately in perspective or isometric projection to show their relationship to each other (*See* Figures E-4 and E-5). Each part is identified by a number that is keyed to a parts list or legend. Exploded views are used extensively in technical manuals to assist mechanics in overhauling and maintaining equipment. They are also used in conjunction with text matter for the disassembly, inspection, repair or replacement, and reassembly of parts. The numbers applied to each part must be assigned in the order of proper disassembly.

Several features shown in Figure E-4 are important in the construction of an exploded view: (1) the assembled view, enclosed within a shadow box or a "TV screen," is oriented in the same plane as the exploded parts; (2) use of the shadow box greatly improves the drawing because it separates the assembled view from the exploded parts; (3) all parts are shaded to show that the light source is coming from the upper left corner; (4) part 9, which is a subassembly, has been disassembled into parts 10 through 12 by the use of a brace (this means that parts 10 through 12 can be ordered

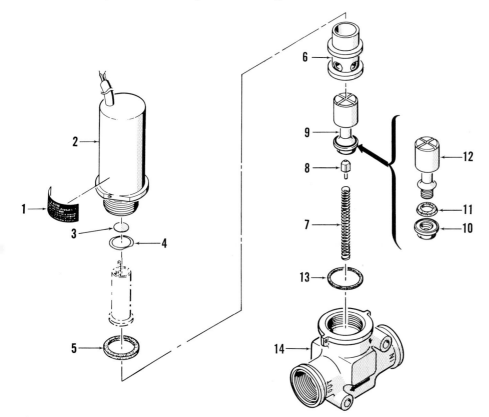
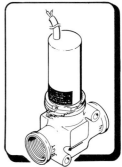

Fig. E-4   Exploded-view illustration.

and replaced as separate parts belonging to assembly part 9); (5) the part directly above part 5, which has no number, appears in phantom with broken lines (this indicates that it cannot be ordered and replaced as a separate part, but is a component of part 2); (6) arrowheads are used with lead lines because there are relatively few parts and they do not clog the drawing or detract from its appearance; and (7) gaskets 5, 11, and 13 are shaded to indicate that they are nonmetallic.

The exploded view in Figure E-5 also shows proper shading for the light source, but here the assembled view merges with the

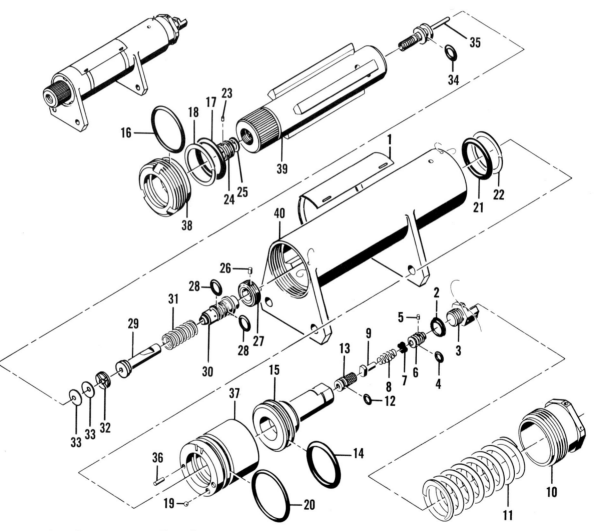

Fig. E-5   Exploded-view illustration.

exploded parts because it is not enclosed. Both views, however, are oriented in the same plane. Arrowheads are not used because they would congest the drawing. O rings are shown in black with highlighted areas. Springs 8, 11, and 31 and the configuration of such parts as 15, 30, 37, and 39, as well as the threaded parts, add to the cost of the view because drawing these parts is time-consuming.

exposure   Quantity of light that is allowed to act on a photographic material. The product of the intensity and the duration of the light acting on the emulsion is the amount of exposure.

exposure index   Number assigned to a photographic material and intended for use with an exposure meter to determine the correct aperture and exposure time for best results.

exposure meter   Instrument used to determine the intensity of light falling on or reflected by the subject that is being photographed.

extended type   *See* EXPANDED TYPE.

extension line   In orthographic engineering and mechanical drawings, a line used to indicate the extent of a dimension. It is designated as a "thin" line. Extension lines should not touch the object to which they refer. (*See also* LINE CONVENTIONS: ENGINEERING DRAWINGS.)

external projection   Exposure of the sensitized copy paper of a microfilm reader-printer outside the machine with room illumination. Speed and light intensity are important factors in quality reproduction. (*See also* INTERNAL PROJECTION.)

extract   Material quoted from another work, usually set in smaller type, indented, or otherwise displayed to distinguish it from the text.

eyeball   Colloquial term meaning to draw lines and objects without reference to scale.

F

face Portion of a type piece that receives the ink and comes in direct contact with the printed surface, thus forming the image. The term is used also as an equivalent of typeface. (*See* TYPEFACES.)

facsimile Exact reproduction of an original.

fade-out blue Very light sky-blue color that is not reproduced by the camera unless it is filtered. It is used for writing on reproduction line copy. Fade-out blue is used also for printing forms employed in the preparation of photographic copy for reproduction. Guidelines showing margin limitations, marginal-data location, columnar arrangement, page-number location, and the like are drawn in black india ink on the original form, which is printed in fade-out blue.

fadeback (also called **ghosting**) Depiction of the central object of an image with full tonal values and the area around the object in flat or less pronounced tones. The heavier tones emphasize the central object. An example is an advertisement showing an automobile engine with an air filter. The manufacturer of the filter shows his product in full, distinct tones and the engine in lesser tones. Thus the physical relationship of the filter to the engine is recognized, and the filter appears as the main object.

fan delivery   Unit on a printing press that transfers folded signatures from a folding section to a conveyor belt. The fan operates in waterwheel fashion. Blades assist in picking up and dislodging a signature at each revolution.

feather   In a printed or duplicated image, an undesirable bleeding effect in which microscopic featherlike indications surround the characters. The effect may be caused by incorrect pressure between printing plate and printing stock, overexposure, excessive diffusion of chemicals, coarse printing stock, or other factors.

featheredge   *See* DECKLE EDGE.

felt finish   Finish applied by a special marking felt on a web of paper as it goes through the papermaking machine.

felt pens   *See* PENS, TECHNICAL.

felt side   Printing side of paper. The felt side is the top side of the paper as it comes off the papermaking machine; it is the opposite of the wire side.

ferrotype   Photograph produced on a thin metal plate by a process in which collodion is used as a vehicle for sensitive salts. As a verb, "ferrotype" means to burnish a photograph by "squeegeeing" it while wet on a lacquered plate.

figure   Line illustration or photograph of any kind used in a publication. A figure may be a graph, a chart, an exploded view, a rendering, a halftone, or any other illustration in which artwork or photography is used to produce the image. Figures in a technical publication should be numbered consecutively throughout or double-numbered by chapter or section, and they should appear immediately following their first reference in text. The figure number and title are placed below the figure.

figure number   Number assigned to an illustration in a publication. Single or double arabic numbers should be used. The two numbers in a double number are separated by a hyphen or an en dash, the first number indicating the section or chapter and the second the sequential order of the figure within that section or chapter.

figure title   Title of an illustration in a publication, usually preceded by a figure number in a technical work. It should be as brief as possible.

file number *See* ART FILE NUMBER.

filler Copy used to fill space in a page or column of a magazine or newspaper. Brief poems, witty sayings, parables, proverbs, and jokes are examples. Cartoons, photographs, and the like may also be used as fillers.

fillet Line impressed on the cover of a book for decorative purposes.

film Flexible, translucent or transparent plastic or other chemically formed base coated with a photographic emulsion. The term may also be applied to a similar material without the emulsion, such as a "wrapping" film.

film base *See* FILMS AND PLATES.

film color sensitivity *See* FILMS AND PLATES.

film negative Photolithographic negative produced by a process camera. The negative has a film base and reflects a translucent (white) image on a black background; it may be a line negative or a halftone negative. While it is called a negative, however, the image is right-reading. The term "negative" is derived from the fact that it is camera-produced. (*See also* NEGATIVE, PHOTOLITHOGRAPHIC.)

film positive Film or material of acetate composition having a black image or definition and a translucent or clear background. It has a right-reading image. Film positives are useful in making additional reference copies on whiteprint machines and as intermediates. The term is also applied to a positive contact print on film-base material that has been produced from a stripped-up negative mask and used for burning in a deep-etch offset plate to expose a silk-screen photostencil. In the case of a continuous-tone print, the film is used for masking an intaglio plate.

film processing *See* MICROFILM PROCESSING; PROCESSING, FILM; PROCESSING, NITROGEN-BURST.

Filmotype Trade name of a phototypesetting machine that sets cold-composition copy. (*See* TYPESETTERS, PHOTOGRAPHIC.)

films and plates The following discussion on films and plates has been made possible through the courtesy of the Eastman Kodak Company and extracted from the copyrighted Kodak publication

Kodak Graphic Arts Films and Plates. Because of space limitations it was necessary to condense the material from this publication.

Composition and physical properties: Generally speaking, photographic films and plates are made up of several layers of extremely thin, carefully coated materials. The most important layers are illustrated in Figure F-1.

Base. Film base or glass is the transparent material that serves as the support for the thin, light-sensitive emulsion. The film base for most Kodak graphic arts films is an improved safety type of great clarity and high dimensional stability. For the utmost in dimensional stability, Kodalith Ortho Type 3 is available on a polystyrene base. Kodak plates are coated on specially selected glass, ranging in thickness with the size of the plate from 0.060 to 0.190 inch. Other thicknesses can be furnished on special order.

Dimensional stability: The dimensional stability of a photographic film depends on many factors. These include not only the chemical composition of the film and the treatment it receives during manufacture but also the form and conditions under which it is stored before and after exposure. The dimensional changes which occur in any photographic film are of two types: temporary, or reversible, and permanent, or irreversible. Temporary expansion or contraction is due to (1) loss or gain of moisture, which is determined almost solely by the relative humidity of the air in contact with the film; and (2) changes in temperature. This temporary type of dimensional change is important in graphic arts use. Expansion due to moisture in the air is generally greater than thermal expansion. Since the relative humidity of most shops and laboratories is more apt to vary than the temperature, the problems caused by humidity changes are the main ones. Permanent shrinkage in a photographic film is caused by loss of residual solvents and plasticizer (softening agent) from the base, plastic flow (shrinkage caused by contraction of the emulsion), and release of mechanical strain. Permanent shrinkage during storage prior to exposure is generally very low and is also unimportant because there is no image on the film.

Film swells during processing and contracts again during drying. If it is brought to equilibrium with the same relative humidity after processing as existed before, a small net shrinkage called "process shrinkage" is usually found. Kodak films for the graphic arts are in equilibrium with air at approximately 40 percent relative humidity at the time of shipment. When the utmost in dimensional stability is required, sheets of film should be conditioned to the air of the workroom before exposure by being hung in the dark for approximately one hour. Gentle circulation of air is beneficial.

If the film is reconditioned in the same atmosphere after processing,

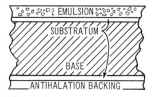

Fig. F-1   Layers of typical photographic materials.

all dimensional changes caused by humidity are eliminated. All Kodak graphic arts films have high dimensional stability, provided they are not stored after processing at relatively high humidities, that is, over 60 percent. It is desirable for conditions in the workroom to resemble those in the storage room. If the relative humidity of the workroom is either low or high, each sheet of film should be conditioned to room air before exposure. A temperature from 70 to 75°F and a relative humidity between 40 and 50 percent are most satisfactory. Too low a humidity is undesirable because it increases static. If this occurs, dust adheres to unprotected unexposed film and spots appear after the film has been exposed and developed. Light penetrating all the way through an emulsion may reflect from the back of the base and strike the emulsion once more, causing halation. Halation is particularly noticeable in areas of negatives that represent excessively bright areas of the original copy.

In graphic arts films, a light-absorbing material is incorporated in the backing layer, which then serves the double purpose of preventing both halation and curling of the film. The light-absorbing material is always bleached out, but the backing is not removed during processing. In graphic arts plates, the backing is bleached and dissolved during processing. An exception is the Kodak Infrared Sensitive plate from which the black backing must be removed by rubbing lightly with cotton after the plate has been fixed. A weak alkali or developer solution often makes this operation easier.

Photographic properties: The photographic properties of a film or plate determine the type of image that results after exposure and processing. If the type of image needed for a particular purpose is known, the proper film or plate can be selected to do the job. Specifying such properties as speed, contrast, and color sensitivity usually narrows the choice to a few materials. The first consideration in the choice of a photographic film or plate is generally the color sensitivity needed. In most cases, this is primarily a choice between materials for use in black-and-white reproduction, on the one hand, and those for use in color reproduction on the other. The former are sensitive to a few colors of light, while many of the latter are sensitive to all colors.

Color sensitivity and types of sensitizing. All photographic emulsions are sensitive to blue, violet, and the invisible ultraviolet light. For many applications, however, this sensitivity is not enough. The photographic emulsions used in photomechanical color reproduction must be able to record densities for the broader range of colors which the human eye can see, that is, the greens, yellows, oranges, and reds. During manufacture, dyes are added to make the emulsions sensitive to these colors. Blue-sensitive photographic materials record high negative densities for blue areas of the original and, in the final reproduction, render blues very light and reds, yellows, and greens very dark. They are very useful in such specialized work as copying black-and-white photographs.

Orthochromatic films and plates are not sensitive to red light and therefore render reds as very dark in reproduction. These materials are normally faster than blue-sensitive materials because they are sensitive to a wider range of colors. Panchromatic films and plates are sensitive to all visible colors, as well as to ultraviolet, and therefore give excellent monochromatic rendering of colored copy. Infrared materials possess a particularly high sensitivity to infrared radiation. Their principal use in photomechanical reproduction is in making black-printer negatives.

Filters: A filter is a device which transmits light of certain colors while it absorbs light of others. The most common types are thin sheets or disks of gelatin or glass that are placed in front of the lens of the camera or in a slot in the lens mounting. By using the proper filters, selected colors of light from a multicolored object are filtered out or reduced. A photograph will then record only the colors transmitted through the filter. Kodak Wratten filters in the form of dyed gelatin sheets are used extensively in graphic arts photography because of their consistently high quality. A filter never

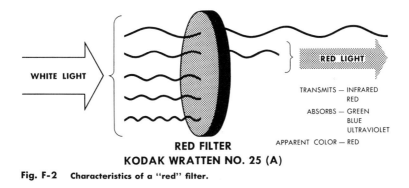

RED FILTER
KODAK WRATTEN NO. 25 (A)
Fig. F-2   Characteristics of a "red" filter.

changes the color of light. It can only allow a part of some colors to pass through and stop other colors. A "red" filter appears to be red because it transmits red light to the eye and absorbs most other colors. This is shown in Figure F-2. All filters absorb some of the light which strikes them, and under the same conditions of illumination longer exposures are necessary than when no filter is used.

There are two basic applications of filters in photomechanical work. In one, filters are used to emphasize tonal areas in making black-and-white reproductions from colored or soiled copy. In the other, filters are used in making color reproductions from color copy. In the latter case, the original is photographed successively through each of three color-separation filters. The three black-and-white negatives thus obtained are called "color-separation negatives" and are used in making the three printing plates that print the respective colors on the paper. (A fourth plate, the black printer, is usually employed to add density to the dark areas of the picture.) Each of the two applications requires a separate method of calculating the correct exposure. The first is based on filter factors and the second on filter ratios.

The recommended filters for photomechanical work are the Kodak Wratten filters, which are made by carefully mixing prepared dyes in gelatin and forming the resulting mixture into thin sheets. Each filter is standardized by comparison with a permanent standard in specially designed instruments. Selected Wratten gelatin filters are available for critical photomechanical work. These filters, designated as Kodak Wratten Photomechanical filters, are particularly useful when partial exposures are to be made through each of several filters, as in the split-filter method of making a black printer. The Kodak Wratten Photomechanical filters are PM8, PM25, PM29, PM33, PM47B, PM58, PM61, PM85B, PM23A, PM47, and PM96 (0.60 and 1.00 densities only).

Materials for general use: The fundamental requirement in a film or plate for photomechanical line work and screened halftone work is high contrast. In negatives of line work, dark lines will then be rendered as clear areas and background areas as extremely dense areas even if the original copy has light or weak lines. In halftone work, the high contrast of the emulsion will produce sharp, crisp halftone dots. A fine-grain emulsion is necessary so that edges of lines and dots will not be ragged. Halftone dots must be of such quality that they can be altered in size by chemical means after development and still retain their opacity. For color copy, it is necessary to use a color-sensitized material that can record colors in their relative black-and-white tone values.

Although emulsions with extreme contrast are slower than continuous-tone materials, high film and plate speed is important in reducing costs by saving time. Kodak graphic arts films and plates combine sufficient speed and sensitivity to provide ease in handling. Of equal importance, films and plates must be physically stable to withstand handling under production conditions. Each of the many photographic materials has characteristics which meet specific needs.

For a more thorough technical discussion of films and plates, it is recommended that the publication *Kodak Graphic Arts Films and*

Plates, a copyrighted Kodak publication, be obtained from a Kodak graphic arts dealer.

filmsetter   Name given to a machine that sets copy automatically on film or on photographic paper. While this term more appropriately describes such a machine because it does not set metal type, the trade has accepted the name "typesetter" as definitive. However, because a photographic process is used, the machine is more correctly called a photographic typesetter or a photocomposing machine. (*See also* TYPESETTERS, PHOTOGRAPHIC.)

filmstrip   Strip of rolled film containing still photographs projected as slides, as opposed to strips of film whose images are projected by motion-picture cameras in rapid succession to simulate motion.

filter   Device, commonly of gelatin or glass, placed between the subject being photographed and the photographic material in order to reduce or eliminate the light of certain colors while allowing that of others to reach the emulsion. (*See also* FILMS AND PLATES.)

filter factor   Multiplication of exposure time necessary when using a color filter under the same conditions as without the filter.

final draft   Text material or copy that is ready in all respects for setting in type.

fine arts   Arts created with concern for aesthetic values rather than for utility. Among them are architecture, sculpture, drawing, painting, and ceramics, insofar as they manifest taste, are responsive to beauty, and are susceptible to aesthetic influences.

finished-sheet size   Overall dimensions of an engineering drawing and of a full-size reproduction made from it.

finisher (inker)   One who applies ink on artwork and generally finishes the work after another has drawn it in pencil.

finishes, paper   *See* PAPER FINISHES.

first generation   Photographically reproduced copy made from an original, either by contact or by photographic reproduction; also, the first impression or copy made from the original.

first parallel fold   Paper fold made in the jaw folder immediately following the former fold. (It is called a "tabloid fold" when the web has been slit in half along the longitudinal dimension.) The result is the printing of eight-page signatures of multiples of the number of webs in the press, the signature size being one-half of the cutoff length by one-half of the web width.

fitting copy   *See* COPYFITTING.

fixative   Any clear solution sprayed or coated on artwork or other material, such as reproduction copy, that "fixes," or stabilizes, the image, rendering it more resistant to wear or smudging. A fixative protects and preserves drawings, photographs, documents, and other papers. An example is a spray coating trade-named Krylon.

flapping   *See* MOUNTING AND FLAPPING.

flare   Nonimage light that reaches a photographic emulsion during a camera exposure. Its source may be any stray light falling directly on or reflected to the lens or internal lens reflections of image light. The general effect is to lower the contrast of the image obtained. Flare is most troublesome when lens surfaces are dirty. It is at a minimum with clean lenses that have antireflection surface coatings.

flash exposure   Second of two process-camera exposures used only in halftone work. The first exposure, the main or detail exposure, is not sufficient to bring out the dot formation required in dark areas of a halftone for proper reproduction in printing. The dots formed during the main exposure will run together, and the halftone will print as solid black in the shadow areas. An additional flash exposure through the contact screen to the negative is required to form halftone dots in the dark areas without affecting the lighter areas.

A flashing lamp is used to make exposures remotely with some cameras. The lamp is located in the darkroom, where it can illuminate the entire film back area evenly. Exposure is controlled manually. During exposure, the vacuum back film holder is lowered and the vacuum retained to keep the film and screen from moving. The exposure must be made on the dots already started on the negative, and any movements of the screen or film would begin new dots, creating a moiré effect.

Flash exposures are also made by retaining the camera setup and flashing through white paper covering the copy on the copyboard. The flashing lamp is gallery-operated, connected to the timer, and mounted on the front-case lens board.

flat   In photographic plate making, a group of pages of copy loaded in the copyholder for photographing. The term also denotes the combined negatives masked and ready for plate making.

flat copy   In photomechanics, images that lack depth, such as line copy, in contrast to images that have varying depths, such as are encountered when photographing outdoors with an ordinary camera.

flat-size copy   Copy made from an original engineering drawing that has a printed format and, because of its relatively small size, can be filed flat.

flat tone (screen tint)   In lithography, a tone without gradation that has only one tone value in the dot formation.

flatbed press   Printing press having a horizontal bed on which forms are locked for relief (letterpress) printing.

flexographic ink   Highly pigmented opaque ink used almost exclusively in flexographic printing. The colors are brilliant and solid.

flexographic printing   Printing with rubber plates and with a liquid ink instead of paste ink, such as that used in letterpress printing. The image is set in relief. The flexographic press prints from rolled stock such as foil, cellophane, and enameled or coated paper. Because of the fluidity of the ink used, the dots in halftones may be lost and papers that are manufactured to absorb ink readily may absorb too much ink, but such items as food cartons, candy and gum wrappers, cellophane bags, and waxed papers are ideally suited for this type of printing. The presses operate at 300 to almost 1,000 feet per minute, the speed depending on the material to which the image is being transferred. A wide range of opaque colors is available for printing such as those seen on holiday gift wrappings.

flip chart   *See* BRIEFING CHART.

flocking   Minute fiberlike particles of wood or cloth in various colors that are blown onto printed matter or painted objects having an adhesive ink. The particles adhere to the ink or paint, producing a decorative effect.

flong   Damp mixture of papier-mâché used as a matrix or negative. The image is impressed in the papier-mâché, which dries and serves as the matrix or negative.

flow diagram   Schematic diagram indicating the course of a material through an object or article, as in hydraulic and pneumatic systems. It shows the direction of flow through the system and the relationship of the components (*see* Figure F-3). Arrows used to indicate direction of flow may be shaded, dotted, or cross-sectioned to show condition or state. Colors may be employed. An accompanying legend, which should be part of the diagram, may show the arrows and key them to the flow system for clarity. If possible, the flow in a system should originate at the left of the diagram so that the direction is from left to right.

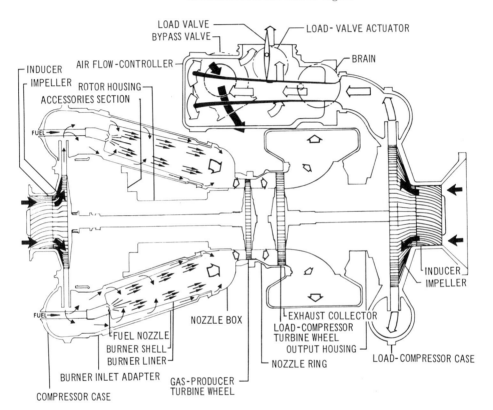

Fig. F-3   Pneumatic flow diagram.

flow line   Line that indicates the physical relationship of parts of an object when the parts are separated in the drawing. It is broken into alternate short and long lines. (*See also* EXPLODED VIEW.)

fluid duplicating   *See* SPIRIT DUPLICATING.

fluorescent ink   Very bright poster and printing ink that contains natural or synthetic phosphorus. It throws off a broad spectrum of visible light while absorbing ultraviolet light. Such inks are effective in briefing charts and advertising displays.

flush   Even with a predetermined point, said of lines of text or of line or halftone copy. For example, this line is flush left and right (because it is justified) with the lines above and below it. When lines are not flush, particularly at the right margin, they are said to "run ragged" (and are therefore not justified). (*See also* JUSTIFICATION.)

flush blocking   Trimming so that a plate and a printing surface are even.

flush cover   Book cover having the same dimensions as the inserted book.

flyer   Broadside, announcement, or circular, usually of inferior quality, printed on one side of the sheet and generally used for advertising purposes.

flying paster   Automatic device that splices a new web of paper onto a depleted roll without stopping the press.

flyleaf paper   *See* ENDLEAF.

fog   Veil of silver of low density on a photographic material. It is most commonly caused by nonimage ink that strikes the material or by incorrect chemical treatment. Correct treatment is of particular importance in maintaining quality in microfilm processing. Fogging is sometimes done intentionally by means of uniform light of low intensity.

foil   Very thin sheet or leaf of metal, such as gold foil, silver foil, and the like, that is used to embellish designs and lettering in a stamping process. The term also denotes a transparent, sensitized acetate film that is used chiefly in whiteprint reproduction to produce intermediates and in making projecturals for overhead projection.

foil stamping   Method of using gold and silver foil to impress an image on a surface. The foil, or leaf, is stamped and laid on the surface by using heat in the relief matrix.

folder   Printed circular folded and used as a mailing piece.

folding: prints   Blueprints, whiteprints, and any prints taken from original engineering, construction, or architectural drawings may be folded to size. A standard method of folding prints ensures visible identifying numbers when the prints are filed or stored. Regardless of the size of flat prints, all are folded to $8\frac{1}{2}$ by 11 inches and filed so that the drawing number is visible on the outside in the upper right corner when a print is being selected (the drawing number also appears in the title block in the lower right corner). So-called "accordion-pleated" folding may be used.

Folding requires a folding board of sheet metal, plastic, or wood, measuring $8\frac{3}{8}$ by $10\frac{7}{8}$ inches with rounded corners, and a small block of smooth wood for creasing. The duplicate drawing number must appear in the upper right corner after folding. Folding procedures for various sizes are as follows:

Size, in.	Folding
$8\frac{1}{2}$ by 11	None required.
11 by 17	One fold to $8\frac{1}{2}$ by 11 in.
17 by 22	First fold to 17 by 11 in.; second fold to $8\frac{1}{2}$ by 11 in.
22 by 34	First fold to 34 by 11 in.; second fold to 11 by 17 in.; third fold to $8\frac{1}{2}$ by 11 in.
11 by 34	First fold to 11 by 17 in.; second fold to $8\frac{1}{2}$ by 11 in.

For all roll-size and flat prints not listed above, accordion folds are made by using the folding board. In each case, the first fold is an 11-inch fold made from the end that carries the drawing number. Each fold thereafter also is 11 inches except the last, which may be smaller. After the length of the print has been folded into the required number of 11-inch accordion folds, the width is folded in $8\frac{1}{2}$-inch folds.

foldout (gatefold)   Insert wider than the page width of a publication. It may require one or more vertical folds so that it will occupy the same area as the page. Foldouts are used to accommodate large illustrations, charts, and the like.

For technical publications measuring $8\frac{1}{2}$ by 11 inches, right-hand page foldouts should have the figure number and title on the right $4\frac{1}{2}$-inch dimension of the $8\frac{1}{2}$-inch width. When a left-hand foldout backs up a right-hand foldout, figure number and title are centered across the page. If a single foldout is interspersed with text, it should be a right-hand page.

folio In papermaking, a paper size measuring 17 by 22 inches; in printing, a sheet of paper folded once; in a publication, a page number.

follow copy Direction to compose or type copy exactly like the manuscript copy without making any changes.

font Complete assortment of characters of one size and style of type, including capitals, small capitals, lowercase, numbers, and punctuation marks. Matching italic and bold characters are often available.

foolscap Any of various sizes of paper measuring from about 12 by 15 inches to about 13½ by 17 inches.

footnote Note of comment, explanation, or citation appearing at the bottom of a page or table. It is usually set in smaller type than the text or table on which it comments. If necessary, a long footnote may be carried over to the foot of the succeeding page. Footnotes are usually referred to in text by superior numbers and in tables by reference marks. When superior numbers are used in text, numbering is generally by chapter in nontechnical books and by page in technical works. (*See also* REFERENCE MARKS.)

forced aging Subjection of a light-sensitive emulsion or material to increased temperature in order to estimate its shelf life in advance of natural aging.

foreshorten In illustrating, to depict an object or line in less than its true perspective.

foreword Statement forming part of the front matter of a book, frequently written by someone other than the author or editor. The term may be used synonymously with preface. (*See also* PREFACE.)

form Type and material secured in a chase and ready for printing or electrotyping.

format General form of a book, brochure, direct-mail piece, or other printed matter, with particular reference to composition, layout, size, and general appearance.

former Triangular device used on a web-fed printing press to make a longitudinal fold. The paper travels over the former and converges at the apex, or nose, of the triangle to make the fold. A roller keeps the web smooth before forming begins. Small air jets along the edges and nose of the former reduce the heat caused by friction.

former fold (newspaper fold) In a web-fed press, a longitudinal fold made by a former as the web travels over it.

foundry proof Last or final proof of type and material locked in a form before electrotyping or stereotyping.

foundry type Type cast in individual pieces.

fountain Ink receptacle attached to a printing press or machine. There is provision for direct application of the ink to distributing plates or rollers.

Fourdrinier machine Papermaking machine whose name is derived from two brothers, Sealy and Henry Fourdrinier of London, who built a successful machine in Bermondsey, England, in 1803. Their machine was perfected from a crude paper machine invented in France in 1799 by Nicolas Robert.

fourth cover Exposed back cover of a book or magazine.

frame Lines drawn or printed around an illustration or other copy in the form of a rectangle. An illustration should never be enclosed in a frame on original artwork; instead, the lines should be ruled on the basic reproduction page of which the illustration becomes a part when copy is prepared for photo-offset reproduction. The term "frame" also denotes an individual picture in a strip of motion-picture film.

free sheet Sheet of paper without wood particles.

French fold Sheet of stock printed on one side only and folded twice to form an uncut eight-page folder.

friction feed Method of feeding sheet paper into a printing press or other device in which rubber rollers are used to transport the paper in its initial progress through the press. Friction feed may be distinguished from suction and hand feeding.

friction-glazed finish Highly polished finish given to coated papers by using wax and processing the paper through friction rollers.

frisket knife   Any small knife with a fine cutting edge used by artists, illustrators, and others for precise cutting.

frisket paper   Thin transparent paper used to block out or mask portions of art during retouching or airbrushing. The paper is cut with a sharp knife after the art has been mounted on a mounting board. (*See also* AIRBRUSHING.)

front cover   Face of a book or magazine. The cover may be soft and flexible or hard, as in a case-bound book. (*See also* COVER PAPER.)

front matter   All matter that precedes the text of a publication, which should begin on page 1, a right-hand page. The preceding material is front matter and may include a half title, frontispiece, title page, copyright, foreword, preface, abstract, table of contents, list of illustrations, list of tables, and the like. Front-matter pages are generally numbered with lowercase roman numerals, but printed numbers do not appear until after the copyright page.

frontispiece   Formerly, the first page or title page of a book; now a photograph, sketch, drawing, portrait, or other illustration prefacing a book or other publication. In a commercial publication, a frontispiece may consist of one or more line drawings or photographs that serve as a visual introduction to the article under discussion. If such a frontispiece is a line drawing, it should be drawn in perspective as an assembled view and show the best angle of view.

fugitive color   Colored ink or other color that is sensitive to light and fades or changes hue with age and exposure.

full binding   All-leather binding of a book.

full measure   Entire width of a line of type measured in picas. A line of type set full measure is flush with both margins.

full-tone   Name applied by some authorities to a halftone, or screened continuous-tone copy. (*See* CONTINUOUS-TONE ART.)

furniture   In hot-metal linecasting work, wood or metal pieces used to fill in the blank areas of typeforms that are locked in a chase.

fuzz   Loose or projecting fibers on a paper surface.

G

gallery In process-camera work, the area in and around the copyboard, camera tracks, exterior control panels, and so on.

galley Long, shallow metal tray used by compositors to hold type after it has been set. Proofs called galley proofs are pulled from the galley. The type in the galley is later divided into pages.

galley proof Proof taken from type while still on the galley, before the material has been divided into pages. It is about 24 inches long. In cold-composition work, the prejustified reproduction copy is sometimes called a galley proof to identify the copy.

gamma In photographic work, the degree of contrast of a photographic image as represented by the slope of the straight-line portion of the characteristic curve. The gamma is equal to the tangent of the angle which the straight-line portion makes with the base line.

gang shooting In photolithographic plate making, photographing several pages of original copy, such as pages of a book or booklet, at the same time. The pages are arranged on a surface so that after printing, folding, binding, and trimming they will be in numerical sequence. To save the cost of separate negatives, unrelated images may also be grouped for gang shooting if reduction or enlargement is the same for all.

gate page   Page having a gatefold.

gatefold   *See* FOLDOUT.

gathering   Collating signatures in the order in which they are to appear in a book. Machines which automatically gather sheets or signatures in page sequence are used when a great number of copies are required. (*See also* COLLATING.)

gelatin process   Direct-image duplicating process. Writing, typed matter, or drawn images are impressed on a master paper by special carbon ribbon or with a hectograph pencil or ink. The image on the master is pressed into a gelatin mass or pad and then transferred from the gelatin to duplicator paper. The copy is referred to as a gelatin or "jelly" print.

geometry symbols   *See* TABLE 12.

ghost   Colloquial term used by draftsmen and others for a smudge or smear, such as a portion of an image left by poor erasing.

ghosting   *See* FADEBACK.

glossary   List of terms in a particular field with their definitions.

glossy print   Photoprint having a glossy finish, as distinguished from one having a matte finish. Such a print is not adaptable for rework, as the glazed surface does not readily absorb ink. If nomenclature is required, an acetate overlay containing the nomenclature should be used. If artwork is not required on the face of a print, a glossy should be used for screening into a fine reproduction halftone. If ink work must be done on a glossy print, the gloss may be erased and the surface will then accept ink.

goldenrod flats   Orange-colored masking paper used in layout and makeup work for stripping in line and halftone negatives for lithographic reproduction. It is preprinted and ruled to serve as a guide for the placement of the stripped-in negative. The paper is opaque so that light cannot pass through it when the negative is exposed, yet it has sufficient translucency so that it may be cut over a light table.

gothic Typeface that is square-cut, sans serif, and without hairlines.

gradation Variation in tonal values from white to black; also, the passing of one tint or shade into another by insensible degrees. The tones between the two extremes are called middle tones.

grain: paper Alignment of paper fibers as a result of the manufacturing process. The grain of paper should be parallel with the binding edge. Grains are classified as long and short. Grain may be determined by tearing the paper; if the paper tears easily with relatively few broken edges, it is torn with the grain. A smooth and even crease results when paper is folded with the grain.

grain: photography Minute variations of density in a developed photographic emulsion. The variations are caused by irregular distribution of the silver crystals.

graph Diagrammatic representation of changes in a variable quantity in comparison with those of other variables. The term is used in preference to "chart" in scientific and technical work.

graphic arts Arts represented by drawing or imposing on a flat surface an image that communicates a message; also the methods, processes, and techniques employed in these arts. The three components necessary for any graphic arts function are the products and tools with which the image is made, the kind of image produced, and the material on which the image is applied or formed. These three components are the theme around which the *Encyclopedia* has been written.

graphic scale *See* SCALE: ENGINEERING DRAWINGS.

graphical map Graphic representation of an area that shows various factors in addition to geographical features. A weather map, for example, reflects conditions such as wind movements and velocities, temperatures, pressures, and rainfall. A graphical map may be constructed to show pictorially farm and industrial products in their respective locations.

graphoscope Optical instrument used to magnify engravings, photographs, and the like.

Graphotype Trade name of a machine that embosses characters on a thin metal plate. It is used largely in producing addresses and lists.

gravure printing   *See* INTAGLIO PRINTING; PRINTING METHODS.

great primer   Old type size. The nearest equivalent in the point system is 18 point.

grid   Spaced vertical and horizontal lines imposed by preprinting or by drawing on a plane surface. Grid lines may be imposed by the arithmetic or by the logarithmic scale. Preprinted grid forms are useful for drawing charts, block diagrams, sketches, and graphs. Artwork may be prepared directly on the grid. Brown or black preprinted grid lines are employed if the lines are to be reproduced photographically, but light blue preprinted or drawn lines should be used if the lines are not to be reproduced. (*See also* GRID DRAWING, PROPORTIONAL.)

grid drawing, proportional   Method of drawing objects in a larger or smaller size by using a grid with evenly spaced vertical and horizontal lines. A translucent or transparent overlay is placed over the original artwork, and the grid lines are drawn on it. A second grid is then drawn on paper with lines in proportion to the reduction or enlargement desired. A reference point is established at each point where a line of the object crosses a grid line. For fine details, finer evenly spaced grid lines are used in the same proportion. For example, to reduce artwork by one-half, a 1-inch grid line is used for the original art and a $\frac{1}{2}$-inch grid line for the reduced art. For fine details, $\frac{1}{4}$-, $\frac{1}{8}$-, or $\frac{1}{16}$-inch grid lines are used with the $\frac{1}{2}$-inch grid scale.

gripper edge (gripper margin)   Forward, or leading, edge of paper held by grippers of the printing press. In calculating the total paper area an allowance must be made for gripper edges, especially in printing from forms.

grippers   Metal fingers that clamp on paper and control its flow as it passes through the printing press.

groundwood   Inexpensive wood pulp, such as that used in the manufacture of newsprint.

groundwood paper   Paper used originally for newsprint. It is manufactured from groundwood pulp and bleached or unbleached chemical pulp. With modern papermaking machines and techniques, the utilization of groundwood pulp has been extended to include the manufacture of many varieties and grades of paper for magazines, catalogs, directories, books, and wallpaper, as well as commercial printing paper.

guide roller   *See* COCKING ROLLER.

gum   Protective substance used to coat offset printing plates when they are not in use.

gutter   Inner margins of two facing pages in a book or other publication; also, the space between two columns.

H

hairline   Finest of an assortment of printing rules. The term also denotes an unfavorable characteristic of the text image mass that shows as impressions around and between printed characters. Found only in hot-metal linecasting work, the hairline condition is caused by the frequent collision of matrices with one another, resulting in a breakdown of their sidewalls. The breakdown leaves a space between adjacent matrices where molten lead escapes and appears on the type slug, thus causing the printed hairline.

halation   Blurring of a photographic image, particularly in highlight areas, caused by light reflection from the back surface of the base of the film. (*See* ANTIHALATION BACKING; *see also* FILMS AND PLATES.)

half title (bastard title)   Title of a book appearing in the front matter, usually immediately following the front flyleaf and preceding the full title page, which not only repeats the title but adds other information such as the author's name and the publisher's name and location. In some technical publications, a half title page is one that bears the title on the upper portion of the first page of text. Such a page must conform to specifications. In government parlance, a half title page is a panel title page. It may also be called a short title page.

halftone   Tone pattern of shades from white through black of a continuous-tone image, made by photographing the image through a finely ruled glass screen with crossing opaque lines. The screening reduces the tones to a dot formation for reproduction by printing. It is claimed that half of the original image is thus eliminated and half of the full tone remains. (*See also* CONTINUOUS-TONE ART; LINE CONVERSION.)

halftone paper   Smooth paper prepared especially for the reproduction of halftones.

halftone screen   Screen placed in front of the negative material in a process camera to break up a continuous-tone image into a dot formation. There are two types of halftone screens, ruled glass screens and contact screens.

halftone screening   Continuous-tone art is composed of tones and lines, the tones ranging from white through a variety of grays to dense black. The intermediate tones are called middle tones. The tones cannot be reproduced as they appear to the eye but must be reduced to many rows of dots that stand apart so that the dots will receive ink.

In photographing continuous-tone art, the photographer or engraver places a fine transparent screen between the camera lens and the film or plate that will become the negative. The image transmitted through the screen registers on the negative as many broken, or dotted, rows or lines. Heavy tones on the photographic copy register as heavy dotted lines on the negative and light tones as light dotted lines; intensity of tonal values is thus reproduced.

Halftone screens vary with the quality of workmanship desired and other factors. Screens are defined and classified by the number of dots that appear per linear inch. The most commonly used screens are 55-, 65-, 85-, 100-, 120-, 133-, and 150-line screens. Screens defined as 55-, 65-, and 85-line screens contain fewer dots and produce coarse halftones as compared with, for example, the 150-line screen. The coarse halftone screens are used for newspaper reproduction and other work not requiring fine quality. The 100-, 110-, and 120-line screens are used for supercalendered papers, and the 133- and 150-line screens are used for printing halftones on coated papers when a very high quality of reproduction is desired. If one looks at a halftone through an ordinary magnifying glass, the rows of dots are readily recognized.

hand composition   Setting type by hand. The type is set on a measured composing stick. When a full measure is being set, quadrats are inserted to make the line flush right with other lines. This is called "justifying" or "justification." (*See also* COMPOSING STICK.)

hand lettering   *See* BRUSHES, ART; PENS, STEEL-BRUSH; SPEEDBALL PENS; STYLUS.

handbill   Printed sheet, usually containing advertising, that is circulated by hand.

hanger marks (edge marks)   Objectionable marks produced on film by the developing hanger. They are usually due to poor agitation in the first developer.

hard copy   General term for original or other copy. Hard copy may include camera-ready, or reproducible copy, original typewritten manuscript copy, or letterpress copy. The term is opposed to "soft copy," such as a whiteprint copy. The expression "hard copy" is sometimes used to describe a reproduced printout made from a microform.

The aerospace industry has also adopted the term "hard copy," with particular reference to computer output, to indicate analogue strip charts, oscillogram records (analyzed and annotated), prerecorded magnetic tapes (analogue and digital), quick-look analysis reports, and other data.

hard-cover book   *See* CASE-BOUND BOOK.

head-to-foot arrangement   Arrangement of copy on both sides of a sheet with the foot of the opposite page aligned with the top of the first page. It is necessary to flip the sheet to view the opposite page for normal reading.

head-to-head arrangement   Arrangement of copy so that the top of the page is at the same end on both sides of a sheet.

heading   Caption or title of a division of a brochure, book, or other publication. Center headings are centered on a page or column. Sideheads may be flush with one side or indented in alignment with other page elements. Headings are printed in type chosen to set them apart from the text and to make a distinction between main and subsidiary headings.

headless paragraph   Paragraph that stands alone without the support of a sidehead.

headline Major caption set above a newspaper or magazine article or advertising text. The size of the type indicates the importance the editor attaches to the topic.

Headliner Trade name of a display typesetter. (*See* TYPESETTERS, PHOTOGRAPHIC.)

headpiece Illustrative image used to decorate a chapter or section heading.

Headwriter Nonphotographic headline composing machine. (*See* VARIGRAPH.)

heat-set ink Special ink used for high-speed printing. It dries rapidly when the web (paper roll) is passed through a dryer at approximately 350°F and then chilled by cooling rollers. The setting temperature is approximately 80 to 90°F.

hectograph Device for making duplicate copies from a prepared gelatin surface to which the original image has been transferred.

height Distance between two points along the vertical dimension. It is perpendicular to the width. When measurements are given for line and continuous-tone copy, the width and the height are stated in that order. (*See also* VERTICAL DIMENSION.)

Helios Line of opaque papers and cloths and transparent papers, cloths, and films manufactured especially for dry diazo reproduction. Helios is a registered trade name of the Keuffel and Esser Company. The opaque materials comprise a series of papers and cloths with black, blue, and maroon lines. The opaque prints, which are produced from right-reading translucent originals, serve as working prints in engineering and production departments and may be used for the reproduction of maps and other types of drawings. They are also used for business forms, duplicate copies, manuals, handbooks, and bulletin-board notices. The blackline papers are obtainable in white, yellow, pink, green, and blue. The several transparent papers are all 100 percent rag papers with sepia lines. The plastic-coated transparent cloths and clear or matte acetate safety films have sepia lines; they are used primarily for making intermediates.

Herculene drafting film Trade name of durable, translucent, and tear-resistant drafting film manufactured by the Keuffel and Esser Company. It has excellent erasing qualities for ink, pencil, or typewritten copy. Herculene film may be obtained in sheet sizes as ordered or in 20-yard rolls with widths of 30, 36, 42, or 54 inches. Base thicknesses are 0.003 and 0.002 inch; a matte finish is available on one or both sides of either thickness. The film accepts printer's ink for title blocks, logotypes, or forms. When a material is translucent, excellent copies are obtained by using the whiteprint reproduction process.

hidden line   Line used to show a hidden feature of a part or article. As used in orthographic engineering and mechanical drawings, it is designated as a "medium" line and consists of evenly spaced short dashes. Hidden lines should always begin with a dash in contact with the line from which they start unless such a dash would form a continuation of a full line. Dashes should touch at corners, and arcs should start with dashes on the tangent points. (*See also* LINE CONVENTIONS: ENGINEERING DRAWINGS.)

High Contrast Pan film   Du Pont separation negative film on Cronar polyester film base. It is used when high gammas are required in making continuous-tone color-separation negatives from reflection (opaque) copy or from low-contrast color transparencies.

high finish   Smooth high-polished paper finish.

highlight   Light portion of a photograph. In a negative, highlights are the areas of highest density since these correspond to the lightest areas of the original.

highlight halftone   Halftone plate in which the dots usually present in highlights have been etched away. The act of etching out or eliminating halftone dots in negatives is called "dropout." Practically all dropouts are confined to continuous-tone copy other than photographs, such as wash drawings, crayons, and charcoal drawings with large white areas.

horizontal bar chart   *See* BAR CHART.

horizontal dimension   Dimension of a plane that extends parallel to the horizon. It represents the width of an image when the image is viewed from the correct left-to-right position. The horizontal dimension is the major controlling dimension in graphic arts insofar as proportions are concerned. Its correlative is the vertical dimension. When used as the controlling dimension, the horizontal dimension governs the reduction or enlargement of line and halftone art as well as text copy and nomenclature for paste-ups. For oversize line and halftone art, the width of the image to be reproduced, from crop mark to crop mark, is the controlling dimension. For a page of solid text that has been set or typed oversize, the dimension is the width of the text area. When a single strip of nomenclature has been set or typed for paste-up and an enlargement or a reduction of the letters is desired, the horizontal dimension is the distance from the left edge to the right edge of the copy. (*See also* SCALING.)

horizontal page   *See* BROADSIDE PAGE.

hot composition   Setting type by machine, as with the Linotype, Intertype, Monotype, and other composing machines, in which characters are cast into slugs of molten metal or as single pieces of type.

house organ   Periodical published by a business organization for its employees or customers.

hydrographic chart   Map that depicts a body of water, sometimes with adjacent land, showing its location, flow, depth, and other significant phenomena.

hyperbolic functions: symbols   *See* TABLE 12.

I

idler rollers *See* WEB LEAD ROLLERS.

illustration *See* FIGURE.

illustration board (artist's board) Heavy paperboard manufactured especially for artists, for both oil and watercolor application. Standard sizes are 22 by 30, 22 by 28, 28 by 44, 30 by 40, and 40 by 60 inches; weights vary from thick to heavy. Thick board is about 8-ply; heavy, 24- to 30-ply. Colors range from white gray to snow white.

illustration file number *See* ART FILE NUMBER.

illustration request Form that requests that an individual piece of art be executed. It is usually filled in by the writer of the text that the illustration is to accompany.

illustration title *See* FIGURE TITLE.

image Any representation of a concept or an object on a paper sheet, plate, or other material. It may be drawn, typewritten, stamped, printed, marked, cut, carved, engraved, typeset, or photographed and be applied by any method or process. The image may be a type mass of text, a line drawing, a photograph, a symbol, or a dot, but only if it was made intentionally and communicates a message. An image is not an ink smear, an erasure ghost, or an unintended mark.

image area Square or rectangular area that encompasses a printed, drawn, or photographed image and the white or dark background space around the image. It is enclosed by imaginary perpendicular and horizontal lines. For artwork, the four sides of the area are established by using crop marks that limit the horizontal and vertical dimensions but are not printed. In text matter, the image area is defined by a line measure along the horizontal dimension and a line count along the vertical dimension, both expressed in picas. The image area may also be expressed in inches, particularly when oversize copy is to be reduced.

imposition Arrangement of the pages that are to be printed on one side of a sheet so that, when cut, folded, and trimmed, they will be right-reading and fall in numerical sequence. After margins have been determined for the outside dimensions of the sheet, it is the practice to allow additional margins of $\frac{1}{8}$ to $\frac{1}{4}$ inch for trimming. When work is tumbled, that is, when a sheet is first sent through the press in a normal operation and then tumbled forward with the top of the second printing engaging the bottom of the first printing, it is imperative that all sheets have the same dimensions to register properly. Figure I-1 shows how various folders and booklets may be printed for correct imposition. Illustration *A* is the simplest form of imposition, if it can be termed imposition at all. One typing is made on the top half of a direct plate or stencil and run through the machine. The paper is then reversed, run through the machine again, and cut in half. Illustrations *A* through *H* show types of imposition suitable for duplicators, whereas those shown in illustrations *I* through *P* must be done on printing presses.

impression Degree of pressure or force required between the printing plate or form and the printing stock. A "kiss" impression is the ideal contact between plate and stock. An impression is also each individual piece of printed matter made during a pressrun, as well as an image of any kind imposed on a surface, such as the impression that printing type makes on a material when the type is inked or in embossing without ink. The term also denotes a printing, or all the copies made in one pressrun.

impression cylinder In a rotary printing press, the cylinder that impresses the paper against the plate or blanket cylinder containing the image.

impression paper Paper that receives the image in any duplicating or printing operation. It is known in the printing trade as printing stock or as the web (rolled paper) and in the reproduction field as copy paper.

imprint Matter printed on a page or sheet which has already been printed. Imprinting is generally confined to printing a name and address, perhaps with a logotype. The term "imprint" also was applied to the first book face that was designed and used in mechanical linecasting composition (1912). Its success proved that it was possible to draw and cut new type designs pantographically and that mechanically set type could rival in appearance the best examples of hand composition.

imprint unit Device used to print imprints on one side of a web (paper roll), usually from rubber plates. For example, each copy of *This Week Magazine*, a Sunday newspaper supplement, bears the imprint and usually the logotype of one of the newspapers whose publishers subscribe to it.

inch-pica-point conversion chart *See* TABLE 7.

incunabula Books printed before 1501.

indention Holding of one or more lines of printed or typewritten matter in from the margin. The first word of a paragraph is usually indented. In a hanging indention, the first line is flush left and subsequent lines are indented 1 or more ems from the left.

index Alphabetical listing of the important topics of a work, accompanied by the numbers of the pages on which they occur. It is the last element in the back matter.

index guide Printed tab or other device marking a division of a publication, card file, ledger, or filing system for quick reference. Several kinds of index guides are used. One method involves printing divisions (dividers) on sheets of the same size as the publication. The guides are not visible when the book is closed but become apparent when it is fanned to locate the division. This type of index is printed with the book and generally on the same grade of paper. Text matter appears on the same sheet.

A second kind of indexing, called "thumb indexing," is often used in dictionaries. A single letter is printed on a black or colored half-round portion of the margin of a page at the beginning of each alphabetical section (sometimes a half-round printed tab is affixed

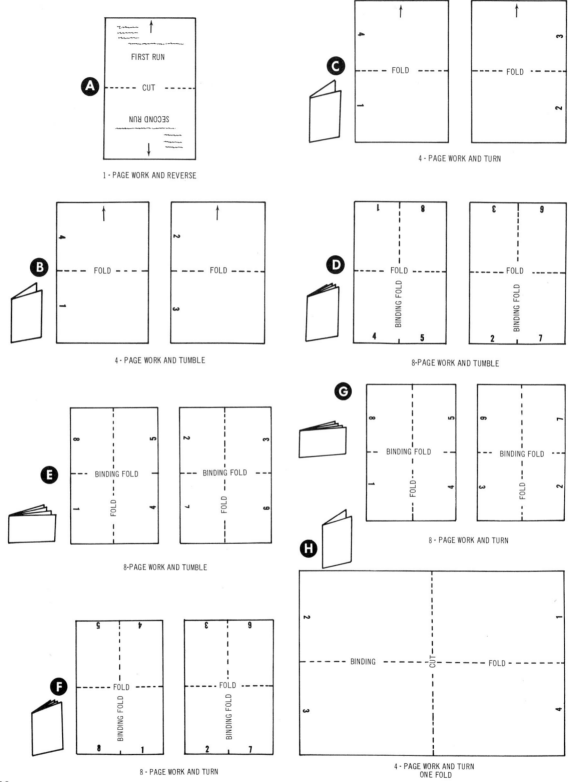

1 - PAGE WORK AND REVERSE

4 - PAGE WORK AND TURN

4 - PAGE WORK AND TUMBLE

8-PAGE WORK AND TUMBLE

8-PAGE WORK AND TUMBLE

8 - PAGE WORK AND TURN

8 - PAGE WORK AND TURN

4 - PAGE WORK AND TURN
ONE FOLD

Fig. I-1   Examples of imposition.

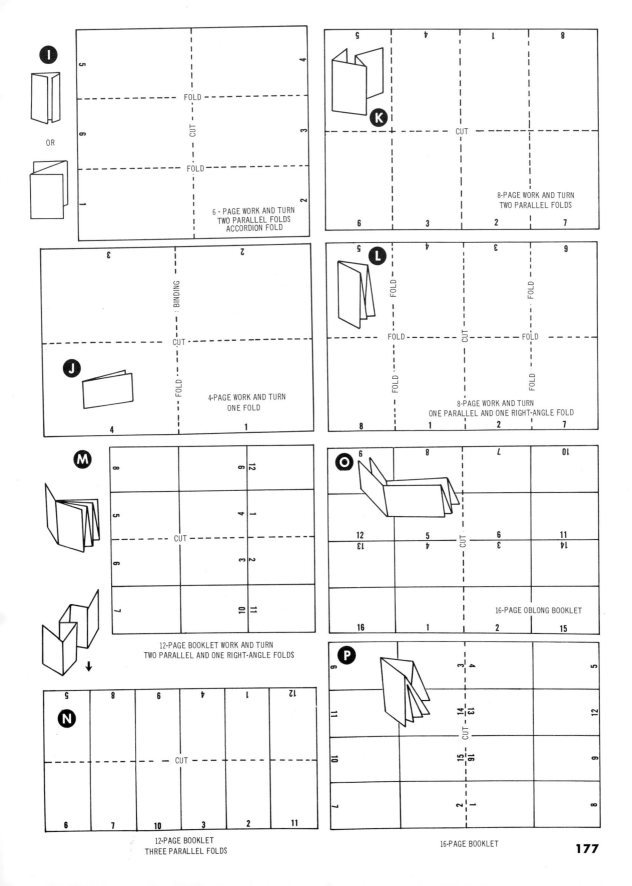

I

OR

6 - PAGE WORK AND TURN
TWO PARALLEL FOLDS
ACCORDION FOLD

K

8-PAGE WORK AND TURN
TWO PARALLEL FOLDS

J

4-PAGE WORK AND TURN
ONE FOLD

L

8-PAGE WORK AND TURN
ONE PARALLEL AND ONE RIGHT-ANGLE FOLD

M

12-PAGE BOOKLET WORK AND TURN
TWO PARALLEL AND ONE RIGHT-ANGLE FOLDS

O

16-PAGE OBLONG BOOKLET

N

12-PAGE BOOKLET
THREE PARALLEL FOLDS

P

16-PAGE BOOKLET

to the page). Pages appearing before the index guide are die-cut to expose the letter. The guides are visible when the book is closed.

A third type of indexing guide extends beyond the standard sheet or card size and is usually printed separately on heavier stock. Such guides are used extensively in industry. Figure I-2 shows a typical arrangement of index guides for a book. There are six units, each of which contains three divisions. The broken lines represent notches that will be cut out. All the divisions are in the order in which they will appear in the assembled book.

To prepare index guides as shown in Figure I-2, proceed as follows:

1. Mark off three even divisions on the edge of the 11-inch dimension of a sheet of quality reproduction paper, using a fade-out blue pencil. Leave $\frac{1}{4}$-inch blank spaces at the right- and left-hand margins.

2. Draw lines for tabs either $\frac{3}{8}$ or $\frac{1}{2}$ inch wide from the edge of the paper along the 11-inch dimension.

3. Apply nomenclature to each position by paste-up, taking care that copy is spaced evenly within each tab. (If this cannot be done, the printer will make the index tabs from furnished instructions.)

4. Use separate sheets of paper for each three-position unit and complete the paste-up.

The index guides are now ready for the printer, who will print from a plate for each unit. After printing, the sheets are notched with a circular die cut.

index letter   Letter of the alphabet, usually a capital letter, used to key a part or item depicted in an illustration to a legend or to a discussion in text. Index numbers are used for the same purpose. (*See also* KEY NUMBERS.)

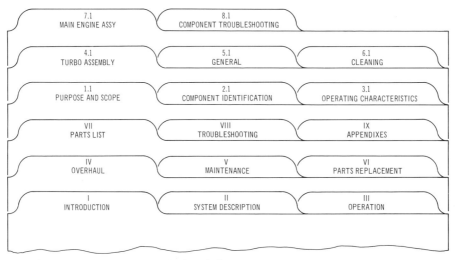

Fig. I-2   Arrangement of index guides for printing.

india ink Pigment made of lampblack and binding material; also this pigment suspended in water as a fluid ink. For good delineation, india ink should be solid black. Some india inks are gray in comparison with others.

india paper *See* BIBLE PAPER.

indirect color separation Color separation in which the various separation exposures are made on a continuous-tone film or plate and halftone screening is accomplished as one of the later steps of the process. Masks for color correction can be applied to the continuous-tone negatives.

industrial-view Land camera *See* POLAROID MP-3 INDUSTRIAL-VIEW LAND CAMERA.

infeed rollers *See* METERING UNIT.

inferior Subscript; a letter, numeral, or symbol written below the line and to the right of another character, in contrast to a superscript. It is set in a type size smaller than the text size. (*See also* SUPERIOR.)

initial First letter of a chapter, section, or article that is set in a type size larger than the text size. When the base of the initial is aligned with the base of the first text line, the initial is said to be a "stickup" initial. When the top of the initial is aligned with the top of the first text line and carry-over lines run around the lower part of the initial, the initial is said to be a "cut-in" initial.

initial caps Abbreviation for initial capital letters. As a direction to the printer, it indicates that only the first word of a heading should begin with a capital letter.

inked art Artwork that has been completed in ink after the penciled drawing has been checked for accuracy. When inked art is ready for reproduction, it is called reproduction or camera-ready copy.

inker *See* FINISHER.

insert Page or group of pages added to a publication during binding. The term also denotes, particularly in rough manuscript copy (copy in the process of being reproduced in one form or another), added text that is keyed to fall in its correct place in the copy. If all pages of the manuscript copy are right-hand pages, the insert may be typed on a separate sheet facing the page in which it is to appear.

This procedure necessitates binding the insert at the right margin. It is a good plan to type inserts on paper of a different color from that used for the original manuscript copy. This lessens the chance of the insert's being overlooked by the typist preparing the final copy.

For copy that is to be set on a linecasting machine, an insert should be stripped in place by cutting the sheet where it falls. When stripping in an insert will leave a sheet longer than other sheets, the copy should be broken at the bottom of the page and carried over to another sheet. When additional sheets are thus required, letters are added to the page number, as in 236A, 236B, 236C, etc.

inspection drawing   *See* DIMENSION DRAWING.

installation control drawing   Engineering drawing that sets forth the dimensions of an item in terms of area and space, sway and access clearances, and pipe and cable attachments for installation and functioning with related items.

installation drawing   In engineering drafting, an outline drawing that shows the form, location, and position of an item and provides mounting instructions with respect to its fixed points and other parts.

Instant Negative Conversion   *See* NEGATIVE CONVERSION.

intaglio printing (gravure printing)   Method of printing used in steel and copperplate engraving. An engraved plate is an exact opposite of a relief plate, the image being depressed below the surface of the plate. Ink floods over the plate and into the depressed areas. The top of the plate is then wiped clean with a "doctor blade," leaving ink only in the depressions. When paper is applied to the plate, the ink held in the depressed areas adheres to the paper and the image is printed. Ink used in intaglio printing must be more fluid than letterpress ink to maintain the flow into the engraved areas. (*See also* PRINTING METHODS.)

interconnection diagram   Connection or wiring drawing that shows the external connections between units. Connections within the units themselves are usually omitted.

interleave   *See* SLIP-SHEET.

interlock   Effect of joining type characters, produced usually in display type set with a photographic typesetter. An interlock is similar to a ligature. (*See* LIGATURE.)

intermediate   Copy of an original on translucent or transparentized film, paper, or cloth from which subsequent copies are made. An intermediate serves as a master only in the sense that it is used to make additional copies so that the original may be filed and saved from wear and tear. More than one intermediate may be made from the same original, thus saving production time in running off copies. Used largely in the whiteprint process, intermediates are required to intensify weak originals and to permit design and copy changes while leaving the original unaltered. The following list of uses and applications of intermediates is made possible through the courtesy of the Charles Bruning Company.

1. Make intermediate prints of original tracings and drawings. Use the intermediates as working originals and keep the originals in the files, where they will be spared frequent handling.

2. If the original is weak, torn, or faded, make an intermediate print of the original copy on translucent material. Use this translucent print in place of the original to produce subsequent prints in the machine.

3. Make design changes without altering or tracing the original by producing a translucent print of the original. Make the changes on the print with pencil or ink and produce as many prints of the design change as are needed.

4. When two or more drawings are to contain basic elements common to all, intermediates eliminate the need for tracing or re-drawing the constant elements each time. Make a drawing containing only the constant elements and as many copies of the original as there are different drawings required. Complete the individual drawings at the drafting board by adding the respective design variations to the translucent prints.

5. Make composite prints of two or more originals by (*a*) reproducing each original on translucent material, blocking out or later eradicating any unwanted portions of the original design; (*b*) superimposing the prints or placing them next to each other in desired registration; and (*c*) running them through the machine as a single original is run.

6. Make several reproducible prints of the original translucent material. Use these as multiple "duplicate originals" in the machine to speed production.

internal projection   Exposure of the sensitized copy paper of a microfilm reader-printer so that light falls on it within the machine. (*See also* EXTERNAL PROJECTION.)

introduction   Preliminary explanatory statement in a book or other publication. There are two kinds of introductions. One, which appears as part of the front matter, comments on the scope and content of the book, how it should be used, and the like. This type of introduction may be made by someone other than the author. The second kind of introduction is the opening chapter or section of a book in which the author introduces the reader to the subject matter.

IPH Abbreviation for impressions per hour.

isometric projection *See* AXONOMETRIC PROJECTION.

italic Slanting type used to emphasize a letter, word, or series of words in text and to print foreign words or phrases. *This sentence is set in italic.* To indicate to the printer that a word or phrase is to be set in italic, underscore it with a single line; in proof, underscore the word or phrase and write "ital" in the margin.

J

jacket Dust cover for a hard-cover book, bearing the book title, the author's and publisher's names, and other information as desired. It is usually designed to have sales appeal. The parts of the jacket that fold inward are called the front and back jacket flaps.

jaw folder Paper folder used with a web-fed printing press. It consists of three cylinders between which the web passes to make one or two parallel folds at right angles to the direction of web travel. First, the leading edge of the web is caught on pins that carry it around the first cylinder. Halfway around, tucker blades on the cylinder force the center of the signature-to-be into folding jaws on the second cylinder. At the same time, a cutoff knife separates the tail of the signature from the web. The signature is then carried around and released by the jaws, and the cycle continues. The signature can be passed to a third cylinder in a similar manner to make a second parallel fold. The folds thus made are called jaw folds or parallel folds.

jelly print *See* GELATIN PROCESS.

job case *See* CASE.

job press   Small printing press into which stock is fed by hand. The platen and bed open and close to receive the stock, which is pressed against the typeform on the bed.

job stick   *See* COMPOSING STICK.

jogger   Vibrating device used to align the edges of stock before trimming, folding, and binding, or to align and position any material for any purpose during production. The jogger may be a separate unit (Figures J-1 and J-2), or a printing-press delivery system may employ vibration to jog printed matter into alignment. Joggers are of many types and may be designed for multiple or specific uses. They are employed at the press or cutter in small printing shops or binderies, in offices and stores, in label factories, and in the gathering machines of newspaper plants. Specific uses include settling the contents of envelopes prior to opening them by automatic machines; aligning invoices, tabulating cards, statements, canceled checks, premium notices, and forms; aligning heavy board stock to onionskin; and adjusting addresses in window envelopes.

Figure J-1 shows the Syntron Model J-2 single-action vertical-vibration hardwood-deck jogger. Stock must be handled manually, the material being jogged first on one side and then turned to be jogged on the other side. Designed for bench and table work, this model has a 17- by 22-inch deck and jogs loads as heavy as 50 pounds. It aligns correspondence, orders, invoices, and other papers.

Fig. J-1   **Syntron Model J-2 jogger.**

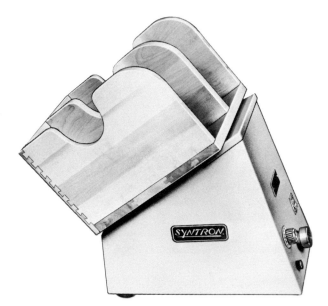

Fig. J-2   **Syntron Model TJ-1 jogger.**

Figure J-2 shows the Syntron Model TJ-1 two-bin single-action jogger. It uses the combination of a tilted bin and vertical vibration to provide automatic jogging.

justification Spacing of lines of type to a predetermined measure so that the margins are aligned. Linecasting machines automatically justify copy, but copy composed on a typewriter and other cold-composition machines must be pretyped (prejustified) to determine the required unit count of each line. Although the VariTyper justifies copy automatically, prejustification is required. Manual justification is accomplished with typewriters that feature proportional spacing such as IBM's Executive series of electric typewriters. (*See also* PROPORTIONAL SPACING; TYPEWRITER.)

Justowriter Automatic cold-composition tape-operated copy-setting machine. Justowriter is a trademark owned by Friden, Inc. (*See* COLD COMPOSITION.)

K

Kalvalith Trade name of halftone contact copy film manufactured by the Kalvar Corporation for Kal/Graphic, Inc. Kalvalith is a high-contrast contact film designed for the production of plate-making negatives or positives. It consists of a nongelatinous resin coating on a 0.003- and 0.005-inch polyester (Mylar) base. Processing is completely dry and does not require chemicals. The image is formed by exposure to ultraviolet light, developed by heat, and cleared by reexposure to ultraviolet light.

The film does not require a darkroom or a safelight, can stand ten to fifteen minutes of normal room illumination before image exposure, and may be handled indefinitely under the lamps commonly used in plate-making areas. It is an ultraviolet-sensitive film that is printed through line and halftone originals in vacuum-frame contact. The fact that the unexposed film is yellow-green provides a quick visual check of the degree of exposure. When verified by reflection under normal tungsten or white fluorescent room light, the fully exposed image is blue-gray and similar in appearance on both sides. A yellow-green image viewed through the film support indicates underexposure.

Kalvar process Photographic processing system. Kalvar is a registered trade name owned by the Kalvar Corporation. Kalvar film consists of stable single-layer coatings of thermoplastic resin on a polyester support. Exposure to ultraviolet light energy releases very small amounts of gas within the coating. When heat is applied after exposure, the gas expands to form microscopic vesicles. Since the quantity, and distribution of the vesicles are proportional to the exposure, they form a light-scattering negative image of a printed original. Sensitivity in coating areas not exposed during the image printing is removed by a final clearing exposure to ultraviolet energy without the application of heat. The gas released by this second exposure escapes by diffusion and does not form vesicles.

The very small light-scattering vesicles in processed Kalvar films cannot be classed as bubbles, such as might be formed in a gelatin emulsion. The hydrophobic plastic matrix forms more highly ordered crystallike shells around each expanding cavity, thus producing a stable image composed of light-scattering vesicles that are highly resistant to change due to age, use, and storage. The earliest commercial applications of the Kalvar process were made in microfilming systems. There the advantages of high resolution, simplicity, and speed earned the process wide acceptance among government agencies and industrial users.

Kalvatone Trade name of a continuous-tone color masking and copy film manufactured by the Kalvar Corporation for Kal/Graphic, Inc. Kalvatone is designed to fulfill the continuous-tone reproduction requirements of photographic color masking. It is a contact film for making same-size continuous-tone copies, either negative from positive or positive from negative. In positive and two-stage masking, its tone scale makes it suitable for use as the primary, the color corrector, or the under-color removal mask. Processing is dry and does not require chemicals.

Kalvatone film does not require darkroom or safelight handling. It can withstand five to ten minutes of low-level tungsten room illumination before image exposure. The film may be safely handled for an indefinite period in a plate-making area illuminated for common use. Kalvatone is an ultraviolet-sensitive film that is printed through the original negative or positive in vacuum-frame contact.

kern Any part of the face of a type letter that extends beyond the body.

key Legend or index identifying components, parts, or other features of an illustration. Keys are used with numerals, letters, or drawn symbols. The term "key" also denotes a code used in an advertiser's address to identify the magazine or newspaper from which an inquiry originates. The advertiser can thus determine the effectiveness of his advertising in a particular medium.

key art *See* BLACK ART.

key letters Identifying letters (or words) used in a layout comprehensive or dummy to indicate that such letters (or words) are to appear as part of the copy at that particular place. The completed text is furnished separately.

key numbers In technical illustrating, index numbers used in sequence with lead lines and arrowheads to key items on an illustration to an identifying legend. When it appears that arrowheads may congest the illustration, only lead lines are used. (*See also* CALL OUT.)

key plate *See* BLACK PRINTER.

Keyline letters Outline characters produced by the Varigraph cold-type composing machine. Keyline letters and numbers lend themselves to color work and special effects.

keystoning Distortion of the screen image in overhead projection. As the height of the image is increased, the image becomes wider at the top than at the bottom. Keystoning is corrected by tilting the top of the screen forward.

kid finish Paper finish similar to that of unfinished kid leather. It is comparatively smooth.

killed matter *See* DEAD MATTER.

kiss impression Near-perfect impression produced by the ideal contact between printing plate and paper. In offset and letterpress work, it may be necessary to build up the plate, form, or blanket with paper to secure a kiss impression.

kit drawing Engineering drawing that depicts a packaged unit, item, or group of items, instructions, photographs, and drawings, such as are used in modification, installation, or survival but in themselves do not necessarily constitute a complete functioning engineering assembly. A kit drawing usually includes a listing of all item numbers, commercial products, and hardware (as applicable) to complete a modification or installation. Only one drawing is usually prepared for a particular kit modification.

kneaded eraser Gum eraser of a special type that is kneaded into a desired shape for pencil erasing. When a portion is kneaded to a fine point, this type of eraser is excellent for cleaning excessive toner from open xerographic plates before the image on the plate is fixed by fusing.

Kodagraph Autopositive paper *See* KODAK AUTOPOSITIVE MATERIALS.

Kodak Autopositive materials Photographic films, plates, and paper proprietary with the Eastman Kodak Company. They are divided into four classifications: (1) Kodak Autopositive film (Estar base), a clear-base film that is thin enough for printing through for lateral image reversal; (2) Kodak Autopositive plates, designed for precision color work and applications for which the utmost dimensional stability is required; (3) Kodak Autopositive projection film (Estar base), for use in the process camera or enlarger in making positive transparencies from line originals and coarse-halftone originals; and (4) Kodagraph Autopositive paper "Ultra-thin, Al," which is used for quick proofing from positives, thus eliminating the need for an intermediate negative.

The basic operating principles are the same for all four Kodak Autopositive materials. The individual processing required in each case is described in instruction sheets packed with the material. With these materials, a negative can be made directly from a negative and a positive from a positive. The materials can be used to make outline effects on lettering and line work in a few simple steps. Portions of a single negative can be reversed so that positive and negative combinations and effects can be combined on the same sheet of film without stripping. Such effects as solid, clear, or tint lettering on halftone backgrounds, halftone tint joined to halftone tint with a clean division between the two, and clear or solid areas set in halftone-tint backgrounds are all produced without stripping. Reflex copies can be made of drawings or printed matter without the use of a camera or an intermediate negative. Blue-key positives can be simply produced instead of the usual blue-key negatives. Exposure is made by high-intensity ultraviolet light; the print is developed, stopped, and washed, but fixing is not required. The printout image has a blue or purplish color; hence the term "blue-key." Stripping to positive keys is easier and more accurate than stripping to negative keys.

The reader is referred to Kodak Pamphlet No. Q-23.

Kodak gray contact screen Photographic screen available in rulings of 65, 85, 100, 110, 120, 133, 150, and 220 lines per inch. Screens of 110, 120, 133, and 150 lines have elliptical dots only. The gray contact screen is designed for making halftone negatives and direct halftone separations from colored originals. It is recommended for processes that do not require the magenta dye for controlling tone reproduction. The controlled-flash method is recommended for controlling halftone contrast. The Kodak gray contact screen will give adequate highlight contrast for most work. For any application requiring additional highlight contrast, however, a no-screen, or highlighting, exposure should be made. Such an exposure is made before the screen is put in place for the main exposure. The highlighting exposure time is 2 to 15 percent of the main exposure time. If this time becomes too short for control, a neutral density filter is used. With a filter having a neutral density of 1.00, the same exposure time as is used for the main exposure will yield a 10 percent highlighting exposure.

Kodak magenta contact screen   Screen developed by the Eastman Kodak Company and used to make halftone negatives for photolithography and photoengraving. It is usable for either the conventional etching or the powderless etch process directly from black-and-white copy, as well as for making lithographic screen positives. The screen is also an improved means of making screened color-separation negatives or positives by the indirect method. One of the advantages of the magenta contact screen is an improvement in sharpness and in reproduction of fine details. Improved tone rendering, especially in the middle tones and highlights, without distortion of dot shapes, simplified contrast control, and elimination of the problems of screen distance ratios are other advantages. The use of multiple lens stops, required with conventional crossline screens, is also eliminated.

Since the lens opening does not affect contrast or dot formation, lens apertures other than $f/16$ can be used. Most process lenses give sharper results in the apertures of $f/16$ and $f/32$. When enlargements or reductions are made, either the aperture or the exposure time can be changed in compensation. An enlargement of the image size necessitates more exposure; a reduction, less. Contrast may be controlled by any of four methods: controlled flash, highlighting exposures with a screen, the use of an appropriate filter, and controlled agitation. Often these methods are used in combination.

Kodak magenta contact screens are supplied in three basic types: (1) Kodak magenta contact screen (negative), for making halftone negatives for photomechanical reproduction; (2) Kodak magenta contact screen (positive), for making halftone positives from continuous-tone negatives; and (3) Kodak magenta contact screen (for photogravure), for making gravure reproductions of high quality. When any positive or negative type of screen is used for its intended purpose, it gives excellent results without complicated exposure techniques. If a positive screen is used in a normal manner for making negatives or if a negative screen is used for making positives, however, the resulting reproduction usually lacks sufficient highlight contrast.

Again, although excellent halftone negatives can be made with a positive screen if a no-screen, or highlighting, exposure is added, there is no way to overcome the loss of highlight contrast when positives are made with a negative screen.

For further information on these screens, the reader is referred to Kodak Pamphlet No. Q-21. Instructions for using Kodak magenta contact screen (for photogravure) are given in Kodak Pamphlet No. Q-22, *How to Use the Kodak Magenta Contact Screen for Photogravure.*

Kodalith Autoscreen Ortho film   Film produced by the Eastman Kodak Company and used primarily to make halftone negatives for lithography from photographic prints. When the film is exposed to a continuous-tone image, a dot pattern is automatically produced as though a halftone screen had been used in the camera. The film can be exposed in an ordinary view-camera film holder without a vacuum frame. As no screen is used, the film is capable of greatly improving detail. All image light reaches the film, and the result is a higher effective speed than is obtained with the conventional screen and film combination. Much wider lens apertures can be used than are considered practical in conventional halftone-screen photography.

For futher information on this film, the reader is referred to Kodak Pamphlet No. P-21.

Koh-I-Noor pen   *See* PENS, TECHNICAL.

Ko-Rec-Copy   Sheet with a white coating on one side that is used for correcting typewritten errors. The trade name Ko-Rec-Copy is owned by the Eaton Allen Corporation. When an error is made, the typist backspaces to the letter or word typed in error. A sheet of Ko-Rec-Copy is placed over carbon-copy errors with the coated side down, and a strip of Ko-Rec-Type (the same as Ko-Rec-Copy except that it is provided in smaller strips) is placed over the original-copy error, again with the coated side down. The error is then retyped. The white coating on the material is thus transferred to the original and carbon copies, obliterating the error. The material is removed, and the correct letter or word is typed.

Krylon   Registered trade name of Krylon, Inc., for a crystal-clear spray coating used to protect artwork, drawings, photographs, documents, papers, or any other material that is to be preserved. The copy is held at a distance, and Krylon is first sprayed to one side to determine the strength of the spray. The image area is then sprayed lightly, the arm moving back and forth over the copy. Several passes with the spray should be sufficient to coat the material.

L

lacquering *See* VARNISHING.

laid antique paper Antique paper with a pattern of vertical and horizontal lines produced either by a hand process or by laid wires in the dandy roll of a papermaking machine.

lamination Flattening into a thin plate; in the graphic arts industry, uniting plastic film by heat and pressure to a sheet of paper to protect the paper and improve its appearance. Lamination is used to protect, preserve, and add luster to documents, valuable drawings and papers, covers for books, booklets, proposals, and specifications, and any material that might suffer from heat, aging, chemicals, water, grease, and other stains. Figure L-1 illustrates the laminating process.

Laminating machines can cover one or both sides of a sheet with laminating material. The American Photocopy Equipment Company's Ply-On laminator is a portable desk-top machine weighing 30 pounds. The General Binding Corporation manufactures an 18-inch laminator. After the film has been loaded in this machine, the operation is controlled by first pushing the PREHEAT button for warm-up, then switching to RUN, and feeding the sheets into the machine for lamination on one or both sides. A sheet 35 inches wide can be accommodated by folding it and running it through the machine twice.

The General Binding Corporation has developed a method of producing full-color transparencies for overhead projection from a printed page. The image to be reproduced must be letterpress printed on clay-coated stock. With this process, two transparencies can be produced at the same time. The two illustrations to be made into transparencies are placed back to back and run through a GBC laminator twice. The excess film is then trimmed off, and the two pages are separated by cutting through the edge of the paper. After soaking, wiping, rinsing, and drying, the transparencies are ready for a final laminating that protects the printed image and adds body for easier handling.

landscape page *See* BROADSIDE PAGE.

lateral reversal Left-to-right, or mirror-image, reversal of an image.

latitude Range of exposures within which a film will produce an acceptable image.

lawn finish Linenlike paper finish.

lay Character of the bed on which paper rests before it enters a flatbed printing press. Register controls, sheet-size alteration, and type of paper grippers are considerations of lay.

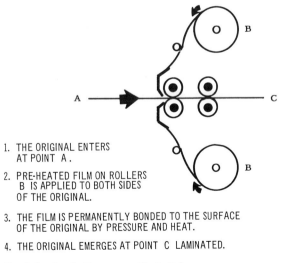

1. THE ORIGINAL ENTERS AT POINT A.

2. PRE-HEATED FILM ON ROLLERS B IS APPLIED TO BOTH SIDES OF THE ORIGINAL.

3. THE FILM IS PERMANENTLY BONDED TO THE SURFACE OF THE ORIGINAL BY PRESSURE AND HEAT.

4. THE ORIGINAL EMERGES AT POINT C LAMINATED.

Fig. L-1 Laminating process illustrated.

layout Arrangement of a book, magazine, or other publication so that text and illustrations follow a desired format. Layout includes directions for marginal data, pagination, marginal allowances, center headings and sideheads, placement and size of display and body type, and placement of illustrations. If time permits, a dummy layout may be made to show how the final layout will appear. Layout may also be defined as "makeup," but this term is usually confined to work handled by printers, whereas "layout" is used for cold-composition copy.

Figure L-2 illustrates a multiple-page layout form for a soft-cover report consisting of 4 pages of front matter and 19 pages of the

PUBLICATION TITLE _____

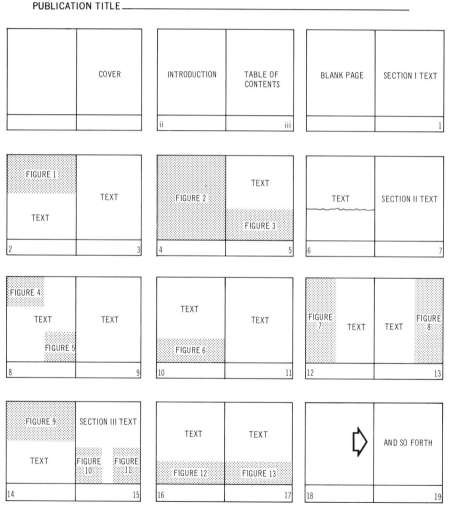

Fig. L-2   Advance multiple-page book layout.

body of the report. Such a form is used before or with individual page makeup, primarily as an advance indication of the placement of copy and its relation to right- and left-hand pages. Note that all right-hand pages have odd numbers and left-hand pages even numbers. The cover or title page does not take a page number, but the page is counted (blind-folioed), as is shown by the succeeding page, which is numbered ii. All front-matter pages preceeding page 1 are numbered with lowercase roman numerals. Page ii will back up the title page. Page iv is left blank so that page 1 can be a right-hand page. From the illustration one can see that each section begins on a right-hand page.

Figures may be designated "F/P" (full-page), "H/P" (half-page), etc. Line art may be identified as "Line," halftones as "H/T," and page foldouts as "F/O." While it is customary for a foldout page to be a right-hand page with the opposite side left blank, an ideal arrangement exists when one page foldout backs up another page foldout. The size of the sheet for the foldouts is determined by the longer illustration of the two. A blank space called an "apron" may be left on either foldout next to the binding margin if one illustration is not of the same length as the other.

Page 19 of the report is backed up with a blank page because it is a right-hand page. The blank page serves as the back cover. When the last page ends as a left-hand page, copy on the page should be protected with a dust cover by adding a blank sheet to the publication.

The term "layout" is also applied to the arrangement of art and of nomenclature used with art. Art should supplement the text and be in proportion to the object depicted, of the right size, and pleasing to the eye. Without benefit of enlargement or reduction, it can be seen that in Figure L-3A the object is drawn in too large a scale because its shape does not lend itself to the size. The layout of Figure L-3B is more in keeping with proper size.

layout typing   Typing text for reproduction copy while allowing space for illustrations or other material. Considerable skill and experience are required for this kind of typing because page layout must conform to acceptable standards. Illustration dimensions, particularly height, must be known. A convenient method of layout typing employs layout sheets printed with fade-out blue perimeters that show the space limitations of the page. Each line of text should be numbered, beginning with 1 at the left margin and proceeding in sequence to the last line on the preprinted page. A line count for each line of text is thus established. Allowance for illustration numbers and titles should be made and the number of lines for titles predetermined.

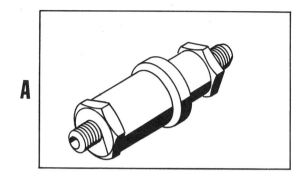

POOR LAYOUT

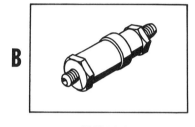

GOOD LAYOUT

Fig. L-3   Art layout.

Fig. L-4   Using preprinted lead lines.

lead line (leader line) Line that leads to and points out an object or a point of interest or reference. Arrowheads may be used with lead lines. When preprinted wax-backed paste-ups are employed, a white lead line (or white arrowhead) should be used when leading into a dark area and a black lead line (or black arrowhead) when leading into a white or highlighted area. A white-and-black lead line should be used to cross both white and dark areas. Figure L-4 illustrates the use of lead lines. (*See also* LINE CONVENTIONS: ENGINEERING DRAWINGS.)

leaders Row of dots, called dot leaders, or dashes used in lists or tabular matter to guide the eye from one item to another. An example follows:

Introduction 1-1

leading Spacing between lines of type, measured in points. Narrow metal strips less than the overall height of the type are inserted between the lines, or the type is cast on a slug that is wider than the point size of the type. If no leading is used, the type is said to be "set solid." If 8 point is cast on a 10-point body (called "8 on 10"), the effect is of leading 2 points.

leading edge Front portion of a moving object that extends beyond the leads the remaining portion. An example is the leading edge of a web (paper roll) as it is fed into the printing press or the front edge of an airplane wing. The term is opposed to "trailing edge."

leaf Sheet of paper in a book. Each of its two sides is a page. The term "leaf" also denotes a thin sheet of gold or similar materials used in die stamping or lettering.

leatherette finish Paper finish giving the appearance of leather. It is made by embossing.

ledger paper (record paper) Smooth-finished paper used for business ledgers and other purposes for which strength, absence of glare, and suitability for pen writing are required. It must be readily erasable. In addition, it must meet requirements for printing headings and ruling. Colors include white, blue, pink, and salmon. Basic weights are 24, 28, 32, and 36 pounds for 500 sheets of the basic size of 17 by 22 inches.

left-hand page *See* PAGE NUMBERING.

legal cap White legal-size writing paper.

legal-size paper Paper measuring $8\frac{1}{2}$ by 13 or $8\frac{1}{2}$ by 14 inches. (*See also* BOXED PAPER.)

legend Key accompanying an illustration; also an illustration title. (*See* FIGURE TITLE; KEY.)

length Longer of the straight-line dimensions of a plane surface, the shorter dimension being the width. While longer drawings, such as engineering schematics, are described as having length, the term is not used in scaling enlargements or reductions of artwork. For this purpose, the horizontal dimension is the width and the vertical dimension the height.

Leroy pens *See* PENS, TECHNICAL.

letter designations: engineering drawings There are ten sizes of engineering drawings, each of which is designated by a letter for flat and roll sizes. For flat sizes, A is $8\frac{1}{2}$ by 11 inches (used both as a vertical and horizontal sheet); B is 11 by 17 inches; C is 17 by 22 inches; D is 22 by 34 inches; E is 34 by 44 inches; and F is 28 by 40 inches. For roll sizes, G is 11 by 42 inches; H is 28 by 48 inches; J is 34 by 48 inches; and K is 40 by 48 inches. The four roll sizes, G, H, J, and K, may extend from the minimum length shown to a maximum length of 144 inches.

letter paper Paper, regardless of size, that is manufactured for correspondence.

letter size Boxed-paper size, ordinarily 8½ by 11 inches.

letterhead Information printed or engraved as a heading on a sheet of stationery; also the printed or engraved sheet itself. The name and address of a person or an organization and sometimes the telephone number, logotype, and other information are included in a letterhead. A properly executed letterhead that reflects the characteristics of the individual or firm it represents is an important factor in graphic communication.

lettering, hand *See* BRUSHES, ART; PENS, STEEL-BRUSH; SPEEDBALL PENS; STYLUS.

lettering engineering drawings Single-stroke uppercase commercial Gothic lettering is generally used for engineering drawings unless typewritten characters are employed. Letters may be freehand or made by means of a template, typewriter, or lettering machine. To ensure legibility after reproduction, inclined or vertical letters are used. Except for titles, lowercase letters may be used on construction drawings. When office typewriters with standard pica (0.10-inch) letters are used, the typewritten characters are uppercase.

Regardless of the lettering method used, all lines must be sufficiently opaque to be legible, either in full size or after reduction, by any method of reproduction. Underlining may be used for emphasis, but it must be less than 0.03 inch below the characters. The division line of a common fraction should be parallel to the direction in which the dimension reads and separated from the characters by a minimum of 0.03 inch. When a fraction is included in a typewritten note, table, or list, however, an oblique line may be used. The size of lettering and the spacing are determined by the size of the original drawing and the amount of reduction to which it will be subjected. Characters should not touch lines, symbols, figures, or other characters. The minimum space between lines of lettering is 0.03 inch. The minimum size of lettering should be in accordance with the following table.

Use	Size, in.
Drawing and part number in title block	0.20
Title	0.12
Subtitle for special views	0.12
Letters and numerals for body of drawing	0.12
Dimensions, fractions, and tolerances	0.12
Designation of section and detail views	
"Section," "Detail"	0.12
"A-A," "B"	0.18

When the need arises, larger characters may be used to provide the required legibility. Lettering and numbering for special notices may be of any suitable size. The spacing between round, full figures such as O, Q, and 6 is smaller than that between straight figures such as I, H, and P. Spacing between words should be not less than the width of one letter O; that between sentences, not less than twice the width of the letter O. Spacing between paragraphs should be at least as wide as a line of lettering. No type smaller than the standard pica (0.10-inch) size should be used. The regular line spacing of typewriters and other lettering machines is acceptable.

lettering guides   Transparent green stenciling aids (Figure L-5). The guides are rectangles with tapered openings for forming letters

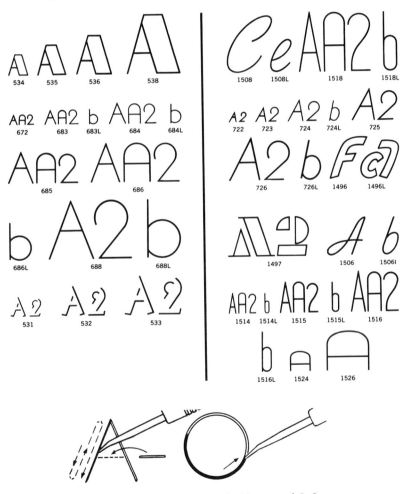

Fig. L-5   **Lettering guides used for stencil work.** (*Courtesy of A. B. Dick Company.*)

and numbers in various sizes and faces to be used in stenciling and reproduction by the direct-plate (stencil) process employed with duplicators such as the mimeograph. They are used also with mechanical negatives in making presensitized plates for offset duplicating.

lettering or type reduction   When lettering or type must be reduced, it must be large enough to be legible after reduction. Furthermore, when a series of drawings (electrical schematics, for example) is to be included under one cover, as in a technical publication, the lettering of all the drawings should be consistent in size. All drawings should have the same image width. When the drawings are reduced, the lettering will be reduced proportionately. If it is not possible to have the same image width on all drawings, the lettering or type applied to them must be proportionately larger or smaller. Lettering or type smaller than 6 point is too small for easy reading. Sizes from 6 to 10 point are recommended. The 12-point size is generally too large for a page size of $8\frac{1}{2}$ by 11 inches.

Lettering and type sizes and drawing-image widths should always be planned beforehand. Figure L-6 is a simple explanation of how this can be accomplished when these factors are known: (1) the image width of the original, (2) the fact that the type size must not be less than 6 point or more than 12 point and that a range from 8 to 10 point is desirable, and (3) the image width of the reduced

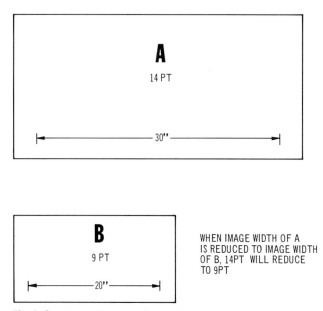

WHEN IMAGE WIDTH OF A IS REDUCED TO IMAGE WIDTH OF B, 14PT WILL REDUCE TO 9PT

Fig. L-6   **Determining type size requirements.**

drawing. The drawing-image width is 30 inches, and it is to be reduced to 20 inches. If 30 inches is reduced by one-half to 15 inches and 12-point lettering is applied, the 12 point will be reduced proportionately, to 6 point. Since the required reduction is to be 20 inches instead of 15 inches, however, a size larger than 6 point must be used. If 14-point lettering is applied to the original copy, the size of the type after reduction can be determined by means of the following formula:

30 in. is to 14 pt as
20 in. is to ?

Algebraically expressed,

30/14 : : 20/x

Multiply crisscross:

14 × 20 = 280

280 ÷ 30 = 9 pt (approximately)

lettering pens   *See* PENS, STEEL-BRUSH; SPEEDBALL PENS.

letterpress printing   Relief printing method in which raised inked surfaces come in direct contact with the paper and the impression or image is transferred. (For the printing process known as offset letterpress, dry offset, or letterset, *see* LETTERSET PRINTING; *see also* PRINTING METHODS.)

Letterpress is one of the major divisions of printing. It includes both hand-set and machine composition. Foundry type, cast in individual pieces, is used in hand composition. In machine composition, type may be cast in slugs of equal lengths or measures by linecasting machines such as the Linotype and the Intertype. These are hot-metal composition machines. The Monotype is also a hot-composition machine, but it produces single pieces of type. The advantages of single-type composition are that individual letters may be corrected by hand and that any portion of a line may be increased or decreased to obtain an even, or justified, right-hand margin. Moreover, in tabular matter vertical rules may run through the type mass. The Linotype, Intertype, and Monotype machines all mechanically compose lines with even right-hand margins. (*See also* LINECASTING MACHINE; MONOTYPE.)

Many books are printed by having the copy first composed by letterpress and then using it to produce plates by the photolithographic process. The printer furnishes etch, or reproduction proofs. Since these proofs are page size, they do not require reduction by the process camera and actual type sizes are used.

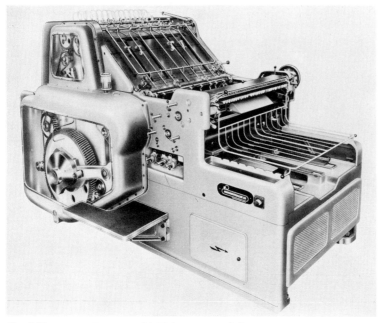

Fig. L-7 **Mergenthaler's Model 38 letterpress printing press.**

Figure L-7 shows the Model 38 Mergenthaler letterpress printing machine. This machine has a mechanism that stops it automatically during a malfunction. A splash lubrication system keeps oil in continuous circulation. Cylinder packing may be exposed by lifting the feedboard. The maximum sheet size is $25\frac{5}{8}$ by 38 inches; the minimum, 10 by 15 inches. The maximum printing area with a normal chase is $24\frac{13}{16}$ by $37\frac{1}{2}$ inches. The feed-pile height is $15\frac{3}{8}$ inches and the delivery-pile height $24\frac{1}{2}$ inches. The maximum speed is 3,600 impressions per hour.

letterset printing (also called **dry offset; offset letterpress; offset relief**) Relief offset printing process. The word "letterset" combines the "letter" in "letterpress" and "set" from "offset." The term "dry offset" is used to describe the opposite of the wet process of planographic printing. Letterset printing differs from planographic printing in that the printing plate is in relief. The image is transferred to a rubber blanket and then to the printing surface. Damping is not required. Any printing process in which an intermediate surface transfers the image from the plate to the stock is an offset process whether the plates are in relief or not. In letterset printing, a thin, flexible, compact relief plate is substituted for the conventional lithographic plate. Ordinary letterpress relief plates and forms must "read wrong" because the impression on stock, which must, "read right," comes in direct contact with the plate. In offset printing, how-ever, the plate must read right in order to read right when printed because of the intermediate step of transferring the image from plate to blanket.

letterspacing Placing of additional space between the letters of words to expand the length of a line or to improve and balance typography. Some typewriters letterspace automatically when a control button is pushed. It is difficult to letterspace lowercase letters without deforming the copy, but headings set in capital letters may be letterspaced to improve their appearance.

lift Greatest number of sheets of paper that can be cut at one time with a paper-cutting machine; also the number of sheets that can be handled in an operation of any kind.

ligature Two or more characters cast on the same body of type and partially joined, as æ, ff.

light table (stripping table) Table having a transparent glass top through which artificial light is reflected from below. Light tables are used for mortising, opaquing, retouching, alignment, and strip-ping negatives into masking paper called "goldenrod flats." Ade-quate light tables are easy to construct and, of course, may be purchased. When a table is being utilized, fluorescent lights should be used instead of incandescent lights to minimize heat and glare.

lightface Typeface composed of fine lines, used for the body of the text, as distinguished from boldface.

line conventions: engineering drawings In engineering drafting there are various standard practices for drawing lines. Ink lines must be opaque and of uniform width. As shown in Figure L-8, three widths of lines, thin, medium, and thick, in the proportions of $1:2:4$, are used. The actual width of each type of line is governed by the size and style of the drawing. The relative widths of the lines are shown in Figure L-9. Pencil lines must be of uniform width and have the same density throughout. Cutting-plane and viewing-plane lines are the thickest lines on a drawing. Outline and other visible lines are drawn prominently. Hidden, sectioning, center, phantom, extension, dimension, and leader lines are not so prominent as outline lines. The minimum space between parallel lines is 0.03 inch. Center lines are composed of alternate long and short dashes, with a long dash at each end. They must cross without voids (*see* Figure L-10). Short center lines may be unbroken if they cannot be confused with other lines. Center lines may be used to indicate the travel of a

NAME	CONVENTION	DESCRIPTION AND APPLICATION	EXAMPLE
LEADER		THIN LINE TERMINATED WITH ARROWHEAD OR DOT AT ONE END	$\frac{1}{4}$ X 20 THD
		USED TO INDICATE A PART, DIMENSION, OR OTHER REFERENCE	
PHANTOM OR DATUM LINE		MEDIUM SERIES OF ONE LONG DASH AND TWO SHORT DASHES EVENLY SPACED ENDING WITH LONG DASH USED TO INDICATE ALTERNATE POSITION OF PARTS, REPEATED DETAIL, OR TO INDICATE A DATUM PLANE	
STITCH LINE		MEDIUM LINE OF SHORT DASHES EVENLY SPACED AND LABELED	STITCH
		USED TO INDICATE STITCHING OR SEWING	
BREAK (LONG)	(WOOD)	THIN SOLID RULED LINES WITH FREEHAND ZIGZAGS	
		USED TO REDUCE SIZE OF DRAWING REQUIRED TO DELINEATE OBJECT AND REDUCE DETAIL	
BREAK (SHORT)		THICK SOLID FREEHAND LINES	
		USED TO INDICATE A SHORT BREAK	
CUTTING OR VIEWING PLANE; VIEWING PLANE OPTIONAL		THICK SOLID LINES WITH ARROWHEAD TO INDICATE DIRECTION IN WHICH SECTION OR PLANE IS VIEWED OR TAKEN	
CUTTING PLANE FOR COMPLEX OR OFFSET VIEWS		THICK SHORT DASHES	
		USED TO SHOW OFFSET WITH ARROWHEADS TO SHOW DIRECTION VIEWED	

NAME	CONVENTION	DESCRIPTION AND APPLICATION	EXAMPLE
VISIBLE LINES		HEAVY UNBROKEN LINES	
		USED TO INDICATE VISIBLE EDGES OF AN OBJECT	
HIDDEN LINES		MEDIUM LINES WITH SHORT EVENLY SPACED DASHES	
		USED TO INDICATE CONCEALED EDGES	
CENTER LINES		THIN LINES MADE UP OF LONG AND SHORT DASHES ALTERNATELY SPACED AND CONSISTENT IN LENGTH	
		USED TO INDICATE SYMMETRY ABOUT AN AXIS AND LOCATION OF CENTERS	
DIMENSION LINES		THIN LINES TERMINATED WITH ARROWHEADS AT EACH END	
		USED TO INDICATE DISTANCE MEASURED	
EXTENSION LINES		THIN UNBROKEN LINES	
		USED TO INDICATE EXTENT OF DIMENSIONS	

Fig. L-8 Line conventions for engineering drawings.

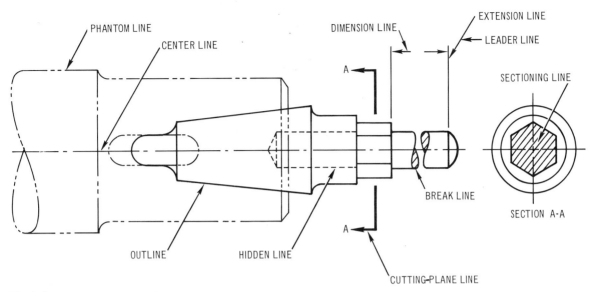

Fig. L-9 Line convention widths.

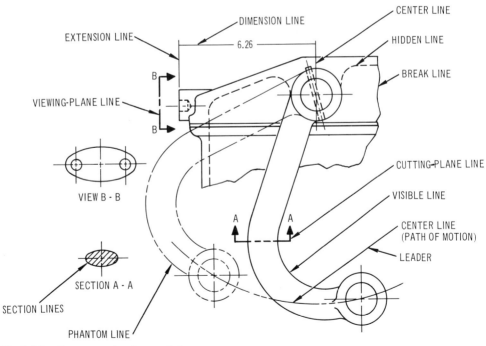

Fig. L-10 Line convention characteristics.

center in an alternate position (*see* Figure L-11*A*). Dimension lines terminate in arrowheads at each end (*see* Figure L-9). They are unbroken except where space is required to insert the dimension.

Leaders are used to indicate a part or a portion to which a number, note, or other reference applies; they terminate in an arrowhead or a dot. Arrowheads always terminate at a line; dots should be within the outline of an object, such as an outline indicating a surface. Leaders should terminate at any suitable portion of the note, reference, or dimension (*see* Figure L-10). Short break lines are indicated by solid freehand lines. For long breaks, full ruled lines with freehand zigzags are used. When a portion of the length of a shaft, rod, tube, or the like is broken out, the ends of the break are drawn as illustrated in Figure L-12. Phantom lines, composed of a series of one long and two short dashes evenly spaced with a long dash at each end (*see* Figures L-10 and L-11), are used to indicate the alternate position of parts, repeated detail, or the relative position of an absent part. Sectioning lines are used to indicate the exposed surfaces of an object in a sectional view. The spacing of sectioning lines may vary with the shape and size of the part but should never be narrower than is necessary for clarity. Hidden lines are evenly spaced short dashes used to show the hidden features of a part. They always begin and end with a dash in contact with the lines from which they start and end unless such a dash would continue a full line. Dashes touch at corners; arcs start with dashes at the point of tangency (*see* Figure L-10).

Stitch lines, which are used to indicate stitching or sewing, consist of evenly spaced short dashes. They are labeled (*see* Figure L-8).

Other conventional lines are visible, datum, cutting-plane, and viewing-plane lines. Visible lines, or outlines, are used to represent the visible lines on an object (*see* Figures L-8, L-9, and L-10). Datum lines, which are used to indicate the position of a datum plane, consist of a series of one long dash and two short dashes evenly spaced unless the plane is established by another line, such as an outline or an extension line (*see* Figure L-8). A cutting-plane line is used to indicate a plane or planes in which a section is taken; a viewing-plane line, the plane or planes from which the surface of an object is viewed.

Arrowheads vary with the size of the object depicted, the ratio of length to width being held to approximately 3:1. An arrowhead denotes the termination of a dimension or leader line, and the tip should end on the line to which it is drawn. (*See also* LETTERING: ENGINEERING DRAWINGS; ORTHOGRAPHIC PROJECTION: ENGINEERING DRAWINGS; SCALE: ENGINEERING DRAWINGS; SIZES: ENGINEERING DRAWINGS.)

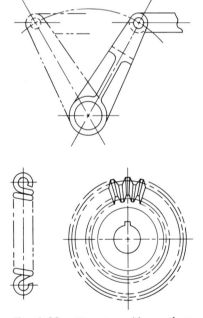

Fig. L-11 **Alternate-position and repeated-detail lines.**

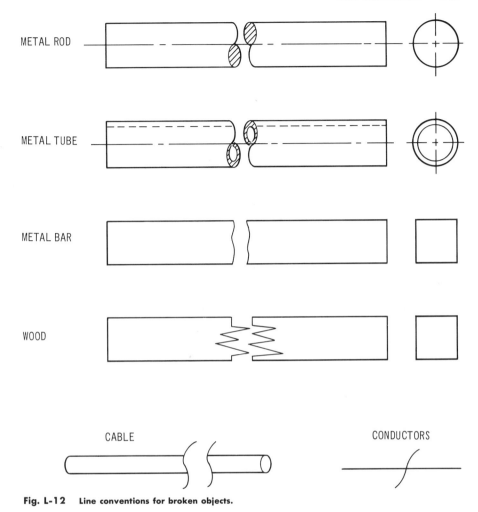

METAL ROD

METAL TUBE

METAL BAR

WOOD

CABLE

CONDUCTORS

Fig. L-12 **Line conventions for broken objects.**

line conversion Photographic process whereby continuous-tone copy is converted to line work. Emphasis is placed on the most important feature of the subject. The process can be used to make duotones from black-and-white photographs, to eliminate halftone screening for wash drawings, and to give photographs a hand-drawn appearance. It also provides contrast from dropouts to solid black, and it can be used in combination with line and halftone work or with other line-conversion special effects. While the process is adaptable to all forms of reproduction, conversion to line work is especially suitable for letterpress, screen-process, and flexographic printing. Special effects have been particularly successful in advertising copy for magazine, newspaper, brochure, poster, and billboard use.

Figure L-13 was produced from an 8- by 10-inch portrait by using a 133-line standard screen. Because of the fine screen, a magnifying glass must be used to observe the dot formation that was necessary for faithful reproduction. However, visible line formations, as shown in Figure L-14, can be used to advantage. These special effects were produced from the photograph used in Figure L-13 and other subjects.

The straight-line effect gives photographs or drawings a scratchboard or hand-engraved appearance. Lines are parallel; they can be horizontal, vertical, or oblique. The angle of the lines and the coarseness of the screen can be selected to intensify dramatic action or to accentuate a subject's characteristics. The mezzoprint adds a hand-drawn effect to photographs or artwork. Contrast is controllable so that textures and details can be held or white dropped out or lost in black shadows. The texture can be fine or extremely coarse.

The contour-line process gives the subject a rounded texture having the appearance of open weaving. The full range, from dropout whites through wavy lines to contour lines of solid blacks, is controlled to give the effect of lines forming and modeling the rounded shapes. Tonal separation simplifies the original copy, resolving continuous tones into clearly separated ones. The process is excellent for multicolor separations from black-and-white copy. As many tones (or colors) can be separated as the original copy allows. Separation can be made on film positives for screen-process printing. The process is effective for billboard and newspaper reproduction, where a posterlike appearance is desired.

The spiral effect of converting continuous-tone copy to line work is effective in focusing the reader's attention on a predetermined point, as shown in the spinning top. The method is effective in combination with line art and continuous-tone copy. The number of lines per inch is controllable to provide spacing as desired. The toneline effect is distinct because of the complete separation of continuous tones into definite lines. The appearance is one of fine pen work, as in a crow-quill drawing in india ink. Tone-line effects are therefore useful in adding an artistic and realistic touch to artwork.

line copy Composition of solid black lines and masses without gradation of tone. It is one of two kinds of copy, the other being continuous-tone copy. In text, line copy consists of letters, numerals, punctuation marks, rules, borders, dots, or any other marks in black and white. Blackline illustrations prepared on white paper are also line copy. The use of preprinted shading mediums does not alter black-and-white illustrations from being line copy. Photoprints made from original line drawings are black and white and therefore are line copy.

Fig. L-13 **Portraiture using 133-line screen.** (Portraiture by Bernie Alden of June E. Lindeman, Miss California.)

STRAIGHT LINE

MEZZOPRINT

CONTOUR LINE

TONAL SEPARATION

Fig. L-14 Line-conversion effects. (*Courtesy of Unigraph.*)

SPIRAL

TONE LINE

line engraving   Method of cutting line images into a copper or steel plate or the like, from which an ink print is taken. Line engraving is distinguished from drypoint, in which ridges of metal are thrown up in relief with a sharp instrument to form the image. In line engraving the background metal is cut away, leaving the image in relief. The term also denotes the engraved plate, or linecut, made by this process and the print made from the plate.

line measure   *See* MEASURE.

line negative   *See* NEGATIVE, PHOTOLITHOGRAPHIC.

line shot   Process cameraman's term for photographing copy without using a screen. A line negative results.

line-tone process   *See* TONE-LINE PROCESS.

line weight   Thickness of pencil, ink, or other lines in artwork or in ruling. Line weights should be consistent within a given group of illustrations regardless of the number of weights used for any one illustration. The amount of reduction of artwork must be taken into consideration. As a simple example, if the width of the original oversize image is reduced from 14 to 7 inches, a line $\frac{1}{16}$ inch thick will be reduced to a thickness of $\frac{1}{32}$ inch. For pencil drawings, the pencil should be sharpened almost constantly to provide a hard, firm line. Present-day process cameras will produce almost as good an image from a good pencil drawing as from ink copy.

Fig. L-15   **Friden's Model LCC-S tape perforator.**

Fig. L-16   Intertype's computer and Intertype linecasting machine.

linecasting machine (slugcasting machine)   Machine that automatically sets slugs of type, such as the Linotype and Intertype machines. Before tape was used in linecasting control, a linecasting machine was run solely by an operator who "keyboarded" the words into the machine as a typist does on a typewriter. With automation it became possible to set type automatically by using punched tape to command the keyboard. Automatic typecasters are employed in the newspaper and commercial printing fields to compose and cast justified copy. Figure L-15 illustrates a tape perforator that punches tape for linecasting control. This machine operates in much the same manner as an electric typewriter. Using the keyboard, the operator types a proof of unjustified copy at normal typing speed. Simultaneously, the unit punches a tape containing the information typed as a combination of holes called "codes." There is a different code for each character and function of the keyboard, as well as for some of the panel switches. A $\frac{7}{8}$-inch-wide tape is punched with a six-hole code structure. The tape is then fed into a tape-operating unit of the linecasting machine for automatic typesetting. With this perforator an experienced operator can produce 375 or more lines of average news text per hour.

Figure L-16 shows the Intertype computer with an Intertype linecasting machine in the background. The computer receives key-

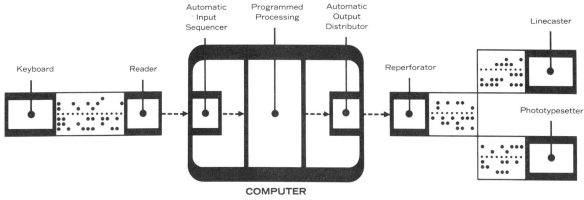

Fig. L-17   Schematic of Intertype's system of automatic linecasting control.

boarded, unjustified, punched paper tape (coded text) from a reader, as selected by an automatic input sequencer. It then processes the copy for justification, hyphenation according to line measure, and typeface and type size and sends processed punched tape to an automatic linecasting or phototypesetting machine (*see* Figure L-17). The

Fig. L-18   Mergenthaler Elektron tape-operated Linotype linecaster.

computer can store and use information on four different type fonts with different brass widths at one time. It can intermix fonts, and it can also provide half-column output while casting on a full line measure. The latter capability is useful for setting "runarounds."

The Elektron Linotype linecasting machine (Figure L-18) is tape-operated and delivers slugs of type to the galley at a rate of 15 standard newspaper lines per minute. Matrices are assembled without interruption and move in a straight line. Justification is accomplished hydraulically. The machine also incorporates a number of safety devices. While the Elektron was designed especially for high-speed tape operation (it can handle the output of two perforator keyboards), feather-touch keyboard has been retained so that the machine can also be operated manually. The machine can accommodate four standard 90-channel Linotype magazines. The starting handle on conventional Linotypes has been replaced by three colored buttons on the keyboard: START (green), READY (yellow), and STOP (red).

The Elektron II Linotype, which is designed for manual operation and for general-purpose composition, incorporates basic features of the Elektron tape-operated linecaster in Figure L-18. The Elektron Mixer is tape-controlled but is designed for manual operation as well. It incorporates tape mixing for mixed and classified advertising as well as straight matter and can produce slugs of type at the rate of 15 standard newspaper lines per minute. The machine can handle advertising work as well as dictionary and technical composition requiring roman, italic, boldface, and special characters in the same line. Figure L-19 shows the basic components of a linecasting machine. (*See also* LUDLOW.)

linecut Metal plate of a line illustration used for printing.

lineup table Device designed to facilitate close register work and alignment of materials before and after plate making. It is used for aligning the components of a paste-up, such as finished art and nomenclature, and for laying out and stripping negatives into gold-enrod flats, ruling and scribing, checking press proofs for dimensional accuracy, handling imposition, assuring correct register for complementary and multiple flats, and many other applications for which accuracy and precise alignment are desired.

Figure L-20 shows nuArc's table-model lineup table. The top tilts forward for convenience, and fluorescent lighting is provided. A floor model is also available. Vertical and horizontal steel straightedges are held at right angles to each other, regardless of where they are placed, because gears at either end of the moving straightedge ride a gear rack. A double hairline indicator over calibrated front and side scales enables the operator to establish any point on the working surface. A pin register system provides an accurate means of register-

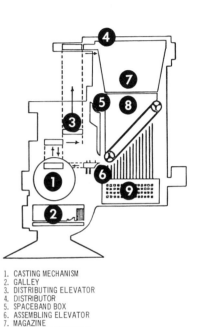

1. CASTING MECHANISM
2. GALLEY
3. DISTRIBUTING ELEVATOR
4. DISTRIBUTOR
5. SPACEBAND BOX
6. ASSEMBLING ELEVATOR
7. MAGAZINE
8. DELIVERING CHANNELS
9. KEYBOARD

Fig. L-19   Basic components of linecasting machine

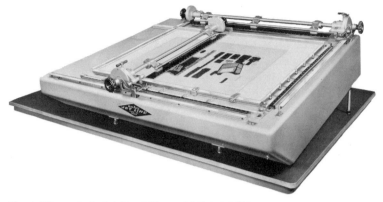

Fig. L-20 nuArc's Jet Line table-model lineup table.

ing layout sheets for complementary and multiple flats before golden-rod layouts are ruled. All layouts are punched simultaneously with a standard $\frac{1}{4}$-inch punch. After the first layout has been positioned on the pins, all succeeding layouts will register. Corresponding pins are positioned directly on the plate or on the vacuum frame of the plate maker to register the completed flats to the plate.

Linkrule   Device used to find the proportion for enlargement or reduction by "stretching" it across copy on the horizontal dimension (*see* Figure L-21). Three graduated color scales are provided. When one scale is used, the others are ignored. View *A* of Figure L-21 compares the increments of a ruler with the zigzag direction of the Linkrule measurements of the Linkrule (view *B*). The Linkrule is a fast and accurate device. It is first extended along the horizontal dimension of the copy to the desired increment as indicated on one of the scales. Without changing the setting, it is then placed along the vertical dimension and the acquired dimension is read on the same scale.

linoleum-block printing   *See* BLOCK PRINTING.

Linotype   Automatic typecasting machine that casts an entire line of type in a single slug. It employs a hot-composition process of typesetting. (*See* LINECASTING MACHINE.)

list of illustrations   Element of the front matter of a publication. It includes the figure numbers and titles and the page numbers on which the figures appear. The list of illustrations, when used, should immediately follow the table of contents. The titles shown in the list should be identical with those appearing with the illustrations.

list of tables Element of the front matter of a publication. It includes the table numbers and titles and the page numbers on which
the tables appear. The list of tables, when used, should immediately
follow the list of illustrations.

Litho T photographic paper Transparent flexible Du Pont photographic paper on a waterproof base. It is a low-cost paper that combines fine resolving power with high contrast. The paper is used
for line reproductions for lithography, quick paper negatives, map
reproduction, and other photographic or photomechanical processes.

Lithofilm Special-purpose sensitized transparent film, used as an
intermediate and for the projection of overlays. Lithofilm is a trade
name registered to the Ozalid Corporation.

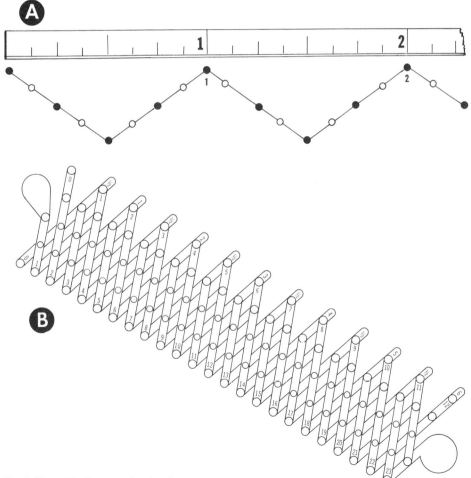

Fig. L-21 **Linkrule proportional scale.**

Fig. L-22 Logotypes.

lithograph Print produced by lithography.

lithographer One who specializes in the art and process of lithographic printing.

lithographic printing Printing from a plane surface, as opposed to printing by the relief or intaglio processes. (*See* PRINTING METHODS.)

live matter Printing forms or copy in current use.

locator *See* SPOT.

lock up In letterpress printing, to secure a form in a chase by means of clamps known as "quoins."

logarithmic scale Proportional scale often used on a chart or graph as a vertical scale with lines varying as to distance; the distances so represented have equal ratios. The horizontal arithmetic scale is often used to represent time; lines are equidistant, representing equal values.

logotype (abbreviated **logo**) Piece of type bearing the name of a company or any name or trademark used with or without a design as a symbol. Figure L-22 shows three examples of logotypes.

long fold Having the grain running along the long dimension, said of paper. It is the opposite of broad fold.

long page Page having one or two more lines of text than the normal page in a publication. One or two lines may be added to a page in order to avoid a bad break during makeup.

long primer Old type size. The nearest equivalent in the point system is 10 point.

loose-leaf binding *See* BINDING, MECHANICAL.

Low Contrast Pan film Du Pont separation negative film on a Cronar polyester film base. It is used for making color-separation negatives when low contrast is desired.

low finish Paper finish without gloss or enamel.

Low Gamma Pan film Du Pont separation negative film on a Cronar polyester film base. It is recommended particularly for gravure work because it offers the negative density range and response to high-activity developers that are required for the separation of long-scale transparencies without correction.

lowercase   Small letters of the alphabet. The term is also applied to small roman numerals.

Ludlow   Trade name of the Ludlow Typograph Company for a system of producing slugline composition by hand-setting large brass matrices. The matrices, which consist of letters, numbers, points, and sorts, are gathered in words or syllables and assembled in a special matrix stick. The stick is locked in the casting machine (*see* Figure L-23), and sluglines are cast directly from hot metal, ready to be placed in forms for lockup. In contrast to setting individual pieces of type in the conventional composing stick, the Ludlow system features setting matrices and then casting the set line as a slug.

The compositor gathers the matrices in word or syllable groups. He then inserts the assembled matrices as groups in the matrix stick. The stick is calibrated in picas so that the desired line measure can be set. It is possible to set matrices up to a measure of $112\frac{1}{2}$ picas in one stick. Spacing units extend beyond the letter matrices and so are readily inserted and removed. Word and letter spacing can be visually inspected for correctness.

After the line has been set, a thumbscrew on the end of the matrix stick is tightened to hold the line of matrices in the machine during casting. There is no need to space the lines so that they are safe to lift. The matrix stick, with secured matrices, is inserted in the casting machine. A lock-down lever holds it in place for casting. Molten metal is forced through the mouthpiece into the matrices,

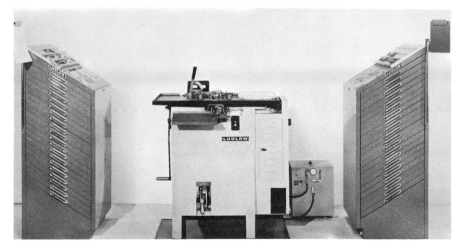

Fig. L-23   **Ludlow Model M caster with matrix cabinets.**

and the finished and justified slug is delivered on the galley at the front of the machine. Any number of sluglines can be cast from the same line of matrices. The sluglines are then made into a form with Ludlow-cast blank slugs or with strip material. Because the matrices are right-reading, it is easy to avoid transposed letters. "Pied type," "work-up," and damaged or broken kerns of italic or script composition are not possible.

The casting machine shown in Figure L-23 is manufactured in both gas and electric models. Pressure and heat in the mouthpiece and throat are thermostatically controlled. The Ludlow Typograph Company also produces an Elrod lead, slug, rule, and base caster. This machine casts strip material in sizes from 1 to 36 points; both gas and electric models are available. Ludlow provides a variety of type styles ranging from 4 to 96 points.

M

machine finish Finish applied to paper as it goes through the paper-making machine. It is smoother than eggshell but not so smooth as English finish.

machine-glazed paper Paper to one side of which a highly polished finish has been applied during manufacture.

magazine Storage unit. In hot-metal linecasting machines, such as the Linotype and the Intertype, a magazine holds the brass matrices that constitute a font of a specific typeface and type size. A machine may have several magazines at a time, making possible a variety of faces and sizes. A single matrix contains the impression for an individual character. When a key is operated on the keyboard, the respective matrix drops into its proper position in an assembler. As each line is completed, molten lead pours into the impressions of the assembled matrices and a single slug of type is produced. The matrices return automatically to their position in the magazine at the top of the machine and are used repeatedly.

magenta Purplish red color, classed as a secondary color in printing inks.

magenta contact screen *See* KODAK MAGENTA CONTACT SCREEN.

magnesium plate   Printing plate of any kind made of magnesium, a metal noted for its durability, light weight, and adaptability for fast etching.

magnetic ink   Special ink containing iron oxide. Its magnetic characteristics permit image code recognition by an electronic reader. The image can thus be sensed for the sorting of bank deposit slips and checks and other applications. Special magnetic inks are required for letterpress and lithographic printing, which vary in the way they deposit ink. A uniform quantity of ink on the receiving substratum is a requirement when images are being sorted by an electronic reader. The silk-screen printing process is used for information recording and storage because a heavier deposit of magnetic ink must be printed in uniform strips for recording.

magnetic-tape Selectric typewriter   *See* COLD COMPOSITION.

mail fold   *See* SECOND CHOPPER FOLD.

main exposure   First of two process-camera exposures used only in halftone work. The main, or detail, exposure is not sufficient to bring out the dot formation required in dark areas of a halftone for proper reproduction in printing. The dots formed during the main exposure will run together, and the halftone will print as solid black in the shadow areas. An additional flash exposure is therefore required. (*See also* FLASH EXPOSURE.)

major axis   *See* AXIS.

makeready   Preparation of a press for printing; specifically, the adjustment of the platen or impression cylinder to compensate for high or low spots in the printing form.

makeup   Arrangement of text and illustrations on a page, generally in conformity with standard practices of the industry or with particular publication requirements. In cold-composition work, it is known as layout. (*See also* LAYOUT.)

manifold paper   *See* ONIONSKIN.

manuscript copy   Text that requires further preparation before it is ready for printing or copying. The term is generally applied to copy in the process of being reproduced. Reproducible manuscript copy is copy that is ready to be converted into reproduction copy. (*See* REPRODUCTION COPY.)

map *See* GRAPHICAL MAP.

marble finish Paper finish resembling the veins of marble.

marking felt In the manufacture of paper, a felt containing a pattern with which the paper pulp comes in contact. The pattern is thus impressed on the felt side of the web of paper as it is processed, resulting in a felt finish.

mask Photographic image mounted in register with a negative or a positive to modify certain tones or colors.

masking Blocking out a portion of an illustration by pasting paper over it to prevent it from being reproduced. Masking is used on reproducible copy before exposure. Opaque material may similarly be used to protect printing surfaces while plates for offset printing are being made. In addition, masking is used in the whiteprint process for changing copy. (*See also* MASK.)

masking, color-separation Any of several methods in which photographic masks are used to obtain better rendition of colors in reproduction. (*See* FILMS AND PLATES.)

Masking (Blue-sensitive) film Du Pont film on a Cronar polyester film base. It is used in making overlay masks for contrast adjustment and color correction of separation negatives, as well as in black-and-white camera-copy work.

masking paper *See* GOLDENROD FLAT.

master Original typed, drawn, typeset, or hand-lettered copy. It may be produced on film, paper, cloth, or almost any other material. Various copy methods and processes are used to produce some form of copy from the master. Additional copies, prints, negatives, or intermediates may be used as masters to produce other copies, but the master itself is the original and first image in the process.

master paper *See* DUPLICATOR PAPER.

master-plan drawing Drawing that is sufficiently detailed to serve as a guide for the long-range development of an area. Such drawings are used in architectural planning and construction.

master plate Paper, plastic, or metal plate installed on a press for offset printing. The image may be applied to the plate directly or indirectly.

Masterfax Trade name for a copying machine. *See* COPYING MA-CHINES.

mat Abbreviation for matrix.

matched negative Combination of negatives of a piece of work that is too large to be accommodated by the available process camera at one exposure. The image must be photographed more than once and the separate negatives "matched" and spliced by taping or other means. When a drawing such as a large schematic is being separated for matching, vertical breaks should be made where horizontal lines are fewest.

matched-parts drawing (matched-set drawing) Engineering drawing that depicts parts, such as special-application parts, which are machine-matched or otherwise mated and which must be replaced as a matched set or pair.

mathematical symbols *See* TABLE 12.

matrix (abbreviated **mat**) Mold in which the face of type is cast, as by using a "flong," a mixture of moist or wet papier-mâché. The papier-mâché dries and forms a mold into which lead is poured. The matrix is then used in stereotyping. Brass dies employed in hot-metal composition are also called matrices.

matrix paper (dry mat paper) Paper ranging in thickness to 0.036 inch, used for making flongs. Matrix paper is a papier-mâché material moistened to make the mold. After molding, the paper is heat-dried, and hot metal is poured into it to form the mold.

matte finish Dull paper finish without gloss or luster.

matte print Photoprint having a dull finish. When line art must be imposed directly on a photographic print, a matte finish should be requested from the photographer. This finish has ink-absorbing qualities not found in a glossy print with its glazed surface. However, if line art is imposed directly on a photographic print without an acetate overlay, it will be screened when the image is screened for plate making. If it is necessary to rework the surface of a glossy photograph, the glaze can be erased from the portion where ink is to be applied.

maximum density *See* DENSITY, MAXIMUM.

measure Printer's term for the length of a line of type measured in picas. The ideal length is about 40 characters of any size. Lines of less than 30 or more than 50 characters should generally be avoided. A good rule to follow is to use $1\frac{1}{2}$ alphabets of lowercase letters, or 39 characters, to the line measure. When printing by typesetters is ordered, the line measure should be specified in picas.

mechanical Page or layout prepared as an original for photomechanical reproduction. It may be a single unit with all the elements of the finished page ready for single-shot photography, or it may have hinged overlays that can be swung into position for making successive exposures of various elements on the same negative.

mechanical binding *See* BINDING, MECHANICAL.

mechanical schematic Engineering drawing that illustrates the operational sequence or arrangement of a mechanical device. Dimensions and relative sizes of items may be shown to indicate mechanical relationships.

mechanical spacing *See* OPTICAL SPACING.

media Means of audio and visual communication, such as books, magazines, newspapers, billboards, direct-mail advertising, radio, and television.

medieval laid finish Finish in paper made by chain lines during manufacture. There is an effect of shading adjacent to the vertical chain-line marks.

Medium Contrast Pan film Du Pont film used to make color-separation negatives from normal transparencies or opaque copy and to serve as camera-copy film when a commercial level of contrast is required.

metallic finish Paper finish having a metallic luster.

metering unit Series of three infeed rollers mounted on the roll stand of a web-fed press. The rollers smooth the web and control paper tension and speed as the web feeds from the roll into the first printing unit.

mezzoprint Line print converted from a continuous-tone photograph or tone artwork by a photographic screening process. (*See also* LINE CONVERSION.)

mezzo-relievo Image sculptured in half relief, between bas-relief and high relief.

mezzotint Method of engraving on copper or steel to produce variations in tone; also the engraving so produced.

MF Abbreviation for machine finish.

mica finish Coated paper finish that contains mica particles. It is sometimes used on greeting cards.

microfiche Sheet of film containing the microimages of pages of technical documents and reports, records, correspondence, instruction manuals, catalogs, or other publications. Each page of the microfiche form can be enlarged and the image read on a reader or viewer or on a reader-printer, which combines showing the page

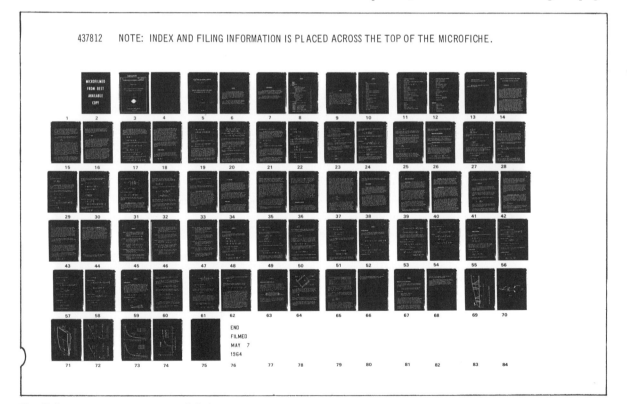

Fig. M-1 Microfiche form (not actual size).

on a screen with making an enlarged printout of the desired page or pages. Microfiches may be 3 by 5, 4 by 6, 5 by 8, $6\frac{1}{2}$ by $8\frac{1}{2}$, and 6 by 9 inches in size. Capacities range from 30 to 100 pages. A 5- by 8-inch microfiche, for example, will hold 84 pages of a standard image on $8\frac{1}{2}$- by 11-inch paper (Figure M-1). It would take only four such microfiche forms to produce a book of 336 pages. Although microfiche sizes vary, United States government agencies now require a standard 4- by 6-inch size. Index and filing information are produced in type of normal size to permit reading with the naked eye.

When duplicate copies of microfiches are required, a microfiche copy is used as an intermediate and a contact print made by such methods as the diazo process or heat-developing film sheets. Duplicates can be extended to four generations without losing readability and reproduction quality. Microfiches may be filed by document number or by cross-indexing the subject matter to the index in a conventional filing cabinet. Filing and selection are generally done by hand, but patented devices are available to speed this work if volume warrants their use. (*See also* MICROFILM; MICROFILM DUPLICATOR; MICROFILM PROCESSING; MICROFILM READER; MICROFORM; PRINTER.)

microfilm   Sensitized film on which microform images are produced. (*See also* MICROFICHE; MICROFORM.)

microfilm duplicator   Machine that produces duplicate microforms from a microform master or from another copy of a microform. Kalvar Corporation's KalKard exposer Model 200 may be used to handle the first step in aperture-card copying. The desired aperture card is selected from a master or satellite file and inserted with a KalKard, an aperture card containing unexposed film, in the exposure slot of the machine. A push button is operated, and a burst of light from an ultraviolet lamp forms a latent image. The microfilm in the aperture card may then be developed by a second burst of light in Kalvar's activator Model 240. The exposer and the activator are each 11 inches long, $12\frac{1}{2}$ inches wide, and 7 inches high, and each weighs 10 pounds. Since light exposes and heat develops the image, need for a darkroom, chemicals, liquids, or vapors is eliminated. (*See also* KALVAR PROCESS.)

Figure M-2 shows the MultiMode Reproducer Model 400 microfilm copier, which produces copies of 16- and 35-millimeter low-, medium-, and high-contrast microfilm as well as direct-image film. Copies are made by using Kalvar film, which is sensitive to ultraviolet light only, and film is developed by heat without the use of chemicals. The Model 400 is 34 inches long, 23 inches wide, and

Fig. M-2 Kalvar's MultiMode Reproducer Model 400 microfilm copier.

19 inches high and weighs 145 pounds. Speed varies from 5 to 20 feet per minute.

Figure M-3 shows the K-10 Colight printer for reproducing transparencies of aperture cards, microfiches, filmstrips, and the like. The transparency is placed in emulsion-to-emulsion contact with Kalvar film and inserted in a vacuum frame. A latent image is created in the film by exposure to ultraviolet light. The Kalvar instant developer (Figure M-4) then develops the image by the application of heat. Chemicals are not used. The developer can handle aperture cards, filmstrips, or sheets of film up to 10 inches wide and 60 inches long. The device is 21 inches long, 7 inches wide, and 4 inches high and weighs 19 pounds.

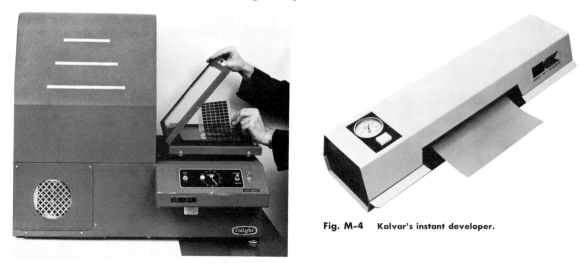

Fig. M-4 Kalvar's instant developer.

Fig. M-3 Kalvar's K-10 Colight printer.

Fig. M-5 DuKane's 576-75 microfilm viewer.

Fig. M-6 DuKane's microphotograph reader Model 576-90.

microfilm processing Development of exposed microfilm to bring out the latent image. Microfilm containing silver halides as the light-sensitive emulsion requires chemical development and washing. This process may be handled by a machine such as the Recordak Prostar. Any length from 2 to 100 feet of 16- or 35-millimeter film can be processed automatically in less than two minutes. The processor is $28\frac{1}{2}$ inches high, 25 inches wide, and $12\frac{1}{2}$ inches deep and weighs approximately 90 pounds.

microfilm reader Device capable of projecting an enlarged microform image on a screen for viewing. Figure M-5 shows DuKane Corporation's 576-75 viewer for reading unitized film. It employs 24-times magnification on an 11- by 14-inch screen. The film is loaded from the front, and spring-loaded glass flats prevent it from buckling. A single knob controls both horizontal and vertical scanning operations. Overall dimensions are 21 by 17 by 17 inches.

Figure M-6 shows the DuKane microphotograph reader Model 576-90, which is used for reading 35-millimeter microfilm mounted in aperture cards. It is designed for desk-top use and is equipped with spring-loaded glass flats for easy loading. A three-position card feed accommodates vertical and horizontal aperture cards as large as military D drawings (22 by 34 inches) and can be removed for cleaning of the aperture glass. A single knob controls both horizontal and vertical scanning operations.

The DuKane microfiche reader Model 576-95 is designed for reading 35-millimeter microfiches in sizes as large as 5 by 8 inches. A single knob controls both horizontal and vertical scanning operations. Overall dimensions are 13 by 15 by 19 inches, and screen size is 12 by 10½ inches with a 15-times magnification.

microform (also called **microtransparency**) Any microimage imposed on film, whether as a microfilm sheet, microfiche, rolled film, individual film, or filmstrip. It may be cut as a unit and mounted in an aperture card. Microforms replace bulk storage of newspapers, books, technical reports, documents, or any other printed or drawn images. They not only save space but facilitate the rapid acquisition and transmission of data. The data thus stored may be retrieved for reading in enlarged form on a viewing screen, or an enlarged printout may be obtained by using a printer or a reader-printer.

Microforms may be positive, negative, or microopaque. A positive microform reflects a black image on a white background on a printout, whereas a negative microform reflects a white image on a black background. (The terms "black" and "white" as used here denote variations of black and white that depend on exposure time and the degree of magnification and development.) A microopaque image is a positive printed on white paper. The paper, of course, reflects light in and around the image area, and the image is produced by reflection and magnification. With negative and positive transparencies, the light passes through translucent areas on the film and reading and printing are also aided by magnification.

Regardless of the type of microform used, original copy must be reduced by photography for storage. In order to be viewed again with the naked eye, the copy must be enlarged to normal or greater size and "read" on a viewing screen. The equipment used to enlarge and read microforms is called a microfilm reader. When a copy of the image is required, a printout of the image is obtained on a microfilm printer. When the image can be viewed and a printout made on the same machine, the equipment is referred to as a reader-printer. If a duplicate copy of a microform is required, it is produced by an exposure unit, a reproducer, or a microfilm duplicator by the processing steps of exposure and development.

Microforms are produced in rolled films of 16, 35, 70, and 105 millimeters. In addition, individual frames may be cut from rolled microfilm and mounted in aperture cards to be used with electrical accounting machines, or the original image can be photographed directly on sensitized film already mounted in an aperture card. Methods of reproduction vary with different manufacturers. Xerography, electrolytic and stabilization processes, diffusion transfer, and conventional photography may all be used in making printouts from microforms.

microimage   Image produced on microfilm; a microform. (*See* MICROFORM.)

microopaque   *See* MICROFORM.

microphotography   Art or practice of producing microscopic photographs. A microphotograph is the photograph so produced.

microtransparency   *See* MICROFORM.

middle tones   Intermediate tones between black and white that compose continuous-tone copy and halftone printed copy.

milestone chart   Chart that lists such information as the elements required to produce an item. By using bars and data points that show scheduled dates in terms of days, weeks, months, or years, production goals can be set and measured. Stages such as prototype manufacture, assembly, first test runs, final delivery, and other aspects are listed on the left side of the chart, and horizontal bars are drawn from them to denote time. When data-point symbols are used, a key should be added to clarify the meaning of each point. Figure M-7 shows symbols used on milestone charts.

Milestone charts are also useful for controlling the production of technical and other publications. Such steps as the starting date, first-draft completion, first-draft review, rewrite or rework, final-draft completion, editing, final-draft review, rewrite or rework as the result of final-draft review, quality control, collating or book makeup, printing, and delivery are milestones that can help control documents as work progresses.

milline   Advertising rate based on the cost of one agate line per 1 million copies of a publication's circulation. Milline rates of various publications may be compared for evaluation.

mimeograph   Duplicating machine that employs a direct-plate stencil process. It is a product of the A. B. Dick Company. Figure M-8 shows the principles of operation of this method of duplication, which has four elements: the stencil, ink, paper, and the mimeograph itself. The stencil, which may be typed, handwritten, or drawn, is placed on the outside cylinder of the mimeograph. As the paper passes through the mimeograph, the impression roller rises automatically and presses it against the stencil on the cylinder. At the same time, ink flows from the cylinder through the ink pad and the stencil openings and makes a copy of the image on paper. The A. B. Dick Model 455 mimeograph produces 12,000 copies per hour. It counts copies automatically and has a jogging receiving tray that

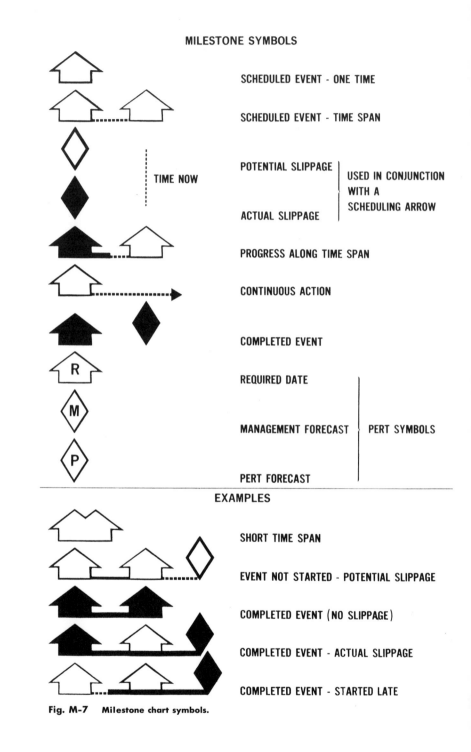

MILESTONE SYMBOLS

SCHEDULED EVENT - ONE TIME

SCHEDULED EVENT - TIME SPAN

POTENTIAL SLIPPAGE

TIME NOW

ACTUAL SLIPPAGE

USED IN CONJUNCTION WITH A SCHEDULING ARROW

PROGRESS ALONG TIME SPAN

CONTINUOUS ACTION

COMPLETED EVENT

REQUIRED DATE

MANAGEMENT FORECAST

PERT SYMBOLS

PERT FORECAST

EXAMPLES

SHORT TIME SPAN

EVENT NOT STARTED - POTENTIAL SLIPPAGE

COMPLETED EVENT (NO SLIPPAGE)

COMPLETED EVENT - ACTUAL SLIPPAGE

COMPLETED EVENT - STARTED LATE

230

Fig. M-7   Milestone chart symbols.

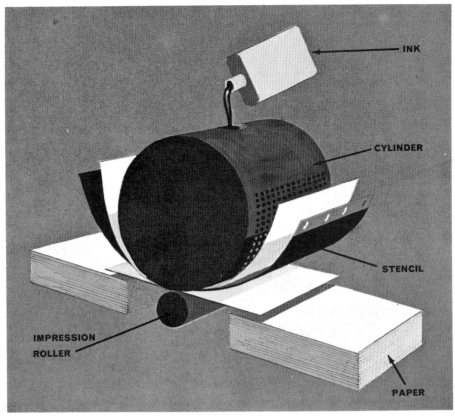

Fig. M-8 Mimeograph principles of operation.

collects and stacks them. There is an automatic fluid inking system. Light or heavy paper, including card stock with a basic weight as heavy as 110 pounds, from postcard to legal size can be handled. Various colored inks are available; paper colors include blue, pink, green, canary, buff, goldenrod, granite, tan, tangerine, terra-cotta, yellow, india, and gray. The A. B. Dick Company publishes a booklet, *Techniques of Mimeographing,* that includes instructions for the operator, typist, and artist and information on such subjects as using colored inks, inking, filing stencils for reruns, ink and pad blockouts, and copy blockouts. In addition to regular typing or drawing stencils, die-impressed and photographically or electronically prepared stencils are available.

mimeograph paper Paper with good ink-absorbing qualities, available in a laid or a wove finish. Considered a boxed paper, it is cut to the letter size of 8½ by 11 inches and the legal size of 8½ by 14 inches. Basic weights are 16, 20, and 24 pounds for 500 sheets of the basic size of 17 by 22 inches.

Fig. M-9   **A. B. Dick Company's Mimeoscope.**

Mimeoscope   Illuminated drawing board or light table (Figure M-9) used in drawing, tracing, or otherwise preparing stencils for mimeographing. Mimeoscope is a registered trademark of the A. B. Dick Company. Sliding straightedges are used for ruling and measuring. The height and slant of the board are adjustable. (*See also* MIMEOGRAPH; STYLUS.)

minimum density   *See* DENSITY, MINIMUM.

minion   Old type size. The nearest equivalent in the point system is 7 point.

minor axis   *See* AXIS.

moiré   Undesirable wavelike or checkered effect that results when a halftone is photographed through a screen. This effect, which is caused by parallel mesh dots, can be avoided by turning the second screen 15 degrees away from that of the halftone.

mold   Wax or other form in which an electrotype is shaped.

monochromatic   Having a single color.

monochrome   Continuous-tone painting or drawing or a printed halftone painting or drawing having a single color or hue. The continuous tone does not become a halftone until it has been screened.

monodetail drawing   In engineering drafting, a separate drawing for a single part.

monogram   Combination of two or more interwoven or overlapping letters to represent a name.

monograph   Written account of a particular subject; a learned treatise on a single topic.

Monotype   Typesetting machine consisting of a keyboard and a caster that produces individual characters and assembles them in justified lines. The Monotype Monomatic keyboard produces perforated tape that is used with a Monotype caster to form the single type letters. A 120-key unit, it is designed for standard typewriter operation with two alphabets, one for lowercase and one for capital letters. Each key can be used to select a character from one of four fonts in the matrix case of the caster by means of one of four shift keys. The matrix case of the Monomatic caster has a capacity of 324 matrices, or eight alphabets. Any font of 81 matrices can be removed to permit changing to a companion boldface or substituting another typeface when two typefaces are to be used in combination.

The Monotype Style D keyboard, shown in Figure M-10, is used to punch tape that is fed into a Monotype caster, such as the composition caster in Figure M-11. The casting machine responds to the coded punched holes and casts individual pieces of hot-metal type to form the text matter. The punched tape can also be used in Monotype's Monophoto filmsetter. (*See* TYPESETTERS, PHOTOGRAPHIC.)

The Style D keyboard generally follows the standard typewriter arrangement, which is based on the frequency of letters and the natural position of the fingers. There are more than 300 keys, which correspond to the matrices in the matrix case of the caster, and seven alphabets can be used. Different-colored key buttons distinguish roman, italic, boldface, and small capital letters. When special characters are required, they may be incorporated in place of characters of the same value not in use. Type sizes range from $4\frac{1}{4}$ to 14 points or, with a large-type composition attachment, to 24 points. Lines may be centered or "quadded out" by operating a key.

Red keys on the Style D keyboard are used for justification. When the operator reaches the end of a line, he refers to the justifying scale to determine which red key to depress in order to produce

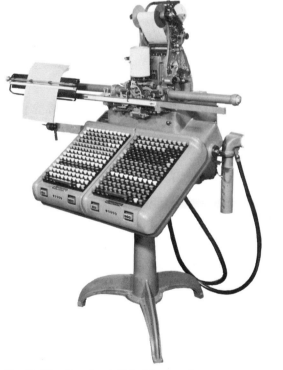

Fig. M-10 Monotype's Style D keyboard for hot metal or film.

Fig. M-11 Monotype's composition caster.

sufficient even spacing between words to justify the line to the set measure. A measure as long as 90 ems can be set and justified with even spacing. Wide tabular settings can be made, and columns can be separated within the overall measure.

Because text matter is permanently recorded on the perforated paper tape, the tape can be run through the casting machine more than once. The rolled tapes are easily stored. When a copy-repeating attachment is installed on the casting machine, a short tape can be used repeatedly to compose running heads or feet, tabular headings, and the like. A Monotype duplex keyboard can be installed for perforating two tapes simultaneously, or tapes can be perforated alternately.

The keyboard can simultaneously compose two different type sizes to two different measures. Because there is no relation between point size, line measures, and spacing, each job can be justified independently. For example, a hard-cover book can be set in a large face while a paperback edition of the same book is being set simultaneously in smaller type. This keyboard can also be employed for alternate settings in which two sizes of tape are used, one for boxheads and the other for books with notes. In addition, it can facilitate setting type when the measure is more than 60 picas long or when additional matrices are required for mathematical symbols.

The punched paper tape is fixed to the tower of the casting machine (Figure M-11), where it unwinds in a direction opposite to that traveled on the keyboard. The tape passes over air vents through which compressed air is directed, and stop pins are caused to rise. The pins control the positioning of the matrix case as the perforations for a particular letter pass over the vents. The case is halted at the proper position over the mold for the fraction of a second required to cast the corresponding type, and then it moves rapidly to the next position.

There are 272 matrices in the matrix case and thousands of matrix-case arrangements. Seven English alphabets—roman capital letters, roman lowercase, italic capital letters, italic lowercase, bold capital letters, bold lowercase, and small capital letters—can be included in one matrix case. This arrangement may be adapted to accommodate different characters of the same typeface for a special job. For example, if foreign-language composition is involved, the bold or the small-capital alphabets can be exchanged for accented characters. Similarly, changes can be made for the setting of mathematical equations, timetables, reference works, textbooks, and other complex jobs that require Monotype special signs.

Casting is fully automatic. The type emerges from the caster and forms into spaced lines and galleys, without manual interference, at a rate as high as three characters per second. The flow of type is uninterrupted. For languages that read from right to left, such as Arabic and Hebrew, a reverse-delivery attachment is fitted to the caster so that lines of type form on the left of the machine.

Various attachments increase the flexibility of Monotype casting machines. A large-type–composition attachment is available for setting type for children's books, Bibles, advertising notices, and other work in sizes from 14 point upward. Larger matrices are used, and about one hundred characters can be obtained in the matrix case. A two-color–composition caster can be provided as an attachment to the keyboard and caster for composing in one operation text matter to be printed in two colors. A technique of four-line mathematical composition with special equipment on the keyboard and caster has been designed to set most such composition mechanically.

A unit-adding attachment on the keyboard enables the set width of a type body to be increased by a fixed amount of one, two, or three units. Letterspacing by this means improves the appearance of words set in capital or small letters or lends emphasis when italics are not used. When exceptionally narrow columns (i.e., left, center, or right runarounds) are being set, a justified letterspacing attachment on the keyboard distributes some or all of the justification space between the characters. Excessive space between words is thus avoided.

montage   Combination of drawings or photographs usually related to one subject and consisting of distinct as well as indistinct images that blend into each other. When only photographs are used, the term "photomontage" is more common.

mortise (mortice)   To secure copy in position on the basic reproduction page; also to cut a hole in two layers of material and replace the undesired cutout piece with the desired cutout piece. The piece to be replaced may consist of one character, a line, a solid block of text, or a complete illustration. To mortise a correction for a word, for example, the word is first retyped on a separate piece of paper of the same kind as the reproduction paper. Ample space is left around the retyped word. The reproduction-copy page is then placed on a light table and the retyped word positioned over the word to be replaced. A sharp knife is used to cut out both layers of paper. The cutout retyped word is set aside. The reproduction-copy page is turned over and a strip of pressure-sensitive mortising tape affixed over the cutout. The paper should not be pulled or wrinkled. The reproduction-copy page is turned over again. The retyped word is picked up with the point of the knife and placed in the cutout space. The adhesive tape will serve as a base for holding the new word in position. When the page has been turned over once more and pressed lightly but firmly, the correction is complete.

Practically anything can be mortised into position. Printing cuts, for example, may be mortised to hold type. While the word "stripping" may be used to define mortising, the former is derived from lithography. Lithographers strip negatives into goldenrod flats before exposing the flats for plate making.

mother-of-pearl finish Paper finish having the effect of a lustrous change of colors.

motorized tape punch Unit that simultaneously produces a punched tape while the Justowriter is operating. It may also be inserted in the Justowriter recorder to set justified copy in a different type size and style. (*See also* COLD COMPOSITION.)

mottle Objectionable cloudy pattern appearing in film because of insufficient agitation in the first developer. Mottle appears especially in color-transparency films exposed to low densities. The same effect is produced in black-and-white film at about 1.0 density unit.

mottled finish Paper finish showing diversified spots or blotches.

mounting, dry *See* DRY MOUNTING.

mounting and flapping Proper protection of line and photographic art requires mounting and flapping. This procedure also makes space available for identifying the art and facilitates filing. Figure M-12 shows a suitable method. The mounting board should be of proper dimensional stability so that it will not warp or bend. A minimum of $\frac{3}{4}$ inch should be provided between the paper edge of the art and the mounting board on all four sides. The tissue overlay, cut to the same size as the board, should be free from wax or grease. It is taped across the top and in two places on the face of the board. The overlay protects the art and may be used for notes and correction marks. It should not be removed until the art has been given a final check. If necessary, a second tissue overlay may be added, but the first one should not be removed. When the art has been completed, a clean tissue overlay is used to replace marked overlays.

Kraft paper is an excellent covering material. It is cut to the width of the mounting board and at least 1 inch longer to permit it to be folded over the top of the board. The corners of the folded edge are tapered, and the flap is affixed with rubber cement. Line art should be fastened in four places with white tape approximately $1\frac{3}{4}$ to 2 inches long and $\frac{1}{2}$ inch wide. Pasting is not recommended because line art must be easily removed from the board for any necessary reworking. Continuous-tone art, however, should be pasted or dry-mounted.

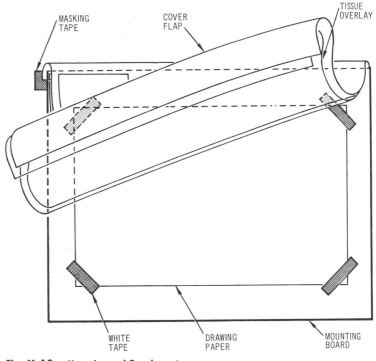

MASKING TAPE

COVER FLAP

TISSUE OVERLAY

WHITE TAPE

DRAWING PAPER

MOUNTING BOARD

Fig. M-12 **Mounting and flapping art.**

mounting board Heavy paperboard in standard sizes of 20 by 20, 22 by 28, 28 by 44, and 30 by 40 inches. The most popular thicknesses are 14-, 24-, and 30-ply. Mounting boards are used for mounting photographs, renderings, and other artwork. They have a smooth finish and vary in color from a slate gray to snow white. The 24- and 30-ply boards are suitable for mounting large illustrations and are sufficiently stable to withstand handling.

mouse *See* PICKUP.

movable type Type consisting of single pieces, as opposed to slugs of type which comprise complete lines cast as one piece. Johann Gutenberg is credited with inventing printing from movable type in the fifteenth century.

MT/ST Abbreviation for the magnetic-tape Selectric typewriter. (*See* COLD COMPOSITION.)

multidetail drawing Engineering drawing that depicts more than one item.

Fig. M-13   Addressograph-Multigraph's Model
250 duplicator.

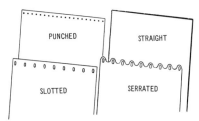

Fig. M-14   Duplicator plate edges.

Multigraph   Relief-process duplicator in which printing is done from a drum. Multigraph is a trademark of the Addressograph-Multigraph Corporation. Individual metal type characters are assembled in slots on the drum in reverse reading. An inked ribbon covers the image area and revolves with the drum, and the image is transferred directly to the paper stock. In addition, paste ink may be fed to inking rollers from a fountain. Apparently, the first concept in marketing such a machine was the rapid duplication of sales letters that simulate typewritten copy. An attachment prints a facsimile of a signature in a color unlike that of the text. Figure M-13 shows the Multigraph Model 250 duplicator.

Multilith   *See* OFFSET DUPLICATOR.

Multilith Duplimat masters   Paper and metal plates used for Multilith duplicators. To meet varying requirements, the plates are available in four styles. The style used depends on the type of master-cylinder clamp on the duplicator and the requirements of the particular application (*see* Figure M-14). Guidelines may or may not be furnished on masters.

The Duplimat masters are classified in numbered series. Series 2000, consisting of direct-image masters, is designed to produce comparatively few permanent high-quality copies. It is well suited to systems duplicating that requires the making of a master from a master to preserve the original format. Information may be added or deleted for each generation. Series 3000 direct-image masters are intended for short and medium runs. Information can be added for reruns. Series 3001 masters combine the surface characteristics of Series 2000 and the body strength of Series 3000. They are suitable for systems duplicating that requires the making of a master from a master, and they can be filed for reruns. Series 4000 direct-image masters produce a greater number of clean, sharp copies than the Series 2000 or 3000 masters; they are used for systems and general office duplicating. Series 5000 direct-image masters are suited for long-run requirements when a fabric ribbon is used; Series 5001, when a paper ribbon is used.

Systemat direct-image masters may be preprinted with business forms, letterheads, or any desired layout in reproducing or nonreproducing ink. Other direct-image masters are available in plain flat packs of various sizes as well as in printed continuous forms with carbon-interleaved work copies. Teletype rolls $8\frac{1}{2}$ inches wide and 333 feet long are also available.

Series 3000 and Series 4000 transfer-image masters are used in the xerographic transfer method. The image may be enlarged or reduced when the xerographic equipment contains a lens. Series 9000 Premier paper masters are presensitized for fine photographic reproduction. They may be exposed to arc lamps, exposure frames, or diazotype machines. Series 9001 presensitized economy master plates are also designed for photographic reproduction. Both types of masters can produce as many as 10,000 copies with a shelf life of one year.

Series 6000 aluminum masters are presensitized for photographic reproduction. The material is resistant to scratches and has a grained surface that simplifies the balancing of ink and moisture. The Pacemaster is a photographic acetate master that is interchangeable with a direct-image master without machine adjustment. It has a short exposure time and is easy to process. The Enco aluminum master is presensitized and exposes any positive image on translucent paper that is applied directly to it.

multiple flats   Separate printing flats, the details of which must match for a particular job, such as successive pages of multiple forms to be printed from separate plates. Multiple flats thus differ from complementary flats, in which several flats are used for the same plate.

multiple-frame microfilm   Arrangement in which two or more frames of microfilm are used to depict a single sheet of an engineering document.

multisheet drawing   Drawing in which two or more sheets are required to cover one item. Each sheet is identified with the same drawing number and numbered as sheet 1 of 5, sheet 2 of 5, etc.

Mylar   Tough, highly stable polyester film used as a base for films for engineering drawings, photographic materials, and other applications. Mylar is a registered trade name of Du Pont. When sensitized, Mylar makes an excellent intermediate for the whiteprint process. The clear film may be used for laminating.

N

negative, photolithographic Film negative having a translucent image and a black background, produced by a process camera and used primarily to make printing plates. An enlargement or a reduction is made from original photographed material. After being developed, the negative is stripped into masking paper called a goldenrod flat, which is placed in a vacuum frame next to a sensitized printing plate. The image is then "burned" through the negative to the plate by exposure to strong light. The light penetrates the translucent image but is blocked by the opaque background of the negative and the masking paper.

There are two kinds of photolithographic negatives: line copy and continuous-tone copy. Line copy is black and white without intermediate tones. The reproduced image will appear as type matter, lines, dots, or other image-forming deposits. Continuous-tone copy has gradations of tone from white to black; when screened, it is a halftone. The printing press cannot reproduce the tone gradations by laying varying amounts of ink on the paper. Instead, it prints various sizes of ink dots. Small dots are printed for light tones and large dots more closely together for dark tones.

The process camera introduces this halftone pattern into the negative by means of a contact halftone screen between the film and the camera lens. Magenta and gray contact screens are widely employed. They are made on a flexible film base that can be used over the film on the vacuum back of the camera. Screens are provided in various rulings and are designated by the number of lines per inch, ranging from a coarse screen of 65 lines per inch, suitable for reproduction on newsprint, to 133-line or finer screens used for quality reproduction of halftones on offset and enamel paper.

Because line copy does not require screening and continuous-tone work does, certain techniques must be introduced when both line and continuous-tone copy are to appear on the same printed page. One method is to take a line exposure of the line work and then, in a second operation, a screened halftone exposure of the continuous-tone copy. The halftone negative is stripped into the line negative, and the result is a combination negative from which a combination printing plate can be made. A second method leading to a combination printing plate is to use masking and stripping film such as Rubylith or Amberlith. Two overlays are required. The first mask covers all the line portions of the image that fall outside the tone area, and a second mask covers the tone values. With the first mask in position covering the line copy and the tone areas exposed, a halftone contact screen is placed over the film and the halftone main and flash exposures are made. With the first mask removed, the second mask is positioned over the copy with the tone areas covered and the line work exposed. A line exposure is made, thus completing the double-exposed film and producing a line and halftone combination negative. This method has many advantages over that of stripping the halftone negative into the line negative.

If art must be reworked, a strip of masking tape may be placed along the bottom of the corresponding negative extending to the width of the crop marks but outside them. Vertical lines are drawn on the tape to show the horizontal limitations of the image. Size instructions are noted on the tape, and the printer will accordingly enlarge or reduce the image to provide a photoprint for reworking.

Photolithographic negatives are excellent for producing reference copies by the whiteprint process. In this process, everything that is white stays white and everything that is black stays black on the copy paper. As the photolithographic negative has a translucent image and a black background, the image on the copy paper will have a white image and a black background. If an 8- by 10-inch negative is positioned to register evenly in the upper right corner of $8\frac{1}{2}$ by 11-inch copy paper, white space is left for a binding margin and for the figure number and title at the bottom.

negative conversion   System of converting metal typeforms to lithographic negatives, developed by the Printing Arts Research Laboratories and designated as the "Instant Negative Conversion" process.

Fig. N-1   Making an instant negative reproduction proof.

Fig. N-2   Developing the instant negative.

Use of a darkroom and camera is not required. To produce a negative, a reproduction proof is made on paper, as in Figure N-1. The proof is then covered with a sheet of instant negative film and heated briefly in a vacuum platen. The film is developed by being wiped, as in Figure N-2.

A special low-tack ink is used in the proof press. The image is transferred immediately after proofing. Vacuum contact and heat between 135 and 145°F transfer the image to the film in about thirty seconds. The latent image is completed when the film is swabbed with a clearing solution. The film is then ready for making an offset printing plate.

negative-reading *See* REVERSE-READING.

neutral density filter Filter that reduces all colors of light uniformly.

newspaper fold *See* FORMER FOLD.

newsprint Paper made from groundwood pulp and varying percentages of chemical pulp and used for printing newspapers.

Newton's rings   Light-interference patterns created where a plane surface and a convex lens (or two lenses with different curvatures) meet, found in photomechanical work during exposure.

nick   Notch found in the body of a piece of type. In hand composition nicks are aligned by the compositor so that type will print properly. (*See also* TYPE DESCRIPTION.)

nickeltype (also called **"steelfaced" plate**)   Copper electrotype plate having a first coating of nickel, used for long pressruns.

nitrogen-burst process   *See* PROCESSING, NITROGEN-BURST.

nomenclature   In artwork, words or symbols used to identify and call out an object (*see* Figure N-3). Nomenclature can be applied

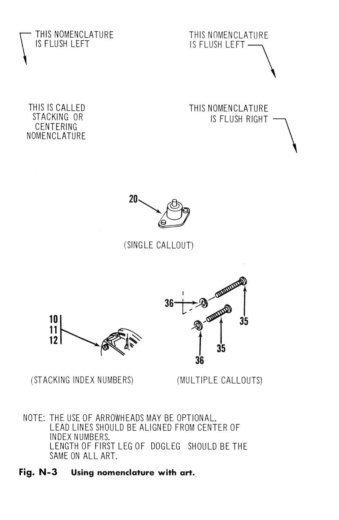

Fig. N-3   Using nomenclature with art.

in several ways. If it is applied by using wax-backed preprints or transfer sheets, it may be on either transparent or opaque paper and be pasted, mortised, or burnished into place. If the background is white, either opaque or transparent preprints or transfers may be used. If the background is gray to black, the nomenclature should have an opaque backing, but preprints should be true rectangles because their background will be defined on the art. If wire numbers are desired for a wiring diagram in which each wire has a number or color designation, the lines should be drawn without breaks. When preprints that have an opaque background are placed over a line, they will then "break" it. (*See also* CALL OUT.)

nomograph (nomogram) Graph or chart that enables one to find the value of a dependent variable by aligning a straightedge with the given independent variable; also a graphic representation of the relation of numerical values.

nonpareil Old type size. The nearest equivalent in the point system is 6 point.

notice of copyright Notice in a book or other printed publication, appearing on the title page or on the page immediately following, that alerts all to the fact and date of copyright ownership. Normally the "page immediately following" is the reverse side of the second title page. The notice in a periodical should appear on the title page, on the first page of text, or under the title heading (title heading may include the masthead). The notice in a musical work should appear either on the title page or on the first page of music. An example of the form follows:

© John Doe 1967

For Classes F through K (generally graphic and artistic works), a special form of notice is permissible. This may consist of the symbol © accompanied by the initials, monogram, mark, or symbol of the copyright owner if the owner's name appears on some accessible portion of the work. (*See also* COPYRIGHT.)

O

office-composition copy Reproduction copy composed on office or similar cold-composition machines. (*See* COLD COMPOSITION.)

offset Unwanted image transferred to the back of a printed sheet by the sheet beneath it as the sheets are stacked after printing. When heavy ink is used on a nonporous stock, a slip sheet must be placed between each two printed sheets. The offset effect is also found on the back of a printed page when the image has been unintentionally imposed on the impression roller because paper and printing plate have not been synchronized. In printing, the term "offset" also refers to the transfer of the image from the plate to a rubber blanket to stock as in photo-offset lithography and letterset printing.

offset duplicator Small offset printing machine that uses the planographic method, or printing from a plane surface by the application of lithography. The image may be applied to the printing plate directly or indirectly. In direct plate making, preprinted matter, an ink pen, graphite or grease pencil, ballpoint pen, rubber stamp, brush, crayon, or other means is used to compose the image on the plate without intermediate steps. Indirect plate making is accomplished by photomechanical means.

The offset method of printing is based on the fact that grease and water do not mix. The master plate is placed on the master cylinder. An aqueous solution applied to the plate is repelled by the grease-receptive image on the master but is accepted by the nonimage area. The ink adheres only to the image and is repelled from the wet nonimage area. As the master cylinder revolves, the various rollers continue to supply the solution and ink to the plate. The image is transferred from the master plate to a cylinder on which a rubber blanket has been mounted. An impression cylinder then brings the paper stock in contact with the blanket cylinder, thus transferring the image from the blanket to paper. (*See also* DIRECT PLATE MAKING; PRINTING METHODS.)

Figure O-1 illustrates the Ditto Model L-16 offset duplicator. Most operations are performed automatically from a control panel. The machine has an automatic blanket cleaner and perforators and slitters for perforating paper during operation. Since a vacuum drum holds the paper master in place, only one end of the master need be attached. An automatic device predampens the master on the machine. The duplicator can handle paper in sizes ranging from 3 by 5 inches to 12 by 14 inches and in weights from 13 to 90 pounds. The maximum image area is $10\frac{3}{4}$ by 14 inches. Speed ranges from 4,500 to 8,500 impressions per hour. The machine has side and center springloaded air blowers. Ink is supplied by a three-roll oscillating roll assembly. Inking of the master automatically stops when the paper action stops. If the feeder skips a sheet, the machine shuts off impression and ink.

Fig. O-1 Ditto's Model L-16 offset duplicator.

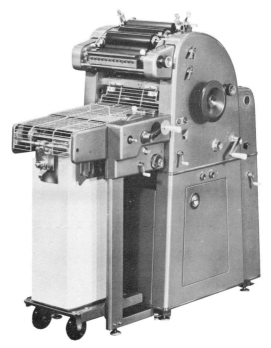

Fig. O-2 A. B. Dick Company's Model 360 offset duplicator.

Fig. O-3 Addressograph-Multigraph's Multilith Class 1250 offset duplicator.

The A. B. Dick Model 360 offset duplicator (Figure O-2) has a chain-delivery system and a receding stacker with a 5,000-sheet pile delivery. Printed copies are automatically stacked on a dolly, which is fully loaded in about forty minutes. The duplicator handles paper in sizes from 3 by 5 inches to 11 by 17 inches. The maximum image area is $10\frac{1}{2}$ by $16\frac{1}{2}$ inches. Speeds range from 4,500 to 9,000 copies per hour.

Figure O-3 shows the Multilith Class 1250 offset duplicator, which is used by printers to support and augment heavier printing presses and by business firms for such applications as systems paper work, multiplication of data-processing output, office communications, business forms, and promotional material. The Model 1250W has a paper capacity of 11 by 17 inches, which permits printing letter-size paper two up on one side of the sheet. Single-lever control simplifies the training of operators. With one hand motion an operator can bring the damping roller, ink roller, and master into contact with the blanket in proper sequence. Attachments provide for automatic blanket cleaning, automatic master ejection, serial numbering, signature printing, and three-color process printing. An automatic copy sorter receives and sorts copies in one operation. A chain-delivery and receding-stacker system controls, delivers, jogs, and stacks as many as 5,000 copies without interruption. Finished copies are stacked directly on a three-wheeled truck. The Multilith Class 1250 duplicators operate at speeds ranging to 150 sheets per minute (9,000 impressions per hour).

offset letterpress *See* LETTERSET PRINTING.

offset lithography Lithographic printing by the method of transferring the image to paper from a rubber blanket. The inked plate prints on the blanket, which then offsets the image to paper stock. (*See also* PRINTING METHODS.)

offset paper Type of book paper. Since the lithographic offset process of printing is based on the fact that grease (ink) and water do not mix, offset paper must be acid-free. Offset book papers are divided into uncoated and coated groups. Both groups may be obtained in basic weights of 50, 60, 70, 80, 100, 120, and 150 pounds for 500 sheets of the basic size of 25 by 38 inches. Uncoated offset paper may be used for magazines, advertising pieces, house organs, and brochures and for single-color and multicolor work. Woven and other finishes are available. Special sizing techniques during manufacture eliminate or minimize fuzz. Coated offset paper is manufactured especially to eliminate fuzz and picking, and sizing processes are included to repel water. This type of paper will reproduce better halftones and colors than uncoated offset paper.

offset perfecting press   *See* PERFECTING PRESS.

offset plate   Paper or metal plate having a right-reading image that is affixed to an offset press for printing. A single plate carries all copy and artwork to complete one impression. The metal plate, which may be made of aluminum, magnesium, stainless steel, or other material, curves around the cylinder of the press. One side of the plate is grained to hold moisture and coated with a solution that is sensitive to light. The coated plate is placed in a vacuum frame with the assembled negative containing the image in front, and the combination is then exposed to arc lights that penetrate the translucent image of the negative. The latent image on the plate is developed by being washed with developer and water. The emulsion on the part of the plate that receives the image hardens and resists the action of the developer, and thus the image is disclosed on the plate.

offset printing press   Rotary press using the offset method of lithographic printing. Offset printing presses are available in a wide variety of designs, sizes, and modes of operation to meet requirements ranging from those of the small job shop to those of medium and large printing establishments and newspaper publishers. Common to all the presses are the rotary cylinders. These in the main are

Fig. O-4   HCM Corporation's Champion single-color sheet-fed offset press.

the master cylinder that holds the plate, the blanket cylinder to which the image is transferred from the master cylinder, and the impression cylinder, which serves as a cushion in conjunction with the blanket cylinder so that the image can be impressed on stock. The stock may be sheet-fed or fed from a roll called a web. Printing-press designers continue to automate offset presses insofar as practicable, arranging for most aspects of operation to be handled at a single control station and incorporating automatic devices to ensure safety and to detect malfunctions.

Figure O-4 shows the Champion single-color sheet-fed offset press. The main operator's station, at the delivery, contains push-button controls for starting, sheet flow, ink and damping, pressure adjustment, tachometer reading, sheet counting, and the like. Colored lamps signal the degree to which the press is switched on and the tripping of the control and safety devices. The press can handle paper from a minimum size of $8\frac{1}{2}$ by $11\frac{13}{16}$ inches to a maximum size of $20\frac{15}{32}$ by $20\frac{1}{2}$ inches. The maximum speed is 10,000 sheets per hour. The height of the paper-feed pile is 43.31 inches; that of the paper delivery, 19.69 inches.

A flatbed offset press manufactured by J. G. Mailänder and distributed by the HCM Corporation is available in six sizes and three models for hand or power operation. It is designed to handle short runs on tin or paper, etched and anodized nameplates, reproduction proofs, metal decorating, and printed circuits. It prints on wood, plastic, and glass, as well as on any paper or board stock. Sheet sizes range from $18\frac{1}{2}$ by $25\frac{1}{4}$ inches to $40\frac{1}{8}$ by $55\frac{7}{8}$ inches.

Figure O-5 shows the Media Master No. 29 single-color sheet-fed rotary offset press. The ink system has large roller diameters and therefore a large distributing surface. A converter transforms alternating current to direct current at a given voltage regardless of the power of the line current. The press incorporates an automatic cylinder-pressure device, an independent motor for the ink-fountain roller, and a device that detects a double, wavy, or creased sheet without touching the sheet. The minimum sheet size is 11 by 15 inches; the maximum, 23 by $32\frac{5}{8}$ inches. The feeder-pile height is 44 inches and the delivery-pile height $20\frac{3}{4}$ inches. Speeds range from 2,500 to 7,500 impressions per hour.

The Chief 15-inch (11- by 15-inch) offset press (Figure O-6) is designed to augment the work of larger presses when makeready time and operating costs are significant. It handles sheets from 3 by 5 inches to 11 by 15 inches and paper weights from 11-pound manifold (0.002 inch) to 2-ply card stock (0.012 inch). The maximum printing area is $9\frac{3}{4}$ by $13\frac{1}{4}$ inches. Speed varies from 3,400 to 7,200 impressions per hour. The inking unit contains 10 rollers and the damping unit 4 rollers. The gripper margin can be adjusted from $\frac{3}{16}$ to $\frac{5}{16}$ inch.

Fig. O-5 Mergenthaler Media Master No. 29 single-color sheet-fed rotary offset press.

Fig. O-6 American Type Founders' Chief 15-inch offset press.

The ATF Solna 230 (23- by 30-inch) offset press prints two colors at speeds as high as 8,000 sheets (16,000 impressions) per hour. Images are printed on paper ranging from 9-pound onionskin to 6-ply (0.024-inch) card stock. Sheet sizes vary from $11\frac{3}{4}$ by $16\frac{1}{2}$ inches to 22 by 30 inches. Plate cylinders with a 0.035-inch undercut are provided for wet or dry printing with photopolymer or metal dry-offset plates or with any conventional wet-offset plate.

The Miehle 29 single-color press handles both planographic and letterset work. Letterset printing uses a flexible, shallow one-piece relief plate and an intermediate blanket cylinder to transfer the image to stock. Because of the intermediate step of transferring the image from the printing plate to the blanket, all letterset plates must have a right-reading image if the stock is to have a right-reading image. With a press of the type of the Miehle 29, both lithography and letterset printing can be used on the same job. This press has a maximum sheet size of 23 by 29 inches and a minimum sheet size of 11 by 16 inches. The maximum speed is 8,000 impressions per hour. Feeder-pile height is 48 inches, and delivery-pile height is $21\frac{5}{8}$ inches.

Figure O-7 shows the Miehle 54/77 six-color offset press with the printing unit for each color in line (a 54/77 four-color press is also available). The press is designed for short or long runs of varied color work. It automatically cuts rolled stock of varied widths to any desired sheet length. The cut sheets then enter the normal stream-feeding process. The maximum sheet size is 54 by 77 inches; the minimum size, 28 by 42 inches. Speeds are as high as 6,000 sheets per hour.

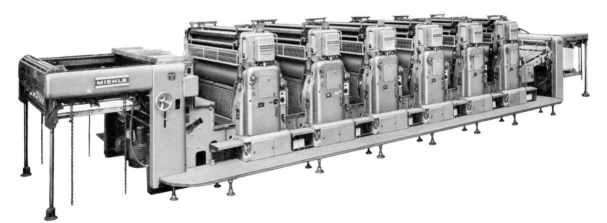

Fig. O-7   Miehle 54/77 six-color offset press.

offset relief   *See* LETTERSET PRINTING.

offset spray   Device that applies a fine mist of powder between two sheets during the pressrun to prevent the moist ink of one sheet from printing on the back of the succeeding sheet.

oiled paper   Paper treated with oil to give it sealing characteristics, often used as a wrapping paper.

once and a half up   In drawing, to a size $1\frac{1}{2}$ times that of artwork as it will appear on the printed page. If a printed page is to have an image width of 7 inches, the art is drawn to that width plus one-half, or $10\frac{1}{2}$ inches, without allowance for boxing. Height must be increased in proportion.

one-scale chart   Bar chart that shows only one quantity by using one scale. The bars, drawn horizontally on the chart from left to right, represent quantity. Such a chart may serve as the basis for constructing other charts in which more than one value can be expressed. A "pie chart" is another example of a one-scale chart. (*See also* BAR CHART; COLUMN CHART; CURVE CHART; PIE CHART; SURFACE CHART.)

one-view drawing   *See* ORTHOGRAPHIC PROJECTION: ENGINEERING DRAWINGS.

onionskin (manifold paper)   Thin, translucent paper used to make a typewriter carbon copy or to serve as a tissue overlay for work requiring correction or protection. The rag content may be 25 to 100 percent, and the finish may be dull or glazed. Basic weights are 7 and 9 pounds for 500 sheets of the basic size of 17 by 22 inches. Onionskin is available in the letter size of $8\frac{1}{2}$ by 11 inches and in the legal sizes of $8\frac{1}{2}$ by 13 and $8\frac{1}{2}$ by 14 inches. It comes packaged in boxes of 100 or 500 sheets.

Onyx   Line of opaque papers and cloth and transparent paper, cloth, and film manufactured for moist diazo reproduction. Onyx is a registered trade name of the Keuffel and Esser Company. Opaque blackline and blueline paper and cloth are produced from right-reading translucent originals. The transparent Onyx paper, cloth, and film produce sepia-line intermediates.

opaque   Impermeable to light; not transparent or translucent. As a verb, opaque means to paint over unwanted areas of a negative with an opaque solution before the negative is exposed for plate making. The painted areas are made impervious to light.

opaque circular   Bond and offset book paper manufactured to provide great opacity. It is used for direct-mail advertising, booklets, house organs, leaf inserts, technical data sheets, and illustrated leaflets.

operating unit   *See* TAPE INTERPRETER.

optical center   Point slightly above the geometric center of a rectangular plane. Objects placed at the optical center appear to be at the geometric center.

optical lantern   *See* EPIDIASCOPE.

optical printing   Any printing method in which a process camera is employed as one step in producing the end item. Reductions, enlargements, or same-size negatives may be produced. If a camera lens is used in the copying process, various sizes may be obtained from the original copy; if a camera is not used, only contact, or same-size, reproduction copies may be had.

optical spacing   Arrangement of spacing between letters for legibility and appearance, as opposed to mechanical spacing, in which the same space is used between all characters. The spacing varies with the shape of the letters to achieve optical equalization.

orange backing   Orange-colored carbon paper used for typing on vellum or other translucent material. The carbon paper is reversed and impresses an image on the back of the original. Orange backing is used to create a dense image and accomplish better reproduction during exposure in the whiteprint machine. Corrections can only be made by erasing, although erasing is difficult because of the carbon characteristics of the orange backing.

order   In styling a manuscript, the ranking of the various headings according to their importance. The major subdivisions of a chapter or section carry first-order headings, their chief subdivisions second-order headings, and so on. The printer is given detailed instructions on the desired typeface, point size and leading, indention, and the like for each heading. Printer's language—picas as a measurement instead of inches, leading, points, and ems—should be used. If key numbers are used to designate the headings, detailed type marking of the manuscript is unnecessary. A similar system may be used in preparing a manuscript for the reproduction typist.

organization chart   Block chart or diagram showing the names, titles, departments, and responsibilities of personnel in an organization

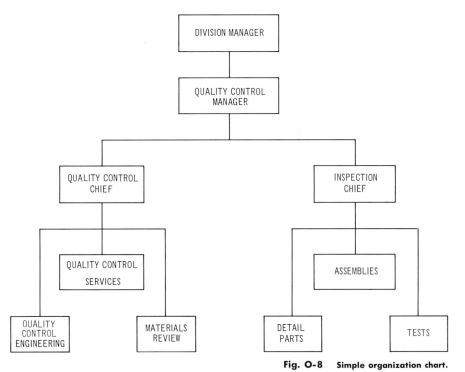

Fig. O-8 **Simple organization chart.**

(*see* Figure O-8). Such a chart serves to outline responsibilities and to show the chain of command. When the information given in each block is not extensive, it should be stacked; that is, each line of type should be centered beneath the preceding line. When a breakdown of the duties of a person or a department or other extended information is given, however, each line should be flush left. The primary title of each block should be set or typed in capital letters and subordinate information in capitals and lowercase. For example, if the subject of a chart is departments or divisions, the department or division name should be in capital letters and other copy in the block in capitals and lowercase. If the subject is the personnel of an organization, then the names of the persons should be in capitals and the other copy in capitals and lowercase.

original *See* MASTER.

orphan In copy layout and page makeup, a colloquial term for a word or syllable that stands alone at the top of a column or page. An orphan is an indication of poor layout and should be avoided. (*See also* WIDOW.)

Ortho A film Du Pont lithographic film on a Cronar polyester film base. Ortho A is designed for halftone and line negatives or positives employed in lithography, photoengraving, gravure, and screen-process printing, and it can also be used to make highlight and color-correction masks. In addition, it finds favor in contact operations because of its ability to perform well in universal developers.

Ortho D film   Du Pont lithographic film on a Cronar polyester film base. Ortho D is designed to produce high-quality line and halftone negatives for Dycril printing plates. Because it has a low-level non-halation backing, it can also be used on deep-etch positives and photoengraving negatives with laterally reversed images for exposure through the back of the film.

Ortho M film   Du Pont lithographic film on a Cronar polyester film base. Ortho M has special surfaces to minimize Newton's rings and characteristics that facilitate contact printing and plate making. It is designed for both camera and contact negatives or positives

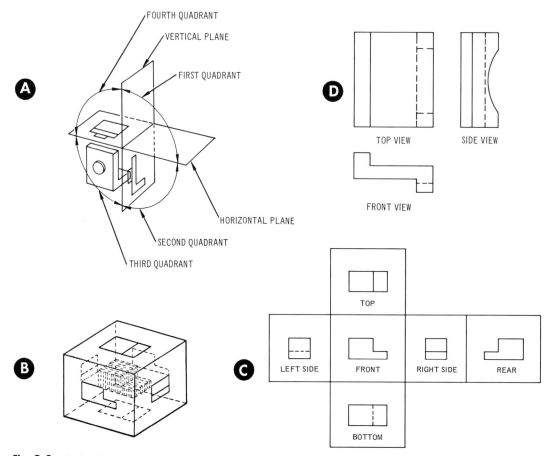

Fig. O-9   Basic principles of third-angle orthographic projection.

for the major printing processes, and it can be used for either halftone or line work.

Ortho S film   Du Pont lithographic film on a Cronar polyester film base. Ortho S is used in making halftone and line negatives or positives for lithography, photoengraving, gravure, and screen printing. The film is recommended for applications where maximum dimensional stability and high-quality camera halftone work are required.

orthochromatic   Designating photographic materials that are sensitive to green as well as blue and ultraviolet light. (*See* FILMS AND PLATES.)

orthographic projection: engineering drawings   Orthographic projection, a method of third-angle projection, is graphically illustrated in Figure O-9*A*, *B*, and *C*. There are six principal views of an object as represented in Figure O-9*C*. Figure O-9*B* shows an object placed in a transparent box, and *C* shows the box unfolded. The projection in Figure O-9*C* shows the object seen by looking straight through each side of the box. When the box shown in O-9*B* is opened and laid flat, the result is a six-view third-angle orthographic-projection drawing. It is seldom necessary to draw all six views to portray an object clearly for fabrication purposes. Figure O-9*D* illustrates an alternative arrangement of three views. Only the views that are necessary to illustrate the required characteristics of an object should be drawn. Almost all engineering drawings used in fabrication are in orthographic projection.

One-view drawings are drawings of objects that are cylindrical, spherical, hexagonal, square, rectangular, or the like or of objects that can be completely defined by one view and by a note of such features as thickness or length (*see* Figure O-10*A*, *B*). Figure O-10*A* shows a cylindrical object, while Figure O-10*B* is a plate.

Partial views of symmetrical objects may be represented by half views, as shown in Figure O-10*C* and *D*. Half views extend slightly beyond the center line of symmetry and terminate in a break line. If the adjacent view is nonstructural, the near half of the symmetrical view is drawn as in Figure O-10*C*; if the adjacent view is a full or half section, the far half of the symmetrical view is drawn as in Figure O-10*D*.

Three-view drawings may be arranged with any three adjacent views in the relation shown in Figure O-9*C*. When space is limited or the part can thus be more clearly indicated, the side view may be placed near the top view, as shown in Figure O-9*D*. When two side views are required to illustrate an object, they may be complete views if together they depict the shape of the object, as in Figure O-10*E*.

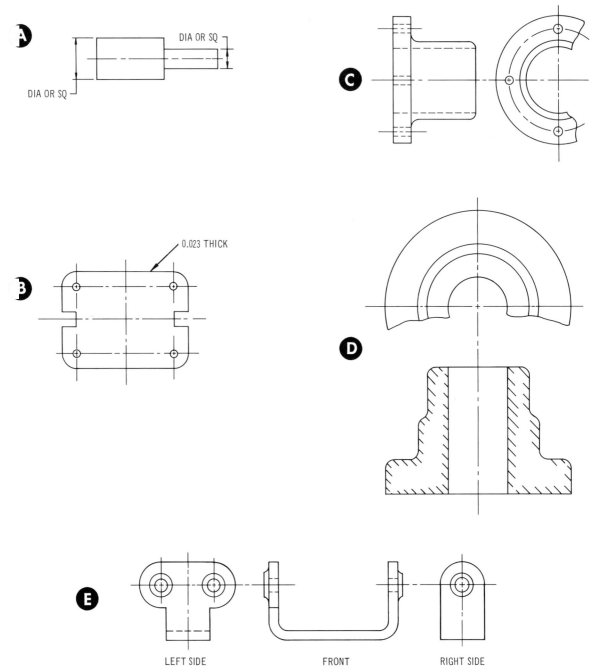

Fig. O-10   One-view, half-view, and side-view drawings are depicted in orthographic projection.

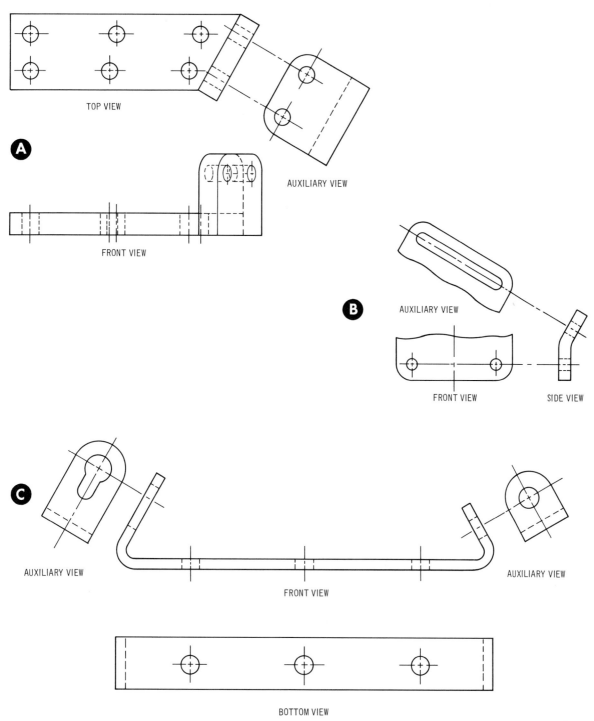

TOP VIEW

A

FRONT VIEW

AUXILIARY VIEW

B

AUXILIARY VIEW

FRONT VIEW

SIDE VIEW

C

AUXILIARY VIEW

FRONT VIEW

AUXILIARY VIEW

BOTTOM VIEW

Fig. O-11   Auxiliary views shown in orthographic projection.

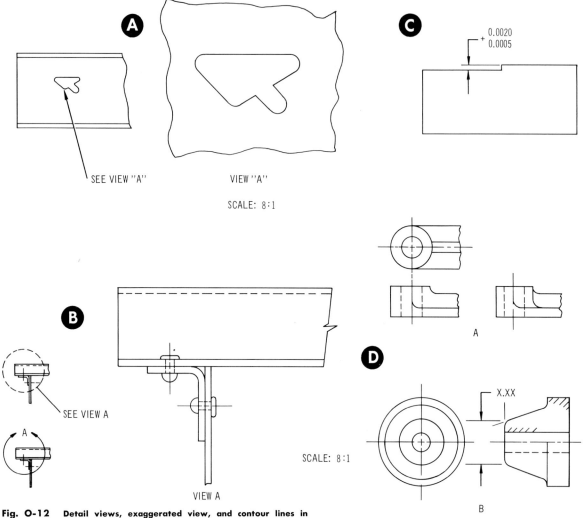

Fig. O-12   Detail views, exaggerated view, and contour lines in orthographic projection.

Objects having inclined faces or other features not parallel to any of the three principal planes of projection require auxiliary views to show the true shape of these features. Partial auxiliary views showing only the pertinent features are employed to illustrate features not clearly shown by the principal views (*see* Figure O-11*A, B, C*).

Auxiliary sectional views may also be employed to advantage to illustrate features not clearly shown by principal views. Views not directly projected must be clearly marked to indicate the location and the direction from which the object is viewed.

A detail view shows part of the drawing in the same plane and in the same arrangement but in greater detail and, if necessary, to a larger scale than the principal view. The part of the drawing to be detailed must be suitably identified (*see* Figure O-12*A, B*). When a feature is too small to be drawn to scale, it may be exaggerated, as shown in Figure O-12*A*. Variations from true projection may be drawn for clarity. For example, the rounded or filleted intersection of two surfaces theoretically shows no line in projection but may be indicated by a conventional line. Contour should be drawn as shown in Figure O-12*D*.

outline   *See* VISIBLE LINE.

outline drawing   In engineering drafting, a drawing that shows the contour of an object, which is usually projected with three views.

overhang cover   Cover larger than the page size of a book. It is the opposite of a flush cover.

overhead projection   System of projecting images over the shoulder of a lecturer, who sits and faces the audience while controlling the projector, which projects the image on a tilted screen. This technique is a flexible method of visual communication and has many advantages over the system in which the lecturer addresses his audience while the projector is operated by a second person. Transparencies, also called "projecturals," visuals, slides, or vu-graphs, are projected from the front of the room with the aid of the projector. By facing the audience at all times, the lecturer not only is in a position to set the pace of his discussion but can observe audience reaction, alter the sequence of projecturals, and operate the projector without interrupting his talk to give an operator instructions.

Fig. O-13   Typical small conference room for viewing overhead projection. (*Courtesy of Technifax Corporation.*)

Figure O-13 illustrates a typical overhead-projection setup, including the communicator and the tilted screen. The projection stage of the projector (the flat surface on which the projectural is placed) permits the communicator to use the screen as a blackboard. Without turning away from the audience, he can write or draw at will with a grease pencil on projecturals or sheets of transparent plastic. He may also use a pointer or a pencil to emphasize important details that are reflected on the screen.

Several sheets of transparent film may be superimposed on the stage and various colors used to identify the elements of the projected image. The communicator can unmask transparent projecturals in his progressive disclosure of information, or he can build several components into a composite image. For instance, it is possible to project the framework of a house in black and, after discussion, to add the electrical system in blue, the plumbing in red, and so forth. Projection is accomplished under normal room lighting conditions.

Standard image-projection sizes are 10 by 10, 8 by 10, 7½ by 10, 7 by 7, and 5 by 5 inches. The larger sizes simplify preparation of artwork and eliminate the need for reduction in most cases. The size of the projection screen is determined by the maximum viewing distance. The width should be not less than one-sixth of the distance from the screen to the last row of viewers. The projector should be adjusted to fill the screen with the projected image. The pro-

Fig. O-14   Technifax Visucom overhead projector.

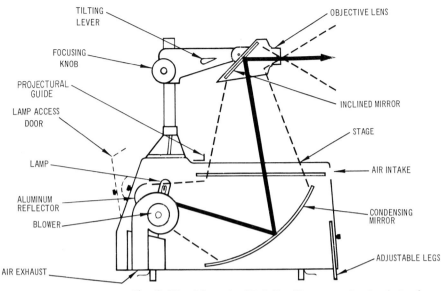

TILTING LEVER

OBJECTIVE LENS

FOCUSING KNOB

PROJECTURAL GUIDE

LAMP ACCESS DOOR

INCLINED MIRROR

LAMP

STAGE

AIR INTAKE

ALUMINUM REFLECTOR

BLOWER

CONDENSING MIRROR

AIR EXHAUST

ADJUSTABLE LEGS

Fig. O-15   Schematic of Technifax Visucom overhead projector showing components.

jector-to-screen location is determined by the size of the screen image desired. The image grows larger as the projector is moved farther from the screen. For example, at a distance of 6 feet from the screen, a $7\frac{1}{2}$- by 10-inch projector produces a 34.4- by 46-inch image; at 8 feet, the projected image is 46.4 by 62 inches.

Figure O-14 shows the Visucom projector, and Figure O-15 is a schematic of its components. The projector has a pure aluminum reflector. Light reaches the screen by means of a condensing mirror, an inclined mirror, and a 14-inch objective lens. The projection head can be tilted as much as 25 degrees from the horizontal to raise the screen image. This feature makes it possible to keep the stage flat in normal operation. The aperture is horizontal, measuring $7\frac{1}{2}$ by 10 inches.

Another projector, the Technifax Transpaque Junior projector, has a 14-inch objective lens and a stage measuring 10 by 10 inches. It provides more than 3,500 screen lumens, making it possible to produce a bright image in a fully lighted room.

The Technifax Acto-O-Matic projector is a dual-position device designed for teaching science in schools and colleges. It has a 5- by 5-inch stage and projects a screen image 5 feet square at a distance of 7 feet. The projector can be converted to the horizontal or the vertical position. The design makes it possible for the instructor to project transparencies and to utilize scientific apparatus for demonstrations in chemistry, physics, biology, and general science. Test tubes, chemicals, electric meters, slide rules, magnets, and the like may be projected on the screen.

Fig. O-16 Technifax Visucom diazo copier.

Figure O-16 shows the Visucom diazo copier, which is designed for producing transparencies for overhead projection. The copier exposes and develops diazo papers and films in sizes as large as 8½ by 11 inches. Materials are exposed by two 15-inch ultraviolet lamps that are controlled by an automatic timer. Exposed films and papers are developed by ammonia vapor in a developing drawer. If a number of overlays are used, they are kept in register by pins during exposure.

overlay *See* ACETATE OVERLAY; CORRECTION OVERLAY; TISSUE OVERLAY.

overprinting Printing of an image over another impression. Overprinting is used particularly in color work. If a tint or a pattern is desired, a secondary color is printed over a primary color.

overrun Printed or duplicated copies of sheets or pages in excess of the specified number.

oversize Designating copy produced in a size larger than the size it will be after it has been reduced for reproduction. The copy may consist of text or line and halftone illustrations. A good deal of copy for reproduction is produced oversize. Technical illustrations, for example, are seldom drawn less than 1½ times the final reduced size, and many are drawn twice up.

The reasons for drawing oversize copy are simple. Critical areas and lines may thus be drawn easily and rapidly with good delineation, and reduction eliminates such small imperfections as fuzziness, smudges, and erasure ghosts. In addition, open spaces are closed up for better appearance.

When nomenclature applied to art is too large, it dominates the object depicted, whereas the object itself should be the dominant factor. If nomenclature is smaller than 6 point, the illustration loses its ability to convey a message. The accompanying table shows the size to which nomenclature will be reduced when the reduced image width is held to 7 inches. (*See also* LETTERING OR TYPE REDUCTION.)

Width of oversize art, in.	Oversize nomenclature, pt.	Reduced nomenclature, pt.
10½	12	8.0
14	14	7.0
17½	24	9.5

Ozachrome Transparent acetate film produced by the Ozalid Corporation. It is sensitized for black, cyanine, magenta, or yellow images and is designed especially for lithographic color. Each film is made directly from the four-color separation positives. Ozachromes are also employed for color overlays in presentations and diagrams and for full-color photographic reproductions for projection booklet use.

Ozachrome view foil Transparent and sensitized film designed primarily for projection viewing and for the preparation of other visual aids. This foil, which is manufactured by Ozalid Corporation, produces strong, vivid images in blue, orange, red, green, and black. View foils are also used in presentations and as overlays for engineering drawings.

Ozalid cloth-backed paper Sensitized white paper having a black image that is used in the whiteprint process. It is backed with scrim, a thin cloth fastened with glue. Its chief applications are flannel-board charts, flip charts, and other visual aids.

Ozalid Dryphoto Special-purpose sensitized material that reproduces a continuous-tone original. Dryphotos are run from a film positive master (a photoprint on film rather than on photographic paper). Positives are made from any photographic negative by using Ozalid reversal film or other photographic means. Sepia Dryphoto produces prints in a warm sepia color; Hi Gloss Black Dryphoto, in a cold, warm, or neutral black.

Ozalid gum-backed paper White adhesive-backed sensitized paper used in the whiteprint process. It has a black image. The paper need only be moistened to be used as a label or sticker.

Ozalid opaque cloth Blackline or blueline cloth manufactured especially for drawings. A tightly woven, sized heavy-duty cotton cloth, it accepts pencil, ink, and crayon. It is recommended for shop prints that must undergo rough handling and for survey maps that are to be bound in ledgers.

Ozalid papers Sensitized papers and card stock used for making copies and reproductions of engineering drawings, office forms, records, etc., from typed, written, or drawn translucent originals. They are available in light (17-pound), standard ($20\frac{1}{2}$-pound), medium (24-pound), and heavy (32-pound) weights. The $20\frac{1}{2}$-pound weight is preferred by many users for most print-making requirements. Blackline, blueline, and redline images may be obtained. Blackline is recommended for the reproduction of typed, written, or printed matter; blueline, for drawings; redline, for prints subject to soiling. Colored stock—blackline on white, pink, green, yellow, and blue; blueline on white, yellow, pink, green, and blue; and redline on white—may also be used.

Ozalid Projecto-Foil Transparent acetate film sensitized with a diazo coating. It is exposed with a translucent original to ultraviolet light in an Ozalid Projecto-Printer or other copying machine. The exposed films are then developed by a dry process to form the desired colored images. Black, magenta, and cyanine are selected for lithographic color proofing. Blue, red, orange, green, sepia, and brown are used for visual aids in selling, teaching, and training programs, presentations, and proposals.

Ozalid reversal foil Positive film made directly from any negative original (or a negative from a positive) in the whiteprint process. The foil provides an excellent original and eliminates the need for photographic processing.

Ozalid Transferon Photocopy papers and films manufactured to produce transparencies, reproduction masters, and standard paper copies from bound and opaque originals. The Transferon group consists of (1) a clear acetate positive that provides a projectable transparency with a black image or a reproducible master; (2) a vellum paper positive that serves as a master for making Projecto-Foil copies for color transparencies or for prints on other Ozalid sensitized materials; and (3) an opaque bond positive for single-copy use.

Ozalith plate Plate made of diazo-sensitized paper or aluminum. It may be exposed with any image printed, typed, written, or drawn on translucent paper in any Ozalid (whiteprint) machine, light box, vacuum frame, or other exposing medium and developed with a fixing solution. The plate is then mounted on an offset duplicator.

Ozaplastic Plastic-coated, sensitized translucent paper having black lines on glossy white. Ozaplastic is a trade name owned by the Ozalid Corporation. The paper is used in the whiteprint process. It is highly resistant to oil and water and is particularly useful for reproducing halftones and for making heavy-duty shop and engineering prints.

P

packing Paper sheets placed under a printing plate or the rubber blanket of an offset press to raise contact surfaces and so improve their printing qualities.

padding Binding printed or blank sheets in units for scratch pads. Base stock is used to separate the units. The pads are secured as a batch, and cement is applied to one side. The units are then separated to form individual tablets.

page One side of a sheet of paper. It should not be called a page until it contains copy or is identified in some manner to show its sequential arrangement.

page-content heading Heading that appears at the top of a page to identify its contents. The headings in dictionaries and encyclopedias that give the first and last entries on a page are examples of page-content headings. In some publications, such as those issued by United States government services, headings showing the section number and paragraph numbers contained on each page are required. The page-content heading is flush right for right-hand pages and flush left for left-hand pages.

page layout *See* LAYOUT.

page makeup   *See* MAKEUP.

page numbering   For most publications pages are numbered with lowercase roman and arabic numerals. Roman numerals are used for pages preceding the first chapter, part, or section of the text. These pages are termed "front matter." The first page of the first chapter, part, or section is then numbered with the arabic numeral 1, and subsequent pages are numbered in sequence. Right-hand pages should always be odd-numbered and left-hand pages even-numbered.

Numbers may appear in the lower right corner of each page for right-hand pages and in the lower left corner for left-hand pages, centered at the bottom of each page, or in the upper right or left corners. Pages are sometimes numbered within each chapter, part, or section. In such a case, the first page of section I is numbered 1-1, the second page 1-2, etc. The fourth page of section III is numbered 3-4. (The roman numeral for the section number is converted to an arabic numeral.) This method of pagination is useful when a contract proposal or other document is being prepared by several departments in an organization. Each department assigns its own page numbers to its sections without waiting until all the material has been collated. Individual sections of the publication can thus be printed before the complete work. If back matter, such as appendixes and indexes, is required, pages are numbered consecutively beginning in most instances with the numeral 1. Exhibits should be identified with capital letters in sequence, such as A-1 or C-5.

page plate   Paper or metal printing plate used to print a single page. The term is generally used with reference to offset duplicators. With large offset printing presses that can accommodate 4, 16, 32, 64, or more pages, the plate is referred to as a "flat." (*See also* FLAT.)

page proof   Proof taken from each page and proofread as a final check. The galley corrections have been made, and illustrations and footnotes have been arranged in their proper places.

paginate   To number pages.

pamphlet   Publication consisting of several sheets of unbound printed matter, either stitched or stapled, or folded only, and having a soft cover or self-cover. It is smaller than a booklet. The term also denotes a treatise published in this format, usually on a controversial topic of interest. (*See also* BOOKLET.)

Pan Litho film   Du Pont lithographic film on a Cronar polyester film base, used for filtered highlight masks. It can also be used in three- and four-color separation systems in which halftone separation negatives are made directly in the camera or enlarger.

Pan Masking film   Du Pont film on a Cronar polyester film base, used as a negative masking material in the contrast adjustment and color correction of color copy. A 0.007-inch version of this film, without antihalation backing, was developed for camera-back masking techniques and for preparing unsharp premasks for transparencies. For multiple overlays and additional image sharpness, the 0.004-inch version of the film is recommended.

panchromatic   Designating photographic materials that are sensitive to light of all colors. Their color-sensitivity range approximates that of the human eye.

panel drawing   In engineering drafting and technical illustrating, a drawing that depicts operating controls and indicators for an item such as a hydraulic or electrical panel. It is used for operating instructions. Relationships and locations appear on the drawing as they do on the item. It is essential that nomenclature appears on the drawing exactly as it does on the equipment and in the same relative location.

panel title page   *See* HALF TITLE.

pantograph   Instrument for enlarging or reducing maps or drawings. It features a hinged parallelogram with a pole, a tracer point, and a pencil point set in the line of the parallelogram's diagonal. If the pole is at one corner and the tracer point at the opposite corner, the pencil will produce a reduction. If the tracer point and pencil are reversed, an enlargement is made.

paper, origin of   Three thousand years before Christ, the Egyptians used a material called papyrus to write on. The papyrus plant was the most important source of writing material before the invention of paper. The Chinese, in about 150 B.C., are credited with making the first pulp from which paper was manufactured. Bamboo shoots were soaked in lime and water, and the fibers were first separated and then pressed together by striking them with stones against a flat surface. The material was dried in the sun. The secret of papermaking reached medieval Europe through the Arabs, who made paper in Spain in the eleventh century. It spread to Italy, France, and Germany between 1190 and 1390, then through the Netherlands to England sometime before 1495.

The first paper mill in America was built on the Delaware River in Germantown, Pennsylvania, in 1690; it was operated by William Rittenhouse. The first paper machine was invented in 1799 by Nicolas Robert, a Frenchman. This machine was later perfected by John Gamble and Bryan Donkin. Henry and Sealy Fourdrinier of London purchased the patent rights and built their first machine in 1803 in Bermondsey, England. The Fourdrinier machine has since become synonymous with paper manufacturing.

paper, reproduction *See* REPRODUCTION MASTER.

paper-base film Sensitized photographic film having paper as a base. It is used in making plates for photo-offset printing.

paper-cutting charts *See* TABLE 3; TABLE 4; TABLE 6.

paper finishes For discussions of particular paper finishes, *see* ANTIQUE FINISH; ANTIQUE WOVE PAPER; CALENDERED FINISH; COATED FINISH; COCKLE FINISH; CRASH FINISH; DOUBLE-COATED PAPER; DRY FINISH; DULL COATED PAPER; DULL FINISH; EGGSHELL FINISH; ENGLISH FINISH; FELT FINISH; FRICTION-GLAZED FINISH; HIGH FINISH; KID FINISH; LAID ANTIQUE PAPER; LAWN FINISH; LOW FINISH; MACHINE FINISH; MACHINE-GLAZED PAPER; MARBLE FINISH; MARKING FELT; MATTE FINISH; MEDIEVAL LAID FINISH; METALLIC FINISH; MICA FINISH; MOTHER-OF-PEARL FINISH; MOTTLED FINISH; OILED PAPER; PARCHMENT FINISH; PLATER FINISH; PYROXYLIN-COATED PAPER; REP FINISH; RIPPLE FINISH; SATIN FINISH; SINGLE-COATED PAPER; SUPERCALENDERED FINISH; SUPERFINE; TEXT FINISH; UNGLAZED FINISH; VELLUM FINISH; WATER FINISH; WOVE FINISH; ZINC FINISH.

paper manufacturing Paper may be manufactured from wood, rags, straw, rope, jute butts, esparto grass, or other materials. Such woods as hemlock, poplar, birch, gum, spruce, and fir are commonly used for paper pulp. Wood may be transformed to pulp by mechanical or chemical means. Mechanical pulp is manufactured by grinding the wood into a fibrous condition. Newsprint, some wrapping papers, and paper bags are made from mechanical pulp. Sulfite, soda, and kraft processes are chemical methods of making pulp from wood. The wood is reduced to fine chips, which are conveyed to a huge digester. There they are pressure-cooked with chemicals until the material has been reduced to a fibrous mass called cellulose, the chemicals having removed such unwanted elements as resin, sap, and lignin. The cooking mixture is drained from the cellulose by continued washing and separation. The pulp is then bleached, washed, drained, and sent to a beating machine. Here begins the actual process of papermaking, in which such additives as clay, rags, various stocks, coloring, and sizing are put in the pulp to give it its special quality and character. At this stage the pulp has the appearance and consistency of milk.

In the sulfite process, the chips are cooked under pressure in a solution of calcium bisulfite. This method produces high-quality fibers for fine book papers. When wood such as gum, birch, or poplar is cooked under pressure with a caustic soda solution, the fibers are soft and short and form a more compact surface than sulfite fibers. Soda fibers are desirable for book papers. The sulfate and kraft processes are used, for the most part, in making wrapping papers and papers for bags.

When the pulp has been reduced to a fine milklike substance, it is piped to the Fourdrinier papermaking machine. The pulp is conveyed along a traveling belt of fine cloth meshed with wire on the underside. The weight of stock to be produced determines the speed of the belt: a speed of 1 inch per second ultimately produces heavier stock than a speed of 10 feet or more per second. The belt vibrates as it moves to set the fibers. At the same time, the liquid content of the pulp either passes through the bottom of the mesh or is sucked off.

After the paper has been dried by heated iron rollers, it is passed through additional rollers, or calenders, where it is finished to the desired quality. Rag pulp is treated in much the same manner as wood pulp. Although the processes of cleaning, sorting, thrashing, bleaching, and digesting differ, the end result is the same when the pulp is ready for the beating process. Rag pulp may be added in various quantities to wood pulp during beating, or paper called "100 percent rag" may be manufactured from rag alone. Rag content, of course, lends a highly desirable quality to paper.

paper master *See* PAPER PLATE.

paper negative Inexpensive negative used for producing printing plates when quality is not of prime importance.

paper plate (paper master) Printing plate used in the direct plate method of reproduction. Typewritten copy, hand-drawn characters, drawings, or any other image may be applied directly to the plate. As no photography is involved, all reproductions are of the same size as the original. If art requires reduction or enlargement, the image may be applied to a paper plate indirectly by means of xerographic equipment or other photographic and exposure units. (*See also* COPYING MACHINES; DIRECT PLATE MAKING.)

paper qualities It is impossible to become an expert on paper without devoting many hours of study to its manufacture and to its use in printing, duplicating, and copying. Whenever an image is created with ink, crayon, camera, airbrush, or pencil, it is paper or a paper-base material that usually receives the image, either poorly or to good advantage. Paper is designed for a particular application, and it can be judged only by how well it fulfills the purpose for which it was manufactured.

Paper should first be judged by the degree of uniformity on both sides of the sheet. Uniformity in a paper surface can be appraised by close inspection under a good light. When paper fibers are compact and uniform, the type impression has less chance of falling on a nonprinting area. Paper may be judged as to whiteness, if this quality is desired, by comparing several samples against a dark background.

There are several tests to determine grain in paper. The most common is to fold the paper in both directions. A fold with the grain is smoother than a fold against the grain. If the paper is fingered delicately, less resistance to coarse friction is experienced when the paper is creased with the grain. Grain may also be determined by tearing a sample of paper slowly in both directions into strips no more than 1 inch wide. In tearing with the grain, the paper has a tendency to tear from edge to edge, whereas in tearing against the grain greater resistance is encountered and a complete tear from edge to edge is seldom achieved.

Durability and tearing resistance are significant primarily in binding and handling. If, for example, paper is to be used in a loose-leaf or other binder and must therefore be perforated or serrated, ability to withstand handling and avoid tearing is most important.

Good folding qualities are considered of prime importance by paper manufacturers and merchants. To test folding characteristics, one can compare a paper of known folding ability with a sample. One can fold and refold the two papers the same number of times, applying equal pressure to both creases across each fold. When the folds have broken the resistance of the paper, each sample should be torn slowly and the difference in resistance noted. This test cannot be applied to 100 percent rag-content paper, which can be folded 500 to 1,000 times before showing any evidence of breakdown.

Good erasure qualities are desirable in certain papers. Paper with rag content and gelatin sizing is better than sulfite-treated paper. To test for erasure qualities, the surface of the paper should be scraped. If the residue is fine and powdery, the paper has good erasing qualities; if it is coarse and fibrous, wood sulfite and starch sizing are evident and erasing qualities are inferior. When good erasure characteristics are desired, papers with gelatin surface sizing are preferable to those with starch surface sizing.

The undesirable surface characteristic called "picking" may be eliminated or minimized by sizing. To test for picking, one can moisten a finger and press it firmly against the paper. When the finger is pulled away quickly, it can be examined for flecks of paper. (*See also* PICKING.)

Another important consideration in determining suitable paper for printing is "show-through" when the copy is printed on both sides of the sheet. If show-through is present, either another grade of paper should be considered or a heavier stock of the same grade selected. (*See also* SHOW-THROUGH.)

The weight of paper is an important factor in book and magazine publishing since postal rates are based on weight. While coated-two-sides book paper will reproduce fine-screen halftones and have remarkable printing qualities, volume mailing costs are considerably higher than if uncoated stock is used. Obviously, additives in paper make it much heavier.

papier-mâché Mixture of paper pulp, clay, chalk, sand, and materials such as glue, resin, and lead acetate. It is molded into shape while moist and then dried until it is firm. Molten metal is poured into a papier-mâché mold for making stereotype printing plates.

papyrus Most important writing material used before the discovery of paper by the Chinese in about 150 B.C. It was made from thin strips of pith from the papyrus plant, which were pressed while wet, covered with a paste, dried, cut to size, and polished with a smooth stone or shell. Papyrus was used by the Egyptians to make writing material 3,000 years before Christ.

paragraph numbering Paragraphs are often numbered in technical manuals, proposals, and reports and in instruction books. Such numbers are useful for reference purposes and as aids to a logical presentation of subject matter. Two types of paragraph numbering are shown in Figure P-1.

1	INTRODUCTION	1-1	INTRODUCTION
1.1	General	1-2	General
1.1.1	Scope	1-3	Scope
1.1.2	Limitations	1-4	Limitations
1.1.3	Use	1-5	Use
2	MECHANICAL SYMBOLS	2-1	MECHANICAL SYMBOLS
2.1	Piping	2-2	Piping
2.1.1	Pipe Systems	2-3	Pipe Systems
2.2	Pipe Fittings	2-4	Pipe Fittings
2.2.1	General	2-5	General
2.2.2	Elbows	2-6	Elbows
2.2.3	Tees	2-7	Tees
3	ELECTRICAL SYMBOLS	3-1	ELECTRICAL SYMBOLS
3.1	General	3-2	General
3.1.1	Schematics	3-3	Schematics

Fig. P-1   Paragraph numbering.

parallel fold   *See* FIRST PARALLEL FOLD; SECOND PARALLEL FOLD.

parallel lines   *See* LINE CONVENTIONS: ENGINEERING DRAWINGS.

parchment finish   Finish that makes paper resemble parchment.

partial view   *See* ORTHOGRAPHIC PROJECTION: ENGINEERING DRAWINGS.

pasted blanks   Stock pasted together to form a thicker ply. Only 12-, 14-, and 16-ply blanks are pasted. (*See also* PLY.)

pastel   Coloring matter mixed with gum to form crayons. The word "pastel" also denotes both such a crayon and a picture produced with the crayon. Pastels are used widely by commercial artists for comprehensives, especially in the range of grays that correspond to the range of tones desired. Pastel colors are those having soft or pale hues.

paster   In a web-fed press, a device that applies a fine line of paste to one or both sides of the paper roll to produce finished booklets.

paste-up   Process of pasting an image or part of an image on a reproduction page or sheet that is to be photographed for plate making and printing. It includes pasting blocks of text, art, preprints, or any other image in position. Before copy is pasted, the paste-up areas should be outlined with a fade-out–blue pencil. Rubber cement is an excellent adhesive for paste-up work. Some types of rubber cement need be used on only one pasting surface, but if a worker is not sure of the cement, he should apply it to both surfaces. All excess cement must be removed. If particles of cement are permitted to adhere to the paper, dust and dirt are attracted and the reflection will show on the negative. A small "pickup" should be used to remove the surplus cement. If the copy is to be stored, it should be covered with a tissue overlay.

patch   Piece of metal with a correction that is affixed to a printing plate, usually by soldering.

patent base   Metal base used for the lockup of irregularly shaped types and designs. It has proved quite successful in the accurate registration of long printing runs.

patent drawing   Precise, carefully executed drawing that depicts all the operational and functional characteristics of an invention, discovery, or design. It should show as many views as patent reviewers may require to understand the invention. Shading mediums, cross-hatching of sectional views, line drawing to portray shapes, and index numbers keyed to explanatory text may all be used. Drawings must be executed in india ink. It is suggested that a patent draftsman or attorney be consulted before making patent drawings if their preparation and handling are not thoroughly understood.

pearl   Old type size. The nearest equivalent in the point system is 5 point.

pebble board   Board stock having a very coarse surface. When it is drawn upon with charcoal or stick pastels, dots are produced, the size of the dots depending on the pressure applied. The work gives a continuous-tone effect but is reproduced as line work.

pencil art   Drawing made with an ordinary graphite or other pencil. It may include lines or renderings (shaded areas) as desired. When pencil drawings or renderings with hard, definite lines are reproduced by the photolithographic process, it is difficult to determine whether pencil or ink has been used. Modern cameras provide quality reproduction of good pencil art.

pencil artist   Technical illustrator who draws in pencil work to be completed in ink by others. Such illustrators are employed in large art departments where volume production is the rule. They are accomplished in art layout and drawing and must be able to convert parts and objects depicted on orthographic engineering drawings into perspective or isometric illustrations. Their work is completed in ink by finishers, or inkers.

The system of employing pencil artists and finishers has both advantages and disadvantages. Good technical illustrators are at a premium, and their knowledge should be employed where the need is most critical. Large art groups are placed at a disadvantage because of volume output and are therefore forced to distinguish between illustrators and finishers. While the distinction discourages initiative, it is followed of necessity. A disadvantage is that the pencil artist, knowing that his responsibility ends when the pencil art is completed, may get out of touch with inking and finishing problems and may not remain so close to the art as if he were to complete the job. The finisher, too, works under a handicap in attempting to interpret what the pencil artist has done. Moreover, he may not be given an opportunity to do creative work or to work with engineering drawings and thus advance to higher illustration techniques.

pens, Speedball lettering   *See* PENS, STEEL-BRUSH; SPEEDBALL PENS.

pens, steel-brush   Flexible pens manufactured by the Hunt Manufacturing Company. They are designed especially for large poster lettering. The pens may also be used as auxiliary brushes for water-

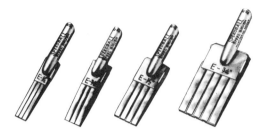

E–1/4" E–3/8" E–1/2" E–3/4"

ADJUST YOUR LARGE LETTERING TO THESE SIZES

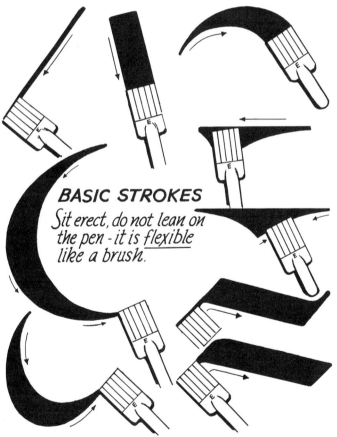

BASIC STROKES

Sit erect, do not lean on the pen - it is flexible like a brush.

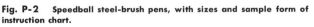

Fig. P-2 Speedball steel-brush pens, with sizes and sample form of instruction chart.

color and oil painting, particularly to fill in large areas of black-ink and color work. The pens work with any india ink or color diluted to a usable consistency. Lettering instruction charts are available on request. The method of illustration and system of instruction shown in Figure P-2 are copyrighted by Ross F. George.

pens, technical   Pens suitable for technical illustrating. Some of the requirements of good technical pens used with regular drawing and writing inks are (1) freedom from clogging, (2) consistency in line weights, (3) ease of filling and cleaning, (4) cleanliness during use, (5) interchangeability of writing points, and (6) adhesion to the material drawn upon.

The Koh-I-Noor Rapidograph No. 3065-H pen is designed for use with acetate inks, which because of their chemical composition have a strong tendency to damage pens during storage. The Koh-I-Noor No. 3065 technical pen set (Figure P-3) is used with regular drawing ink for drafting and technical illustrating, ruling, guide and freehand lettering, tracing, writing, and commercial artwork. The set is composed of seven interchangeable point sections

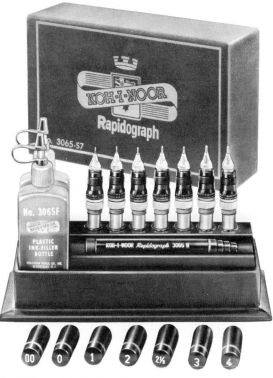

Fig. P-3   Koh-I-Noor Rapidograph pen set.

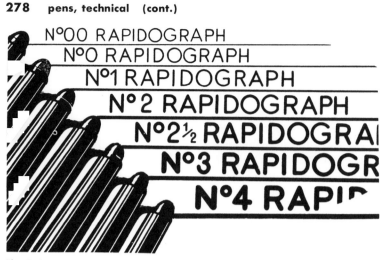

Fig. P-4   Koh-I-Noor Rapidograph pen line weights (actual size).

Fig. P-6 Leroy lettering scriber with reservoir pen.

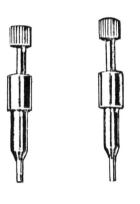

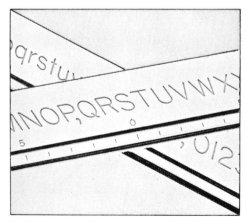

SIZE
0000
000
00
0
1
2
3
4
5
6
7
8
9
10
12
14

Fig. P-5 Leroy pen and line-weight sizes (actual size).

Fig. P-7 Leroy lettering guides.

and one holder. Each point section has an individual line weight, as illustrated in Figure P-4.

Figure P-5 shows the configuration of the Leroy technical pen, as well as the range of line weights from 0000 to 14 (0.008 to 0.250 inch). Leroy pens are used in technical and commercial artwork and also in conjunction with a scriber (Figure P-6) and templates (Figure P-7) for lettering. The standard pen consists of a penholder and socket holder (not shown), a plunger or needle, and a point. The reservoir pen shown with the scriber in Figure P-6 is available with lettering guides in sizes from 00 to 5. To use the lettering pen one proceeds as follows: (1) a template is chosen in the size and style desired (there are many sizes and styles of alphabets, numerals, and symbols, including Greek letters) and placed along a straightedge; (2) the tailpin of the scriber is set in the straight guide groove of the template; (3) the recessed letters on the template are traced with the tracer pin on the scriber, and the pen reproduces the character in full view above the template. Pens with long points are available for use with straightedges, curves, and cutout templates. One model of the scriber permits the height and slant of characters to be varied. Other templates produce line weights up to $\frac{1}{4}$ inch wide with characters 2 inches high. A letter-size adapter, used with certain scribers, extends and condenses lettering by increasing or decreasing heights by as much as one-third.

The standard Wrico pen (Figure P-8) is used by engineering draftsmen, artists, and technical illustrators when fine delineation and workmanship are required. The same inkwell, points, and needles are used with the AR Wrico pen, which is designed to be held in a writing position. The designations of the points for the two pens are shown in Figure P-9.

STANDARD		STYLE AR
No. 2		No. 2AR
No. 3		No. 3AR
No. 4		No. 4AR
No. 5		No. 5AR
No. 6		No. 6AR
No. 7		No. 7AR
No. 7T		No. 7ART

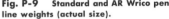

Fig. P-9   Standard and AR Wrico pen line weights (actual size).

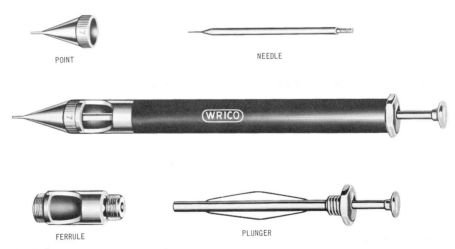

POINT

NEEDLE

WRICO

FERRULE

PLUNGER

Fig. P-8   **Standard Wrico pen and components.**

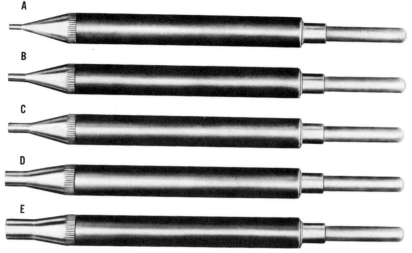

Fig. P-10   Wrico brush pens.

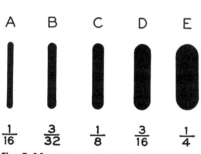

Fig. P-11   Wrico brush-pen line weights (actual size).

Lettering guides are divided into two groups, those used with the Wrico scriber and those used with the standard and AR Wrico pens. Lettering-guide characters used with the scriber range from 0.060 to 0.625 inch; capital and lowercase letters and numerals are available. A pencil-lead adapter may be employed in the scriber. Lettering guides for use with the pens provide a variety of styles and sizes, including vertical and slant letters. Guide holders are used against a straightedge, and the underside of the guide is grooved so that ink will not be smeared when the guide is moved horizontally.

Wrico brush and felt pens are manufactured for use with special lettering guides with characters from 0.040 to 3 inches high. Figure P-10 shows the brush pens in sizes from A through E, and Figure P-11 shows actual line weights that correspond to the alphabetical designations. Various colors may be lettered with Wrico felt pens.

perfecting press (perfector press)   Printing press of any kind that prints one color on both sides of a sheet in one operation for each unit. The Solna 24-inch perfecting offset press (Figure P-12) is designed for printing light to medium forms in sizes as large as $18\frac{1}{2}$ by $24\frac{1}{2}$ inches. Short-run book editions, newspapers, telephone directories, and business forms are a few examples of printable material. A color can be printed on one side, the same color can be printed on both sides, or a different color can be printed on each side. The minimum sheet size is $8\frac{1}{2}$ by $14^{15}/_{16}$ inches, and the maximum printing area is $17\frac{1}{2}$ by $24\frac{3}{8}$ inches. Stock capacity ranges from 27- to 100-pound book paper; speeds, from 1,700 to 6,000 sheets per hour. (*See also* BLANKET-TO-BLANKET PRESS.)

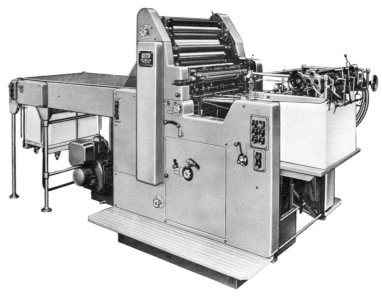

Fig. P-12   American Type Founders' Solna 24-inch perfector offset press.

perforate   To cut minute holes in stock in order to facilitate separation of individual units, as in sheets of postage stamps. Perforation may be performed on machines designed for the purpose. It may also be accomplished during or after the printing run by inserting cutting dies. Perforation differs from scoring in that it is used to separate units, whereas scoring breaks the molecular structure of the stock to permit easy folding.

perforating, schoolbook   Perforation of sheets during the printing cycle, made parallel to the binding edge of jaw-folded signatures. This type of perforation is used extensively in school examination books from which students tear answer sheets, leaving the question portions of pages bound in the books. A similar perforation is used for checkbooks, from which checks are detached, leaving the stubs bound.

perforator   *See* TAPE PERFORATOR.

perspective drawing   View of an object as it appears to the naked eye. A perspective drawing shows a solid object on a flat surface so that the position, distance, and magnitude of the object appear as seen with the eye. A camera photographs pictures in perspective. (*See* Figure P-13.)

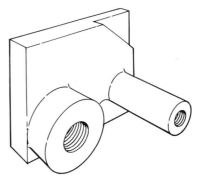

Fig. P-13   Simple line drawing in perspective.

PERT chart Flow-chart network that shows the relationship between events and activities in a program. PERT (program-evaluation and review technique), which was first developed by a project team in the Navy Special Projects Office, was used successfully in the Polaris weapons system and became popular in military and industrial applications. The PERT display of information may be adapted to many phases of programming projects. The basic concept is to control the completion time of a project by showing the events that must take place, the activities required to accomplish them, and the relationship and interdependency of the events. During the course of a program, the chart will reveal remedies that must be adopted to control the program with respect to time. Figure P-14 illustrates a simple PERT chart without identifying events.

pH Symbol used to express hydrogen-ion concentration and thus acidity and alkalinity. The relative acidity or alkalinity of the solution used in offset press work has a tendency to change, primarily because of exposure to the atmosphere. Small kits with litmus paper and a color chart are provided to test this condition. The paper is dipped in the solution fountain, and the color it assumes is compared with the colors on the chart. Corrective action is taken if the solution is unbalanced.

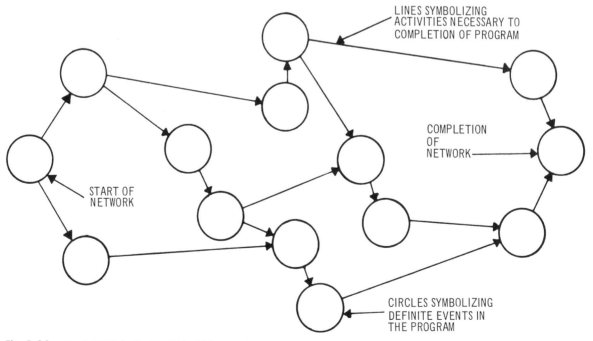

Fig. P-14   Simple PERT chart without identifying events.

phantom lines (alternate-position lines)   Lines used in orthographic projection on engineering and mechanical drawings, consisting of one long and two short dashes, evenly spaced, with a long line at the end. Designated as "thin" lines, they indicate the alternate position of parts of the object delineated, repeated detail, or the relative position of an absent part. (*See also* LINE CONVENTIONS: ENGINEERING DRAWINGS.)

Photact   Trademark of the Keuffel and Esser Company for a process of making blackline contact-size reproduction copies, including equipment and materials. One of two methods may be used, the choice depending on the characteristics of the original that is to be copied. The first method is direct printing in which negatives are made from originals that either are transparent or have a fair translucency, such as tracing paper or cloth, provided the original has an image on one side only. The original is placed in contact with the emulsion side of the negative paper, which is exposed to light through it. A reverse-reading negative results. Reverse-reading negatives are recommended for making the best positive tracings or prints. When a right-reading negative is desired, the original is placed in the printer facedown instead of faceup. The same method is used to make prints or transparent tracings from the negatives. The emulsion side of the reverse negative is placed in contact with the emulsion side of the translucent paper or cloth. Exposure is made behind the negative. This procedure produces a right-reading tracing or print.

The second method uses reflex exposure to make negatives from opaque originals or originals with an image on both sides. The face of the original is placed in contact with the emulsion side of the negative paper, and exposure is made behind the negative. This procedure results in a reverse-reading negative from which tracings or prints may be made. Negatives may be made on several weights of paper. Tracings and prints may be made on card stock, opaque paper sensitized on both sides, 100 percent rag translucent tracing paper, tracing cloth, and transparent and opaque films. (*See also* REPRODUCTION FLOW CHARTS.)

Photo-Draft system   System of automated photomechanical schematic drafting. When the keyboard unit of the system (*see* Figure P-15) is operated, it punches a tape that carries all the control data and simultaneously types a proof for error detection. The unit employs a layout for electric-circuit diagrams. Each of its 42 character-bearing keys controls the coding of four different symbols. A freehand sketch is first drawn on graph paper and scaled to the Photo-Draft typesetter's units of movement. The sketch pattern copy

Fig. P-15 Keyboard unit of American Type Founders'
Photo-Draft system.

is surprinted with equivalent typewritten characters during keyboard-
ing, thus permitting the diagram to be checked before photodrafting.
The verified tape is inserted in the photographic unit (not shown),
and under tape control the complete schematic is drawn automatically on clear film. The film is processed by standard developing
methods.

photoarc process Conventional method of preparing a printing
plate by photographing the original with a process camera and then
using an arc light to "burn" the image from the negative onto the
plate. (*See* ARC LAMP.)

photocomposition System of producing copy by photographic
means. A camera photographs each letter of a desired font as the
operator operates a keyboard in much the same manner as an automatic typesetting machine. Justified copy is produced on film or
paper. Different sizes of a font are produced by enlargement or
reduction. (*See also* TYPESETTERS, PHOTOGRAPHIC.)

photocontact paper negative Contact negative made from an
opaque or a translucent material. The scale maintained is good,
and the material is permanent. Such a negative has a reverse reading
from which positive prints may be made by the reflection process.
Any part of the image not wanted in the positive print can be
opaqued.

photodrafting Drafting by revision or tracing onto a print, such as
a "printout" or a "blowback," of an engineering or design drawing.
The printouts may be made in any manner; the blowbacks are

derived from microfilm images. Photodrafting is useful for revising similar drawing configurations or for tracing the desired portion of an image.

photoengraving   Making a relief printing plate by utilizing photographic means to obtain a chemically resistant image on a metal surface. The unprotected metal is etched away, leaving the protected areas in relief. The term also denotes the plate made by this process. (*See also* CUT.)

photogelatin process (collotype process)   Planographic, screenless printing process similar to lithography. It is based on the fact that oil (ink) and water do not mix. The image area on the gelatin plate is made water-repellent, whereas the nonimage area is receptive to water.

A bichromated gelatin solution is floated onto a thick sheet of glass, which becomes the plate. When dry, the sensitized gelatin coating is exposed through a continuous-tone negative. The plate is developed by a wetting process. The tones from white to black reject or accept the water in the proportion to which they have been exposed to light. With the introduction of reticulation, the entire surface of the plate is divided into minute and mutually independent areas that repel or accept water and ink in direct proportion to tone values. The printing stock is brought in contact with the gelatin plate.

Copy prepared for the photogelatin process may be a paste-up or any other form suitable for photo-offset printing. The process is effective for short runs of fine color work. (*See also* PRINTING METHODS; RETICULATION.)

photogrammetry   System of making maps from photographs, especially aerial photographs.

photograph   Picture of an object formed on sensitized paper, film, or other material by the action of light.

photographic properties   *See* FILMS AND PLATES.

photographic typesetters   *See* TYPESETTERS, PHOTOGRAPHIC.

photogravure   Intaglio printing in which photographic methods are used in the production of the printing plate. (*See also* PRINTING METHODS.)

photolisting   Method of reproducing lists with a sequential-card camera. (*See* CAMERA, SEQUENTIAL-CARD.)

photolithographic camera   *See* CAMERA, PROCESS.

photolithographic negative   *See* NEGATIVE, PHOTOLITHOGRAPHIC.

photolithography (photo-offset)   Photographic method of plano-graphic printing, based on the fact that grease (ink) and water do not mix. Photolithography encompasses all the steps necessary to arrive at the end item: photographing the copy, developing the negative, making the printing plate, and printing the image on stock from the plate. (*See also* PRINTING METHODS.)

photomap   Map constructed from a series of photographs taken from an airplane. The photographs are matched to compose the photomap. Photomapping is also used extensively in space technology to photograph planets through satellite control from the earth. (*See also* PHOTOGRAMMETRY.)

photomechanical   Pertaining to any process of printing or duplicating images by mechanical means from a photographically prepared printing plate.

photomicrography   Art or practice of producing photographs of minute objects such as organisms by using a camera and a microscope. A photomicrograph is the photograph so produced.

photomicroscope   Combination camera-microscope for taking photographs of microscopic objects.

photomontage   *See* MONTAGE.

photomural   Photograph enlarged many times to serve as a decorative piece, especially for wall display.

photo-offset   *See* PHOTOLITHOGRAPHY.

photosensitive material   Any material coated with a light-sensitive emulsion, one which responds chemically to light.

Photostat   Registered trademark of the Photostat Corporation for a photographic copying machine. The Photostat machine has a prism attached to the front of the lens that turns the image to read from left to right instead of in reverse. Thus a right-reading image is made directly. A particular feature of the many Photostat models is the ability to produce copies continuously while developing, fixing, washing, and drying are handled successively in various contained units without attention from the operator. Depending on the model, copies of original material may be made at the same time with a 50 percent reduction and a 200 percent enlargement, as desired. Copies may also be made in sizes between these extremes. Special models used in advertising work enlarge by as much as 350 percent. Sensitized paper for the photoprints is furnished on rolls and housed in the unit. Some Photostat models have a cycle control that permits continuous operation for producing as many as 23 (or 399) prints without the operator's attention. Some of the models may be adapted to make paper prints from 16-, 35-, and 70-millimeter film.

phototypesetting Cold-composition method of producing text matter by successively projecting the images of evenly spaced characters on light-sensitive film or on photographic paper. The images may be developed automatically within the machine as the images are set, or the latent images may be developed in a remote darkroom. The term "phototypesetting" is a misnomer because actual type is not used, but it is accepted in the printing trade as the photographic equivalent of setting type. (*See also* TYPESETTERS, PHOTOGRAPHIC.)

Photo-Typositor Trade name of a photographic typesetter manufactured by the Visual Graphics Corporation. (*See* TYPESETTERS, PHOTOGRAPHIC.)

pi Spilled type. When the type in a galley has been pied, it often must be completely reset.

pica Unit of measurement used in printing. The pica is equal to 12 points; for practical purposes, 6 picas are equal to 1 inch. The pica is used to measure the width and length of pages, columns, slugs, and so on. The term "pica" also denotes a size of typewriter type measuring 6 lines to the vertical inch and 10 characters to the horizontal inch.

picking Lifting of particles of paper from stock during printing. The ink may be sticky or the paper inadequate. In addition, a rubber blanket on an offset press may tend to pick up particles because of suction created by the blanket.

pickle jar Tubular glass jar with a sponge in the bottom that absorbs pure ammonia. A lid prevents the escape of ammonia fumes. The jar is used to develop latent images exposed on diazo-treated foil (film), paper, and cloth. Such a jar is the Technifax Deluxe pickle jar (Figure P-16). The image must first be exposed for several minutes in a printer (Photo-Printer) in contact with the diazo-treated

Fig. P-16 Technifax Photo-Printer and Deluxe pickle jar.

material. The copy material containing the latent image is then rolled and inserted in the jar. The latent image can be seen coming to life through the sides of the jar. The completed print is removed in a dry state.

This method of exposing and developing images is a whiteprint process of reproduction, for which whiteprint machines may also be used. This process is well suited to the making of projecturals for overhead projection, when the image must be on transparent film. (*See also* WHITEPRINT PROCESS.)

pickup Small rubberlike pad or sponge used to pick up excess rubber cement from a paste-up. A pickup is sometimes called a "mouse" by those working in the trade. As a verb, "pick up" means to reuse an illustration or text for a new publication.

pictorial drawing Any drawing that depicts an object with such clarity that it can be recognized. This type of drawing is used with electrical, pneumatic, and hydraulic schematics to show the relationship of a system's components. Pictorial drawings are also used to advantage in overhead projection if the projectural is not cluttered with copy.

pie chart Circular chart divided into wedges resembling the cuts of a pie (Figure P-17). Each wedge represents a percentage of the whole "pie." This type of chart is easy to understand, but its use is limited because only one quantity can be compared with the

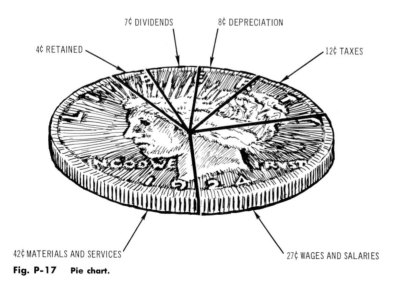

7¢ DIVIDENDS   8¢ DEPRECIATION

4¢ RETAINED   12¢ TAXES

42¢ MATERIALS AND SERVICES   27¢ WAGES AND SALARIES

Fig. P-17   Pie chart.

whole. (*See also* BAR CHART; COLUMN CHART; CURVE CHART; SURFACE CHART.)

pile height   Height of a pile of sheets of stock that equals the normal maximum capacity of the feeder and delivery mechanisms of a printing press. The term is also used to indicate the maximum pile height of other types of machines, such as paper joggers and cutters.

pinhole   Very small light spot that appears on a developed photographic negative. Pinholes result from photographing particles of dust and lint deposited on the unexposed negative, camera lens, vacuum-board glass, or other parts of a camera. The negative may be placed over a light table and the pinholes blotted out with a small brush and opaque solution.

piping diagram   Line drawing of a fluid system or of part of such a system. It shows the routing of components, their physical location and arrangement, and such other characteristics as differences in levels, pipe diameters, materials, types and sizes of fittings, flow, pressure, and volume. Information may be listed in tabular form on the engineering drawing.

placard drawing   Drawing that shows instructions for the maintenance and operation of an article. It can be reproduced in a reduced size and mounted on the article itself. It may be affixed to the underside of the cover of the article or printed on its surface.

plan drawing   Drawing that depicts plans for the foundation, framing, floor or deck, or roof of a structure. It may indicate the shapes, sizes, and materials of foundations, their relation to the superstructure, and their elevation with reference to a fixed datum plane; the location of walls, partitions, bulkheads, stanchions, companionways, openings, columns, and stairs; and the shapes and sizes of roofs, parapet walls, skylights, stacks, and ventilators. The drawing shows materials for construction, arrangement of structural framing, and location of equipment or furniture as appropriate. A plan drawing for services may depict individual layouts for heating, plumbing, air-conditioning, electrical, and other utility systems.

planimeter   Precision instrument for measuring any plane area. A tracing point or lens is moved around the perimeter of the plane, and the area is read from a measuring wheel and indicator dial.

planographic printing   Printing from a flat surface. (*See* PRINTING METHODS.)

Fig. P-18 **A. B. Dick Model 106 plate exposure unit.**

planography Art or practice of planographic printing.

plastic binding *See* COMB BINDING; *see also* BINDING, MECHANICAL.

plastic plate Direct printing plate made on a plastic base. (*See* DIRECT PLATE MAKING.)

plat drawing Engineering drawing of an area in which structures are shown together with detailed information on their relation to other structures, to existing and proposed utilities, and to the terrain, roads, boundary lines, walks, fences, and the like.

plate, photographic Rigid glass base coated with a photographic emulsion.

plate, printing Any printing surface except a form. A form, which is the surface used in letterpress printing, is known as such in the trade. The plate may be an offset plate, a gravure plate, or a photogelatin plate. (*See also* PRINTING METHODS.)

plate cylinder Printing-press cylinder to which the printing plate is attached. In letterpress printing, the opposing cylinder is the impression cylinder, which cushions the stock as it is fed between them. In photo-offset or letterset printing, the opposing cylinder is the blanket cylinder and, in turn, the impression cylinder.

plate finish *See* PLATER FINISH.

plate-making equipment Photo-offset printing plates are made in exposure units. Some units are complex self-contained devices, such as the Itek Platemaster, which produces duplicate plates from original copy. Other units use photolithographic negatives through which the image is "burned" onto presensitized paper or metal plates. (*See also* CAMERA, PROCESS: PAPER PLATES.)

The A. B. Dick Model 106 plate exposure unit is shown in Figure P-18. A presensitized plate is placed in the contact frame with the lithographic negative, the image being positioned over the plate with the right-reading face up. The contact frame is closed, the automatic timer is set, and the switch is turned to ON. A 500-watt reflector photoflood lamp penetrates the translucent image area of the negative and burns the image onto the plate. The plate is then processed with a developer to bring out the latent image. The Model 106 unit holds plates as large as 10 by 16 inches. A portion of the negative may be blocked out by covering the unwanted area with opaque stock. This technique may be used to make separate plates for color runs from one negative.

Figure P-19 shows nuArc's Model FT-26 Flip-Top plate maker, which is operated in three steps: loading, flipping, and exposing. The unit contains a high-intensity point-light source and a vacuum frame. It has an automatic arc control. The inside blanket-beading size is 23 by $26\frac{3}{4}$ inches. In operation, the glass frame is lifted back on its supports, and the plate is positioned on the blanket. The flat (the assembled negative or negatives stripped into an opaque masking sheet) is placed on the plate, with the tail edge of the flat matched to the plate clamp edge. Room should be allowed for clamping when the flat is stripped. The frame glass is closed and latched. The master switch and then the vacuum-pump switch are turned on. When the vacuum gauge registers the desired vacuum, indicating that the plate and flat are in good contact, the frame is flipped and the flat and plate face the light source. The timer is set to the recommended exposure time, and the lamp switch is

Fig. P-20 nuArc's Model FT-40NS nonstop Flip-Top plate maker in frame-flipped position.

Fig. P-19 nuArc's Model FT-26 Flip-Top plate maker in loading position.

T A B L E P-1 **Plate-making Troubleshooting Information.**

Problem	Appearance	Solution
Blinding.	Image may look strong on the plate, but the plate prints very weakly or not at all.	1. Excess gum on the plate may be covering the image so that it will not accept ink. Use correct chemicals as directed for final gumming. Have pressman rub the plate down with fountain solution to remove excess gum. Certain plates require going over with developer. Follow the manufacturer's directions. 2. Plate will not accept ink because ink rollers are glazed. Fountain solution may be too strong and may have worked into the ink, causing the ink to emulsify.
Scumming	Plate picks up ink in the clear areas and transfers it to nonimage areas of the press sheet.	1. Nonimage areas of the plate may not be desensitized properly to resist ink. Reetch the plate or make a new plate. Always work the entire plate, including nonimage as well as image areas, with gum and developer. 2. Scumming may be a press problem because of dirty damping rollers, skidding from the roller, a loose blanket, or an improper fountain-solution mixture. Check press conditions.
Halation	This condition appears as dot spreading, copy enlarged at the edges, and shadows of type.	1. Overexposure may accent poorly stripped areas. Use nuArc Sensitivity Guide to check exposure and replace the guide periodically. A yellowed guide can cause overexposure. 2. There is poor contact during exposure. Check flat for improper stripping, such as "fat" stripped areas, thick tape, or overlapped film. Check vacuum gauge and also check contact visually when making the exposure.

T A B L E P-1 (Continued)

Problem	Appearance	Solution
		3. Use strong point-light source for exposing plates to avoid long exposure and undercutting.
Broken images . . .	Image is missing in certain areas; fingerprints develop on the plate.	1. Examine stripped flat. Tape or opaquing solution may be covering the portion of the image that is broken. 2. Check vacuum-frame glass. Wet opaquing solution or tape adhesive may come off on the underside. Always make sure the glass is clean. 3. The plate may be underexposed. It may appear to develop properly, but the image "walks off" after a few impressions. Check exposure with nuArc Sensitivity Guide. 4. Irregular broken-image areas may be due to moisture on the plate prior to exposure. Handle plates by the edges only and avoid fingerprinting. Store plates in lighttight containers away from moisture.
Plugging	Press sheet looks dirty, dots have been filled in, or "plugged," and the image is spotty.	1. Old, dried developer in the plate sponge or pad may be dissolving in the fresh developer, causing plugging. Always use a clean sponge and pad. 2. Dried gum and developer on the plate working surface or table may work into the plate when it is wet with new solution. Keep the developing table clean. Always use a flat surface so that low areas on the table will not cause incomplete development. Apply additional developer on a clean surface and redevelop according to the manufacturer's instructions to correct plugging.

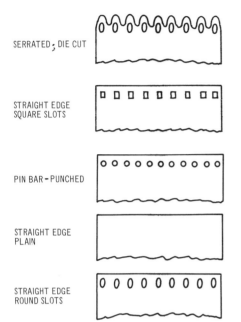

SERRATED; DIE CUT

STRAIGHT EDGE
SQUARE SLOTS

PIN BAR - PUNCHED

STRAIGHT EDGE
PLAIN

STRAIGHT EDGE
ROUND SLOTS

Fig. P-21   Plate type edges.

turned to the ON-TIMER position. The light source turns on and then off when the desired exposure time has elapsed. The vacuum-frame latch is released and the frame returned to the loading position. The vacuum pump is turned off to release the vacuum, the glass-frame catches are released, and the plate and flat are removed.

Figure P-20 shows nuArc's Model FT-40NS nonstop Flip-Top plate maker. It contains all the operating features of Model FT-26, but two independent vacuum frames can be used instead of one. While one frame is being exposed, the second frame is reloaded for the next plate. The FT-40NS has an inside blanket-beading size of 30 by 40 inches. A plate-making troubleshooting chart is shown in Table P-1.

plate type edges   The edges of paper and metal plates vary with the particular clamping devices of presses and duplicators. When plates are being ordered, they should be described as shown in Figure P-21, which illustrates typical plate edges for duplicators and presses.

Platemaster   Trade name of Itek Business Products' process camera for producing paper plates. (*See* CAMERA, PROCESS: PAPER PLATES.)

platen   In a job press, the flat surface that holds the paper as it is pressed against the printing form. In a cold-composition machine such as a typewriter, the platen is the round rubber cylinder that supports the paper and receives the impact when the keys are operated.

platen press   Printing press in which an impression is taken by bringing together two flat surfaces, one holding the stock and the other the printing surface. In some presses, the form moves up against the platen; in the universal type, the platen is first placed in a position parallel to the bed and then pressed against the bed. Platen presses are used for simple one-color work and for high-quality color work in which fine register is required. Large platen presses are used for stamping, die cutting, creasing, and embossing.

Figure P-22 shows a D series Kluge automatic platen press. The D series includes models with sheet sizes of 11 by 17 and 13 by 19 inches. These presses are designed to accommodate thicknesses from onionskin to wallboard (to 0.200 inch). They will print on shapes varying from circles to quadrilaterals and on material ranging from tags to wooden rulers and snap-out forms. The minimum sheet size is $1\frac{7}{8}$ by 3 inches for both models. Feed- and delivery-pile heights are both 14 inches. Speeds are 4,000 impressions per hour for the 11- by 17-inch model and 3,500 impressions per hour for the 13- by 19-inch model.

The Kluge HD series automatic die-cutting, embossing, and foil-stamping platen press handles round, oblong, and rectangular stocks from onionskin to a thickness of 0.200 inch. Either regular or continuous-feed magazines are available. Heavy stock, made-up boxes, book covers, and all-around converting work can be handled. The maximum sheet size is 14 by 22 inches, and the minimum hairline-register sheet size is 3 by 3 inches. Magazine and delivery capacities are each 14 inches. The maximum speed is 3,000 impressions per hour.

Kluge platen presses are designed for delayed dwell, which is the time delay necessary in quality foil-stamping and embossing work. A combination of heat, impressional strength, and dwell-on impression is required. The heat is necessary to soften the binders and coatings in paper, board, and other materials. Once softened, the fibers in the stock can be realigned and reshaped to permit a sharp embossment. Heat is also required for foil stamping, and the increased dwell allows time for the heat to penetrate from the embossing or stamping die to the foil and then to the stock. Otherwise the foil would not adhere properly to the stock.

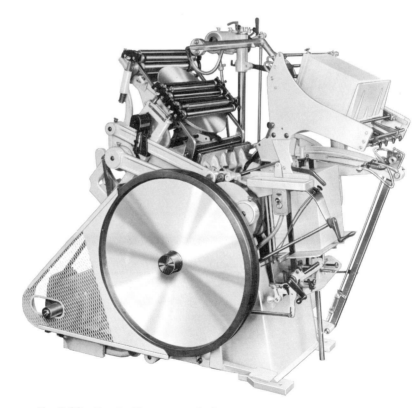

Fig. P-22   D series Kluge automatic platen press.

plater finish (plate finish) Glazed paper finish achieved by introducing sheets of paper between platers, or plate calenders.

plot To establish reference points on a grid. The points so plotted are connected by lines.

plugging In photomechanical plate making, an unfavorable condition of printed copy in which the copy looks dirty, dot areas have been filled in, or "plugged," and the image is spotty. Deposits of dried developer on the sponge or pad may have dissolved in the fresh developer, causing plugging. A clean sponge and pad should always be used. In addition, dried gum and developer on the plate working surface or table may penetrate the plate when it is wet with new solution. A flat surface should always be used and the table kept clean. The condition is corrected by applying additional developer on a clean surface and redeveloping according to the manufacturer's directions.

ply Thickness of blanks and heavy paper stock expressed in the number of layers of which they are composed. The following table gives the equivalent of ply ratings in fractions of an inch.

ply	in.
2	0.012
3	0.015
4	0.018
5	0.021
6	0.024
8	0.030
10	0.036
12	0.042*
14	0.048*
16	0.056*

*Double-pasted sheets.

point-of-sale (point-of-purchase) In advertising, designating a device or display of any kind installed near merchandise to aid sales. Display racks, animated and action pieces, and banners are point-of-sale devices.

point: paper Thickness equivalent to 0.001 inch.

point system Method of measuring type sizes. The point system is based on the pica, which is equivalent to 12 points. Each point measures 0.013837 inch, or almost $1/72$ inch. When 12-point type is set solid, without leading, 6 vertical lines of type measure 72 points, or almost 1 inch. The point size of type is determined by dividing 72 by the number of lines per column-inch when the type is set solid. Thus, 12 lines of type to the column-inch divided into 72 is 6 point, 8 lines is 9 point, and 6 lines is 12 point.

Polaroid MP-3 industrial-view Land camera Stand-mounted camera designed primarily for use in science and industry. It delivers photographs on the site in the same manner as the regular Polaroid camera popular in family picture taking but has greater capabilities. The MP-3 has an adjustable hooded reflex viewer. The hood keeps out stray light and tilts to permit eye-level viewing regardless of the height of the camera head. The base supports four incandescent floodlights.

The camera head, which is spring-loaded on an aluminum support column, may be moved up and down. It may be converted from making on-the-spot Polaroid Land prints and transparencies to shooting with either conventional 4- by 5-inch color or black-and-white films. Five types of photographic films may be used: (1) Polaroid Land transparency film rolls for either line copy or continuous-tone slides, (2) Polaroid Land picture rolls that produce positive prints, (3) Polaroid Land 4- by 5-inch film packets, (4) conventional 4- by 5-inch color film, and (5) conventional black-and-white film.

Five interchangeable lens and shutter combinations are available. A 65-line glass optical screen fits into the focal plate of the camera; it is easily removed for line copy. The scribed ground glass of the screen permits exact sizing. The image may be enlarged to a maximum size of $3\frac{1}{2}$ by $4\frac{1}{2}$ inches, as well as reduced. The print is developed within ten seconds in its own packet. When it is peeled apart and coated, it is cut out, silhouetted in black or white, retouched if desired, and pasted into an assembly with type ready for a page negative. As the photograph has already been screened, only a line negative is required of the page negative.

Figure P-23*A* illustrates the method of copying photographs of any size or format or as $3\frac{1}{4}$- by $4\frac{1}{4}$- or 4- by 5-inch prints. Photographs may also be copied on Type 55 P/N 4- by 5-inch film, which develops a positive and a finished negative in twenty seconds. The negative can be enlarged to 25 times its original size with almost no evidence of grain. Color copy can be photographed with sixty-second Polacolor film or conventional color film.

Figure P-23*B* illustrates photographing small objects. The MP-3 camera is useful when a large number of pictures or slides of objects are required, as in the preparation of catalogs or in gross-specimen photography in hospitals. Each object is precisely focused by employ-

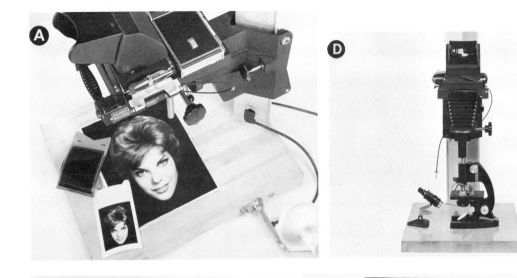

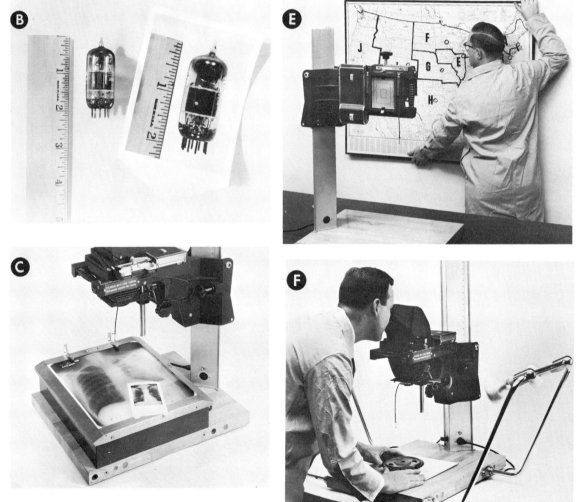

Fig. P-23 Photographing with Polaroid industrial-view Land camera: (A) copying photographs; (B) small-object photography; (C) X-ray copying; (D) photomicrography; (E) copying large material; (F) photographing actual objects.

ing the reflex ground-glass viewer and framing the object for the particular film being used.

Figure P-23*C* shows X-ray copying for slides. A 14- by 17-inch light table is placed on the base with the X-ray on top of it. Opaque copies or transparencies (3¼ by 4¼ or 2½ by 2¼ inches or 35-millimeter film) are made for showing in a standard projector.

Figure P-23*D* illustrates the use of the MP-3 camera in photomicrography. A lensless shutter with a light-baffle tube is available for use with microscopes. The microscope and illuminator are placed on the camera base, and the lensless shutter is attached to the camera and lowered over the eyepiece of the microscope. The microscope is focused to produce a sharp image on the ground glass. A wide variety of films may be used.

Figure P-23*E* shows the method of photographing large objects. The camera head is pivoted, and the floodlight arms are removed. Charts, maps, blackboard instructions, and blueprints may be photographed. Large objects may be reduced to the size of a lantern slide and the photographs later enlarged for projection.

Any object that can be placed on the 24- by 27-inch base of the MP-3 camera can be copied and reproduced for catalogs, as shown in Figure P-23*F*. A white material is placed beneath the object for background consistency.

polyester film base   *See* CRONAR.

portraiture   Process or art of depicting an individual by drawing, painting, or photographing from life, particularly an individual's face; also, the depiction so produced. (*See also* LINE CONVERSION.)

positive   Photographic image usually made from a negative, in which tones are not reversed as in a negative. A positive on paper is called a "print"; one on a transparent base such as film, a "positive transparency." (*See also* FILM POSITIVE.)

positive-reading   *See* RIGHT-READING.

poster   Large cardboard or thick-paper display sign. It is known as a poster chart when it is used as a visual aid in a presentation.

Posteriter   Trade name of a photographic typesetter. (*See* TYPESETTERS, PHOTOGRAPHIC.)

pounce   Powderlike material distributed by the Keuffel and Esser Company for improving the ink-absorbing qualities of reproduction tracing cloths and papers. The powder is sprinkled on the surface, and the excess is removed by brushing with a felt pad or brush.

powder ink *See* DRY INK.

PP Abbreviation for pages.

preface Statement forming part of the front matter of a book in which the author or editor states the purpose of the work and his expectations for it and sometimes expresses appreciation for assistance.

prejustification *See* JUSTIFICATION; *see also* COLD COMPOSITION; TYPEWRITER.

preprint Any letter, number, symbol, design, logotype, shading, or line that is printed beforehand and subsequently pasted or mortised in place on a material or a mechanical for reproduction. Preprints are used in visual aids, television and screen titles, display advertising, commercial art, technical illustrations, and other applications. Almost any design, letterhead, trademark, or logotype may be had on order. Preprints may be typed or drawn on adhesive-backed transparent sheets, or the sheets or images may be opaque. Special preprints may be ordered from the typesetter for paste-up or mortising. In addition, preprints may be typed on coated stock and pasted as desired. The underside of the image should be covered with rubber cement and, when dry, placed lightly on a piece of waxed paper with the adhesive side down. Only sufficient pressure should be applied to make the preprint adhere to the paper. Burnishing is not necessary. The surface of the drawing or other material is then painted with a light coat of rubber cement, and the preprint is ready to be pasted in place by pressing it lightly. Excess rubber cement is removed with a pickup. The tissue overlay should be burnished lightly and care used in handling so that the work is not smeared.

presensitized plate Aluminum printing plate or a paper plate used in offset printing that has been coated with a sensitive emulsion for image reception.

press proof Proof removed from the press to inspect line and color values, registration, quality, and so forth. It is the last proof taken before the complete run.

press-wire tape converter *See* TAPE CONVERTER.

pressrun (run) Total number of copies of a publication printed during one printing.

pressure frame Frame for holding copy while the copy is being photographed; also, a frame for holding plate and negative during exposure. Such a frame holds the elements by pressure alone, without the use of a vacuum. (*See also* COPYBOARD.)

pressure-sensitive material Any material, such as adhesive- and wax-backed tapes, that will stick to another material when lightly pressed on that material. (For pressure-sensitive tapes and sheets, *see* CHART-PAK; *see also* ARTIST AID; AVERY; CRAFTINT.)

pressureless printing *See* ELECTROSTATIC SCREEN PRINTING PROCESS; *see also* PRINTING METHODS.

primary colors In printing inks, yellow, red, and blue. Orange, green, and magenta are secondary, or derivative, colors. The primary colors are used with black. Tints and patterns in color may be overprinted with a combination of primary and secondary colors.

print and tumble *See* WORK AND TUMBLE.

print and turn *See* WORK AND TURN.

Printasign Trademark for a display typesetter manufactured by the Reynolds Printasign Company. (*See* TYPE WRITER, DISPLAY.)

printed circuit Electrical or electronic circuit reproduced by a printing process.

printer Machine other than a printing press that prints out a previously made original, operating either from opaque, translucent, or transparent copy or from a microfilm image. It has a lens for reduction or enlargement of the original. Printers thus differ from copying machines, which produce an exact facsimile of the original (the Xerox 813 copier, however, has a built-in 6 percent reduction factor). Photocomposing machines, too, are in a class of their own. They are neither printers nor copying machines because their primary purpose is to compose cold-composition copy. With the advent of xerography, electrostatic screen printing, stabilization and electrolytic reproduction, and other processes, the classification of equipment has become complex. A printing press imposes an image by depositing ink on a surface, whereas electrostatic copying and printing utilize a very fine powder called "toner" that ultimately forms the image. Not only are the steps required to place an image on a surface entirely different, but magnification, mirror projection, and image sources vary.

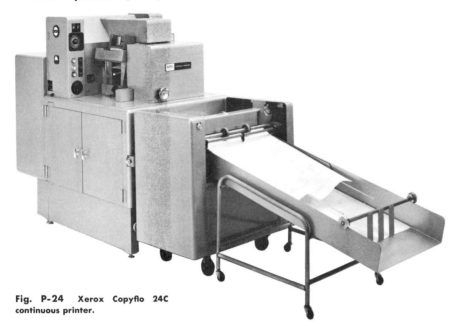

Fig. P-24   Xerox Copyflo 24C continuous printer.

Fig. P-25   Xerox Copyflo 11 continuous printer, Model 2.

The Xerox Copyflo 24C continuous printer (Figure P-24) is designed primarily for large users of engineering drawings. Dry positive-reading prints are made on ordinary paper, vellum, or offset paper masters from 35-millimeter film mounted in aperture cards or from 35-millimeter roll microfilm. Prints are made from a web (rolled stock) up to 24 inches wide at a rate of 20 linear feet per minute. This rate is the equivalent of a 24- by 36-inch print every ten seconds. Prints are cut automatically as they emerge. The printer accepts webs in 2,000-foot lengths. Standard widths are 11, 17, 22, and 24 inches, but other sizes may be accommodated by adjusting a paper spindle.

The Xerox Copyflo 11 continuous printer is manufactured in several models. Model 1 reproduces from 16- or 35-millimeter roll microfilm. Model 2 (Figure P-25) reproduces from opaque originals; Model 3, from either roll microfilm or opaque originals. Copies are produced automatically on a continuous roll of ordinary paper, vellum, or offset masters up to 12 inches wide. The enlargement range of the microfilm-input printer is 7 to 24 diameters in 15 magnification steps within a finished-copy width limit of 11 inches. Opaque-input printers make copies ranging from 45 to 200 percent of the original size within the 11-inch width limit. Prints emerge dry at a rate of 20 feet per minute.

These printers operate in five steps: (1) the image from the microfilm or original copy is projected on a charged selenium-coated drum, where it forms a pattern of electrically charged and discharged areas corresponding to the image and nonimage areas of the original; (2) the surface of the drum is positively charged as the drum rotates; (3) the latent electrostatic image is developed by a cascade of toner over the drum; (4) the powder image is transferred electrostatically from drum to stock; and (5) the image is fused by heat for permanence.

The Xerox 1824 printer is 65 inches high, 32 inches wide, and 32 inches deep and weighs approximately 600 pounds. It delivers prints from 35-millimeter microfilm mounted in military D aperture cards, in which the aperture is set in $1\frac{5}{8}$ inches from the right edge of the card. Exposure, development, and front-end delivery are automatic. Printouts from $8\frac{1}{2}$ by 11 to 18 by 24 inches are provided on ordinary paper, vellum, or offset masters. Enlargements are made in a ratio of 14.5:1.

printing density   Measure of the opacity of an image to the exposing radiation. In the whiteprint process, a mercury arc is the usual light source, and the 3660, 4046, and 4358 A lines of mercury are the exposing radiation.

printing down   Making a photographic print by placing the original film image between a light-sensitive coated material and a source of light. The material may be intended for letterpress, gravure, or photo-offset. The film image and the sensitive material should be kept in close contact by using a vacuum frame during exposure. The term "printing down" is also used in making a printing plate from a photolithographic negative.

printing methods   Printing is the art of causing a plate image to be transferred to a surface regardless of the method used. Conceptions of the major divisions and the various subdivisions of printing differ. With the many advances and the introduction of new technology in printing methods, the identity of the major divisions and subdivisions is open to discussion. Probably no industry has been hindered so much by differences in terminology as the graphic arts. The graphic arts industry has elected to call the function of printing on small offset presses "duplicating," whereas in fact it is printing. The size of the press has nothing to do with the method. The industry has also elected to call certain machines "printers." These machines are copiers because they do not themselves make originals; they merely copy from originals made by another method.

It is important to understand the various methods of printing and the selection of the best one for the particular application. These methods may be classified into major divisions by several criteria: the type of printing plate or material containing the image to be

RELIEF
(LETTERPRESS, MULTIGRAPHING, FLEXOGRAPHY, RUBBER STAMPS)

INTAGLIO (GRAVURE)

PLANOGRAPHIC
(LITHOGRAPHY, SPIRIT DUPLICATING, PHOTOGELATIN, HECTOGRAPHIC)

LETTERSET

STENCIL
(PAPER STENCIL, SCREEN PROCESS, ELECTROSTATIC SCREEN)

Fig. P-26   Methods of printing.

printed, the method of forming the image on the plate or material, and the way in which the image is transferred to a surface. These divisions are relief, planographic, intaglio, letterset, and stencil printing (*see* Figure P-26).

Relief Printing

Letterpress. The printing plate is in relief, and the image is transferred directly from plate to stock. The image on the plate always reads wrong because the printed image must read right. Most letterpress printing is set with hot-metal linecasting or Monotype machines, although type is also set by hand. Whether set by machine or by hand, the copy is said to be "typeset."

Multigraphing. Type is set on a composing stick and transferred to a drum incised with slots for receiving lines of type. A large inked fabric ribbon covers the type mass on the drum, which is rotated to impress the image on paper. Paste ink may also be used in Multigraph work.

Flexography. Rubber plates having a relief image are used in flexographic printing. The flexographic press prints from rolled stock such as foil, enameled or coated paper, and cellophane. Food cartons, candy and gum wrappers, waxed bags, and similar items are ideally suited for this type of printing. The flexographic method is excellent for printing solid opaque colors such as are found in Christmas wrappings. A fluid ink is used.

Planographic Printing

There are more variations of planographic printing, or printing from a flat surface, than there are of any other major division.

Lithography. The most popular method of planographic printing, lithography is based on the fact that grease (ink) and water (aqueous solution) do not mix. It begins with a process camera that photographs original copy to produce a photolithographic negative. The translucent image on the negative is transferred to a sensitized flexible metal printing plate by light exposure. The exposed and unexposed image areas on the plate vary in molecular structure because of the breakdown of image-area emulsions during exposure, and a latent image is formed on the plate in the areas that have been penetrated by light.

In contrast to letterpress printing, in which the image is transferred directly from plate to stock, an additional cylinder containing a rubber blanket is used in lithography. When the plate cylinder is rotated, the aqueous solution and ink are transferred to the flat image. The inked image repels the solution and therefore accepts ink, whereas the nonimage area accepts water, which repels the ink. The operating sequence is plate to blanket to stock.

The lithographic method is also called "photo-offset" because photography is used and the image is offset from the rubber blanket cylinder to stock. In addition, it is known as "offset lithography."

Spirit duplicating. The image is typed, drawn, or written on a paper master that is backed with a separate sheet coated with aniline dye. The dye is transferred to the back of the master and reflects a wrong-reading image. The master is then attached to the cylinder of the spirit duplicator with the dye side up. With the rotation of the cylinder, spirit vapors activate the dye image, transferring the image to stock.

Photogelatin process. This process, which is similar to lithography, is also based on the fact that grease and water do not mix. The image area on a gelatin plate accepts ink but repels water, and the nonimage area accepts water, which repels ink. A bichromated gelatin solution is floated onto a sheet of glass, which becomes the plate. When dry, the coating is exposed through a continuous-tone negative. The amount of light passing through the negative hardens the gelatin in proportion to the light and dark areas. Thus the tones reject water and accept ink through the range of tonal values. The photogelatin process is effective for short runs of fine color work.

High-fidelity reproductions of posters, murals, calendars, and oil and water paintings may be made by this process.

Hectographic printing. An aniline dye is deposited on a master by typing, drawing, or writing with a special hectograph ribbon, ink, or pencil. The master is then placed facedown on a moistened gelatin plate, to which the image is transferred. Copies are made by pressing paper lightly against the plate.

Intaglio Printing

This method of printing is used in steel and copperplate engraving. The intaglio plate is the exact opposite of a relief plate, the image being formed by incised cuts. As the plate cylinder rotates, fluid ink floods over the plate and into the recesses of the image. The top of the plate is then wiped clean with a doctor blade, and the ink that remains in the recesses is transferred to stock to form the image. Intaglio printing is also known as "gravure printing," as "photogravure" when photography is used, and as "rotogravure" when rotary cylinders are employed.

Letterset Printing

In this method of printing, a relief image is produced and is then transferred to a rubber blanket, from which it is offset to stock. The process is also referred to as "offset letterpress," as "offset relief," and as "dry offset" because an aqueous solution is not required. Letterset forms a division of its own because it is neither letterpress (the relief image is not transferred directly to stock) nor lithography (a damping solution is not required). A thin, flexible, compact relief plate taken from the relief image is substituted for the conventional lithographic plate. The image is transferred from the relief plate to the rubber blanket and then to stock.

Stencil Printing

A printing stencil is a paper or metal sheet in which an image is perforated. The perforated image permits ink or other substances to pass through the openings onto stock or other material. A paper stencil is typed, written, or drawn and is then placed on the cylinder of a mimeograph, or duplicator. As the paper passes through the duplicator, the impression roller rises automatically and presses it against the stencil. Ink flows from inside the stencil cylinder through the ink pad on the cylinder and the stencil openings and prints the image on paper.

Screen-process printing. This method of printing utilizes a silk, nylon, or metal screen containing the image. A squeegee forces the ink through the screen to form an image on paper or other material. Early screens were made by painting the image on silk with a fluid, resistant to ink. Masking materials blocked out unwanted printing areas. Now hand-cut stencils or photomechanical means are used in screen-process work. One technique involves coating the material with a light-sensitive emulsion and placing a photographic film positive in contact with it. Exposure hardens the surface of the screen in proportion to the penetration of light; hardened areas are then made insoluble to water while the image area is made soluble.

Thick deposits of ink compounds and paint make a wide variety of printing possible. Fabrics, plastics, metal, heavy card stock, and paper are a few of the materials that are receptive to screen-process printing.

Electrostatic screen printing. In this process, electrostatic forces cause the image to be formed on the receiving surface. Electrostatic screen printing is known also as "electronography" and as "pressureless printing" because the plate containing the image does not come in contact with the material to be printed. A thin, flexible printing element (stencil), with finely screened openings defining the image to be printed, is used. Electroscopic dry-ink particles, known originally as toner, are metered through the stencil and attracted to the printing surface, where they are held by electrostatic attraction until they have been fixed by heat or chemical means to make the image permanent.

printout Enlarged copy made from an original microform, particularly by a microform reader-printer or printer. Printouts are used for reference or for correction and revision of engineering drawings or other images. They are sometimes called "blowbacks."

process camera *See* CAMERA, PROCESS.

process lens Lens for use with a process camera. It is designed to give best results with flat copy of about the same size as the original rather than with subjects of varying depth, such as are photographed with a snapshot camera. (*See also* CAMERA, PROCESS.)

process plates Two or more color plates used together to reproduce artwork or other copy. The primary colors for printing inks, yellow, red, and blue, are used with black; tints and patterns may be produced by overprinting with a combination of primary and secondary colors.

processing, film Development and treatment of film by chemical means or washing after exposure. LogEtronics' Model LD-24 automatic film processor (Figures P-27 and P-28) handles film-base thicknesses of 0.002 to 0.0075 inch and accepts film up to 24 inches wide. Halftones, line negatives, and positives are processed interchangeably.

Fig. P-27 LogEtronics' LD-24 automatic film processor.

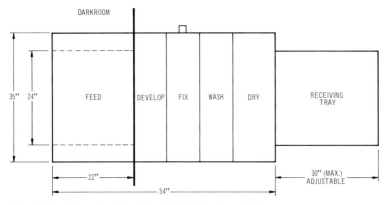

Fig. P-28 Schematic of LogEtronics' LD-24 automatic film processor.

The processor, dryer, and temperature-control unit are incorporated in the machine. The developer is replenished automatically on the basis of film length and width and the percentage of exposed silver. A recirculation unit maintains a given temperature with a variation of plus or minus 0.2°F in the tank. Speed varies from 4.8 to 8 feet per minute; developing time, from one to six minutes. The machine will process 90 sheets of 20- by 24-inch film per hour in 1.5 minutes developing time, 78 sheets in 2 minutes developing time, and 63 sheets in 2.5 minutes developing time.

processing, nitrogen-burst System of using inert nitrogen gas to agitate sensitized materials during the film-developing process. The advantage of the nitrogen-burst process is that each set of developed films exhibits the same density, contrast, and evenness regardless of the operator or the time of day.

Figure P-29 shows a nitrogen-burst processing unit. A basic processing machine contains four lighttight nitrogen-burst tanks and one quick-dump washing tank. Separation negatives usually require a developer tank, a second tank for diluted masking developer, a short-stop (stop bath), and a fixer. For screened material, the masking tank developer is replaced by a high-contrast replenishing developer. The setup also requires the connection of a $\frac{1}{2}$-inch hot- and cold-water line, a $1\frac{1}{2}$-inch drain manifold in the bottom of the unit, and a flexible nitrogen pressure hose from a nitrogen bottle.

The film is loaded in a film sheath similar to that of the conventional film hanger, which supports it on all four sides. The sheath is dimpled and allows the solution to flow freely on both front and back of the film. After loading, the sheath is placed in a channel hanger rack. Film guides facilitate darkroom loading. The nitrogen burst is timed automatically. The operator first turns on the nitrogen-burst system and inserts the rack in the lighttight developing

Fig. P-29 Calumet's nitrogen-burst processing unit.

tank. (White light may therefore be turned on during the developing cycle.) An even layer of gas is injected through a distributor into the tank, where it immediately displaces the entire solution, moving it upward and thus agitating the material. The vigorous boil produced as the gas moves upward mixes the development byproducts and moves fresh chemical to all parts of the sensitized material. The washing tanks also receive a nitrogen burst. When the process has been completed, the film is "squeegeed" and dried in the conventional manner.

processing, stabilization Developing process that makes use of light-sensitive material incorporated in the emulsion of photostabilization papers. Unlike the conventional method of dissolving the silver halides in the nonimage area and retaining those that compose the image, the stabilization process, by chemical treatment of the exposed and developed image, retains the silver halides in the nonimage area but renders them inert. This treatment eliminates the step of washing out the silver halides. The developing agent is in the copy paper itself instead of in a separate developing solution.

Stabilization processors are reproduction machines that utilize this method. They are not necessarily document-copying machines but serve primarily to reproduce high-quality line and continuous-tone images. Figure P-30 shows an Ilfoprint processor. The Ilfoprint system consists of stabilization papers, the processor itself, and chemicals. The papers, which are available in a number of common sizes, are classified by their suitability for continuous-tone work, document copying, phototypesetting, and contact and projection printing.

Figure P-31 shows a Fotorite rapid-print processor. Various models accommodate paper in maximum widths ranging from 14 to 24 inches. Paper sizes range from 4 by 5 inches to 24 inches by 100 feet. In addition, a selection of materials for use in cold-composition phototypesetting machines can be employed. Continuous-tone papers in a variety of finishes, weights, and contrasts and in sheet

Fig. P-30 **Ilfoprint stabilization processor.**

Fig. P-31 **Fotorite rapid-print processor.**

and roll sizes for darkroom and room-light printing are available for contact and projection work. There are also papers suitable for line production, translucent papers for whiteprint reproduction, and paper negatives for offset plate making. Screened Veloxes may be produced by placing the negative to be printed in a standard enlarger and then inserting a sheet of Fotorite enlarging paper in the vacuum frame. The process is as follows: The continuous-tone art is cropped to the desired size for reproduction, and a gray or magenta contact screen is placed on the frame, emulsion to emulsion. When the paper is exposed, light passes through the screen and records the halftone dots on the print. The result is a screened Velox print. A 100-line screen can be held without difficulty.

profile grid *See* RECTANGULAR GRID.

progressive proofs *See* PROOFS, PROGRESSIVE.

projection Act or art of projecting lines and planes in isometric, dimetric, trimetric, perspective, and orthographic drawings. In map making, projection is the representation of a plane on the earth's surface; in visual communications, it is the causing of an image to fall on a surface.

projection, overhead *See* OVERHEAD PROJECTION.

projection machine Any mechanical device that throws an image on a surface from transparent or opaque material by utilizing light and lenses.

projection print Print made from a photolithographic negative by projecting the image. An enlarged or reduced matte or glossy print is obtained. The desired size is indicated by (1) placing a strip of masking tape along the controlling dimension of the copy, (2) drawing a line on the tape with arrowheads to show the image width, and (3) noting the size in inches of the reduction or enlargement. A matte or glossy print having the same dimensions as the negative is called a "contact print."

projectural (also called **visual; vu-graph**) Transparent or opaque material from which an image is projected on a screen; also, the image so projected. (*See also* OVERHEAD PROJECTION.)

proof: photography Sample test print made from a negative.

proof press Hand-operated press for running off proofs; also, any press used to produce reproduction proofs.

proof: printing Impression of the type image taken for examination.

proofreader's marks Standard marks that indicate corrections to be made in typeset copy (*see* Figure P-32). They are placed in the margin that is nearer to the word being corrected.

proofreading Reading copy to detect typographical or other errors. Proofreading should be performed by two persons and from the original copy rather than from an intermediate draft copy, such as that used in prejustifying cold-composition copy. If the material to be proofread is manuscript or other typed copy, a typist should not hold and read her own typing while proofreading. When two persons proofread copy, one is called the "copyholder" and the other the "proofreader," who uses proofreader's marks to correct any errors. Exceptional alertness is required for good proofreading. The copyholder should speak distinctly and fairly quickly. Slow reading places a burden on the proofreader, whose eyes can follow copy much more quickly than the copy can be read. Reading speed is increased when such abbreviated forms as "semi" for "semicolon" and "super" for "superscript" are used. Words difficult to spell or pronounce should be spelled out.

proofs, progressive Set of proofs of all color plates used separately for one operation and of the plates in combination. Progressive proofs give an indication of color quality and serve as a check against requirements. Registration, tonal values, impression characteristics, and the like are determined before the pressrun.

proportional grid drawing *See* GRID DRAWING, PROPORTIONAL.

proportional spacing (differential letterspacing) Spacing of characters in proportion to size by means of the typewriters and office composing machines used in the preparation of cold-composition copy. The keyboard characters have different values that are measured in units. The letter M, for example, has a unit count of 5 and the letter i a count of 2. Thus, characters are well balanced and spaced in proportion to their respective sizes.

With the attachment of a mechanical device, typewriters equipped with proportional spacing may be used to justify copy. Justifying may also be accomplished manually by subtracting units between words on lines that exceed the line measure and adding units between words on lines that are shorter than the line measure. The Vari-Typer is a proportional-spacing machine that justifies copy automatically after the first typing to establish the line count. The IBM Executive series of typewriters are also proportional-spacing machines. (*See also* TYPEWRITER.)

	Marginal Marks		Example
Delete; take out	*d*		Draw a diagonal line thus; show the symbol in margin.
Left out; insert	*ar*		Use a caret and write in mgin.
Insert a question mark	?		Use a caret. What
Insert a colon	⊙		Use a caret and circle. As follows
Insert an exclamation mark	!		Use a caret in text. Write in margin. No
Insert an apostrophe	⌄'		Proofreaders marks. Insert it in margin.
Insert a semicolon	;/		Use a caret in text write in margin.
Insert a hyphen	⹀		Checkout. Show two parallel lines in margin.
Delete and close up			Counter clockwise.
Insert en dash	1/n		Counterclockwise
Insert em dash	1/m		Counterclockwise
Insert a comma	⌃		Use a caret in text write in margin.
Insert a period	⊙		Use a caret in text Draw circle around it in margin.
Insert quotation marks	⌄'' ⌄''		He said, I will not.
Insert brackets	[/]		The result: H_2O
Insert parentheses	(/)		The result: H_2O
Stet; let it stand	*stet*		Do not make correction. Place dots under crossed-out word.
Insert space	#		For better reading.
Equalize spacing between words	eg #		Too many spaces are not good.
Spell out	*sp*		The U.S. government.
Transpose			Written for a purpose. Or, in order reverse.
Align text or columnar matter	‖		43879 76120 34827 63001

Fig. P-32 Proofreader's marks.

	Marginal Marks		Example
Change capital letters to lowercase	*lc*		Do not use ~~CAPS~~.
Change lowercase to capitals	*caps*		Williston, North Dakota
Change to small capital letters	*sc*		Small capital letters.
Use boldface	*bf*		Draw a wavy line under the word. Write in margin.
Use roman letters	*rom*		Use (roman) letters.
Use italic	*ital*		Use italic.
Raise copy; move up	⌐⌐		Use ⌐caution⌐ in drawing angles.
Lower copy; move down	⌐⌐		Use ⌐caution⌐ in drawing angles.
Move copy to left	⌐		The word "the" will be moved left to the vertical line.
Move copy to right	⌐		The word "the" will be moved right to the vertical line.
Make a new paragraph	¶		Use the symbol with a caret.∧This sentence will then begin a new paragraph.
No paragraph	*run in*		Use a line. Connect the sentences.
Insert a superscript	ˇ°ˇ		$32^\circ F$.
Insert a subscript	∧2∧		H_2O
Bad letter; change	X		Circle letter.
Letter is inverted	ↄ		Underline and use symbol in margin.
Straighten jumbled type	=		The letters are uneven.
Push space down	⊥		Draw a diagonal/through it; mark in margin.
Indentions	▭▭▭		▭ ▭ ▭ This indicates an indention of three ems.
Wrong font; change	*wf*		The letter is not of the same face or size.

proportional wheel Circular scale used to determine proportional reductions and enlargements of copy. It may be made of card stock, plastic, or metal. Linear scales may be used for the same purpose.

Prostar Trade name of the Recordak microfilm processor. (*See* MICROFILM PROCESSING.)

protective margin *See* APRON.

protractor, orthographic Instrument used to determine the degrees of an isometric ellipse, angle, or plane. The protractor transposes the angle of an orthographic drawing to a like angle on an isometric projection.

pseudoperspective Any deviation from drawing a true isometric image in order to portray the image in perspective to avoid distortion. For example, lines of an assembled view of an engineering item may be foreshortened to produce a lifelike appearance rather than a distorted one as in an isometric projection.

PSM Abbreviation for proportional spacing machine.

public domain Property rights belonging to the public at large because of the loss or lack of patent or copyright protection. (*See also* COMMON-LAW COPYRIGHT; COPYRIGHT.)

publisher Individual or firm that reproduces for sale to the public books, periodicals, pamphlets, sheet music, maps, and the like. The publisher prints or, more generally, causes to be printed the copies of the work to be sold.

pyroxylin-coated paper Paper treated with pyroxylin lacquer to make it water-repellent.

Q

QA Abbreviation for "query author," used as a marginal notation to question an author regarding the meaning or accuracy of copy. It is the author's responsibility to check and revise the copy accordingly.

quadrat (usually abbreviated **quad**) Piece of type metal of less than the height of the typeface, used to insert spacing in lines of printed matter. It is measured in ems and ens of the point size of type used. As illustrated in Figure Q-1, an en quad (nut quad) is one-half of the em-quad width, a 3-em space one-third of the width, a 4-em space one-fourth of the width, and so forth.

quarto Book size in which sheets of paper are folded twice to form eight pages.

quire Twenty-four or twenty-five sheets of paper (one-twentieth of a ream) of the same size and quality.

quoin Expandable device used to secure forms in a chase.

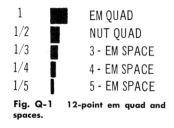

1	EM QUAD
1/2	NUT QUAD
1/3	3 - EM SPACE
1/4	4 - EM SPACE
1/5	5 - EM SPACE

Fig. Q-1 **12-point em quad and spaces.**

315

R

raised printing Printing in which a raised design is produced. (*See* EMBOSSING; THERMOGRAPHY.)

rapidograph pen *See* PENS, TECHNICAL.

ratchet Toothed wheel installed on the end of a typewriter platen to control vertical spacing. As the carriage return key is operated, a prong engages a tooth on the ratchet, thus moving the platen and paper to the next line of typing. Ratchets may be changed to produce desired spacing between lines. While this is a simple procedure, a serviceman must make the final adjustment because a change of parts is necessary.

rate card Card issued by a publisher showing the insertion rates of display and classified advertising and other pertinent information. It is usually assigned a number, such as Rate Card No. 5, which indicates that four previous rate cards have been superseded. Rate cards may include information on mechanical requirements, contract and copy regulations, finished artwork, bleed pages, inserts, mailing instructions, closing dates, special position of advertisements and cover rates, commissions and discounts, production charges, additional charges, subscription rates, and circulation.

reader   (also called **tape interpreter**)   Device that operates a line-casting machine such as the Linotype or the Intertype. As the tape runs through the reader, the device senses the code (punched holes in the tape) and automatically translates, or reads, it into mechanical movements. Thus the reader performs the same function as a manually operated keyboard on a linecasting machine.

reader screen   Viewing screen for reading enlarged microimages from microforms and microfiches. (*See also* MICROFILM READER; READER-PRINTER.)

reader-printer   Machine that magnifies a microform for reading on a viewing screen and, if necessary, produces an enlarged printout of the image. Light must fall on the microimage or pass through it and be reflected by magnification for the image to become large enough to be read on a viewing screen with the naked eye. A second requirement is that the enlarged image be exposed to a light-sensitive material. The latent image must then be developed by some means, usually a chemical process.

A reader-printer is a form of information storage and retrieval. Using microforms to replace bulky material reduces storage and filing space and facilitates the acquisition and distribution of material needed in research. A reader-printer must (1) produce a readable printout under ordinary room lighting conditions without the necessity for a darkroom, (2) produce a dry or almost dry print instantaneously without recourse to conventional film processing, (3) reflect a readable image on the viewing screen, and (4) be so simple that the operator need have only minimal skill and knowledge. Electrolytic processing, stabilization processing, diffusion transfer, and xerography are several methods used to reproduce the enlarged printout.

The Itek 18.24 Standard reader-printer (Figure R-l) accommodates aperture cards, acetate jacketed film, and microfiches. The Itek RF model accommodates, in addition, 16- and 35-millimeter roll film. The inclined viewing screen is of the rear-projection type. The size of the viewed image and printout varies from 8 by 11 to 18 by 24 inches, with a maximum image area of $17\frac{5}{8}$ by 24 inches. With the aid of a control dial a printout length from 8 to 24 inches may be selected. The printout is then automatically cut from the roll in the selected length. Masking a portion of the screen to delete unwanted portions of the image allows drafting and designing revisions to be made on the printout. Similar configurations can thus be produced without tracing. Prints with a 14.7-times magnification are produced in approximately thirty seconds. (Slight variations in magnification may be had on special order.) Special paper for both positive and negative reading and translucent stock for making additional copies on a whiteprint machine are available. Drawings measuring 34 by 44 inches may be reduced to 17 by 22 inches on the translucent stock for smaller whiteprint copies. The processing unit is fed from disposable solution containers. When the hinged reservoir is raised, the unit is filled automatically. Lowering the reservoir returns the developer to containers for evaporation-proof storage when the reader-printer is not in use.

The Filmac 100 reader-printer (Figure R-2) is 16 inches wide, 16 inches deep, and $24\frac{1}{2}$ inches high and weighs 80 pounds. It has a 7- by $8\frac{1}{2}$-inch viewing screen. Printouts from 16- and 35-millimeter film and from microfiches measure $8\frac{1}{2}$ by 11 inches, with a print image size of 7 by $8\frac{1}{4}$ inches. The machine contains optical and illumination systems, a transport for film and copy paper, and a tray and sponge for an activator. A lens projects the image upward to a mirror, and the mirror reflects the image onto the viewing screen. When a printout is to be made, the mirror is moved from the path of the image, which is projected by the lens onto the sensitized copy paper. For viewing, a microform is placed under the lens and the control switch turned to *ON*. The intensity of the image is governed by a control knob. A printout emerges from a 298-foot roll of copy paper at a dispensing slot at the top of the machine, where it may

Fig. R-1   Itek's 18.24 Standard reader-printer.

Fig. R-2   Minnesota Mining and Manufacturing Company's Filmac 100 microfilm reader-printer.

be torn off. While the copy paper is being dispensed, it passes over the sponge moistened with the activator, which develops the exposed image. The unit employs the electrolytic process of reproduction. Magnification lenses having powers of 7, 9, 13, 19, and 26 times are available.

reading type *See* BODY TYPE.

ream Unit of quantity consisting of 500 sheets of fine writing or printing paper or 480 sheets of wrapping or tissue paper.

reciprocity-law failure Apparent mathematical exception in photography. Whereas 6 times 4 is the same as 12 times 2, photographic materials do not attain the same density from an exposure by a high-intensity light source acting for a short time as from an exposure by a low-intensity light source acting for a longer time even though the product of time and intensity is the same in both cases. For example, when the intensity of the light is doubled, halving the exposure times does not rcsult in exactly the same density. Reciprocity-law failure occurs to some degree in all photographic materials.

record paper *See* LEDGER PAPER.

recorder One of two units composing the Justowriter. (*See* COLD COMPOSITION.)

rectangular grid (profile grid) Grid of lines that are closer together in one direction than in the other. Rectangular grids are used in sketching vertical sections (profiles) for railroads, roads, embankments, subsurface formations, reservoirs, and so forth. Contractors use profile grids to determine grades for sewers, inlets, flumes, aqueducts and the like.

recto Odd-numbered, right-hand page. The even-numbered, left-hand page is the "verso."

red streak Streak of red ink appearing along the right margin of the front page of some newspapers to indicate a specific edition, such as the final edition, when more than one daily edition is published. Ink is applied with a cylinder wheel mounted on the press. The device has its own ink supply.

reducer Chemical that decreases the density of a photographic image by removing silver halides.

reference marks Symbols used to key text or tabular matter to footnotes. They are *, †, ‡, §, ¶, used in that order.

references Books, articles, or papers cited by the author of a published work. The name of the author of the cited work, the title of the work, the publisher, the place and date of publication, the volume and page or pages from which the material is cited, and any other pertinent information should be given for each reference. References may be listed in the back matter or included in footnotes appearing at the bottom of the pages in which the works are cited. (*See also* FOOTNOTE.)

reflected light Light that is reflected on an image and is then directed back through the camera lens.

reflection copy Original copy for reproduction that is viewed and must be photographed by light reflected from its surface. Examples are photographs, paintings, dye-transfer prints, and Ektacolor and Kodacolor prints.

reflex copy Copy made by placing a special photosensitive material, emulsion side down, on an original and exposing the original through the back of the material. More light is reflected from the light areas of the original than from the dark areas. (*See also* REFLEX EXPOSURE.)

reflex exposure Method of making copies from originals by light reflection during exposure. As shown in Figure R-3, the original *A* is placed facedown on the emulsion side of the sensitized material *B*. Light rays pass through the underside of the sensitized paper and are reflected by the bright areas (nonimage area) indicated by the letters *D* and are absorbed by the dark areas (image area) indicated by the letters *C*. The areas of the sensitized material under the light-absorbing image area remain white during development. When a very thin original is copied by the reflex method, a sheet of white paper should be placed on top of it. This paper will have a tendency to reflect the light where further light is absorbed around the dark areas.

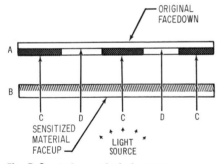

Fig. R-3   Reflex method of exposure.

reflex print Print made by the reflex method during exposure. The Charles Bruning Company manufactures a line of reflex materials used in conjunction with whiteprint materials. Bruning reflex prints can reproduce originals that are too opaque for regular contact printing, such as drawings on heavy paper, and originals that are drawn, printed, or written on both sides, such as magazine articles and catalog pages. The reflex film uses a 300- line screen.

Negative, darkroom, and developing trays are not required. This film provides a permanent positive film copy without intermediate steps. The film copy, which is made in any Copyflex machine, can be filed and used to produce additional copies.

register   In printing, to align a type page so that it exactly backs the type page on the reverse side of the sheet; also, to match the position of successive color impressions.

register marks   *See* ACETATE OVERLAY.

register motor   Optional attachment to a printing press that permits circumferential and lateral register adjustments to be monitored by remote control.

relief   Raised printing surface such as that used in letterpress or flexographic printing. (*See* PRINTING METHODS.)

relief printing   *See* PRINTING METHODS.

rendering   Drawing in which tonal values vary from white through black or from light to dark shades. It may be executed in watercolors, oils, pencil, pen and ink, charcoal, chalk, or airbrush, singly or in combination. A typical rendering is a wash drawing of a house, such as those displayed by real estate firms. For fine reproduction, any drawing with a gradation of tones must be screened for printing as a halftone. (*See also* ARCHITECTURAL RENDERING; WASH DRAWING.)

rep finish   Ribbed paper finish produced during the manufacturing process.

reprint   Additional printing of all or part of a publication.

reproduce   To make a copy from an original. When a camera is employed in the copying process, the image may be reduced or enlarged or be produced in the same size as the original.

reproducer   One of two units composing the Justowriter. (*See* COLD COMPOSITION.)

reproducibility   Ability of line or halftone copy to be reproduced as acceptable and legible copy. Firm definitions of black and white produce good copy, but grays and broken lines do not photograph well. Gray, weak, soiled, or broken copy will photograph as seen by the camera and will be reproduced slightly better than as seen by the eye. Modern cameras are of such good quality that a fine, hard pencil line will reproduce almost as well as an inked line. For reproducing text material, a good grade of coated paper with a basic weight of 60 to 80 pounds should be used. The paper should be sufficiently translucent so that corrections can be made by mortising over a light table. Reproduction proofs of typeset copy are produced on much lighter stock.

reproducible area   Image area on reproducible copy or on a typeset reproduction proof that will appear in final form. Crop and register marks, title blocks, and file numbers are excluded.

reproducible art   Second generation of art made from the original art and mortised into or pasted on the basic reproduction page. Original art is generally drawn oversize. Reproducible art consists of a matte or glossy print made from the art negative of the original art and reduced to the size of the area it will occupy on the basic reproduction page. It should remain free from revisions; only the original art should be altered. The term "reproducible art" may also denote art from which a quality image can be obtained. (*See also* BOARD ART.)

reproduction copy (also called **camera-ready copy**)   Typeset copy or copy composed on an office machine, together with line drawings and continuous-tone copy, that is ready in all respects for photomechanical reproduction. When copy is typeset, the printer refers to it as "etch proofs" or "reproduction proofs." Reproduction copy may also be called "black and white" when continuous-tone copy is not included.

A page of copy is called a "basic reproduction page." Each such page is photographed by the process camera, and a right-reading photolithographic negative is produced. The image is translucent, but the rest of the negative is black and therefore opaque. For printing the negative is stripped in position on ruled orange-colored masking paper called a "goldenrod flat." The flat is then placed in a vacuum frame in front of a sensitized plate and the image "burned" into the plate with a strong arc light. After processing, the plate is attached to the press for printing. Reproduction copy may be oversize or of actual page size. Figure R-4 shows an assembly of reproduction copy ready for the camera. Note that the small line art has been mortised or pasted in position on the basic reproduction page. It will be photographed with the text material on the page because the text also is line copy. Note also the black patch on the page. The area that the black patch occupies will be occupied on the page negative by one of the photographs keyed to it after the photograph has been screened and stripped into the negative. The large line illustrations, of course, are too large to be mortised into the basic reproduction page. They will become separate pages with their own page numbers.

The reproducible pages shown may be of the same size as those produced by letterpress printing, or they may be oversize when composed on a cold-composition machine. In the latter case, each page will be reduced to page size; for an 8½- by 11-inch publication, the image width will be reduced to 7 inches. The letterpress copy requires no reduction, as the copy is set in actual type size. The photograph will be screened for halftone reproduction and reduced to the exact proportions of the area covered by the black patch. The halftone negative is then stripped into position in the negative on the basic reproduction page.

Nomenclature should be of relatively the same size on all art in a given publication. It must be large enough so that when it has been reduced, it will be legible, comparable in size to the nomenclature of other art in the publication, and of good appearance. Reductions of the art for normal reproduction pages and of the

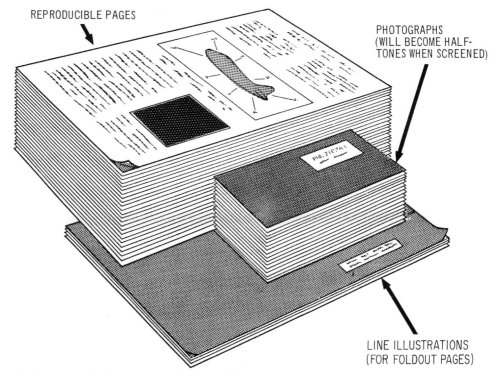

REPRODUCIBLE PAGES

PHOTOGRAPHS
(WILL BECOME HALF-
TONES WHEN SCREENED)

LINE ILLUSTRATIONS
(FOR FOLDOUT PAGES)

Fig. R-4   Reproduction copy assembled as a publication.

large line art are not the same. Therefore, care must be taken that marginal data such as the page-content heading, page number, and illustrations title for large line art are consistent in size with marginal data in other pages of the publication. The practice is to type or typeset all such data on a separate sheet of paper of the same quality and texture as that of the other pages. Following instructions, the photographer will reduce the marginal data to the same size as that on other pages. From this negative, he strips the data into the negative of the large line illustration.

reproduction flow charts　Figures R-5, R-6, and R-7 illustrate reproduction possibilities. The process used or the steps taken depend on the purpose of the end item. Several fundamentals should be recognized:

1. An enlargement or a reduction can be made only when a camera lens is used.

2. When light is employed to penetrate sensitized copy paper during exposure, the original must be on a translucent or transparent material for whiteprinting.

3. A camera lens can photograph any object seen by the eye.

4. An intermediate is a copy on paper, cloth, or film of the original from which additional copies are made.

5. A negative may be right-reading or wrong-reading.

6. There are only two kinds of copy, line and continuous-tone.

7. In direct, or contact, printing the original is in direct contact with the copy paper, cloth, or film during exposure. Therefore the copy will be of the same size as the original.

8. Continuous-tone copy requires screening, whereas line copy does not.

9. The image can be on translucent, transparent, or opaque material.

10. The image is either right-reading or wrong-reading.

reproduction master　Any master used to make copies by the whiteprint or other copying processes. The typesetter refers to the set copy as "reproduction proofs," "etch proofs," or "black and whites." All three terms denote copy that is to be printed by some method. The term "reproduction proofs" is the most common. Copies (usually two or three are furnished) are run off on a proof press. The typesetter has the copy set on a linecasting or Monotype machine (some large type may be set by hand) on a good-quality coated stock, which may be coated on one side only. Paper weights vary from 45 to 70 pounds, the lighter papers being more popular. A hard coated stock gives high-fidelity reproduction because the typeface makes a solid impression with good serif definition.

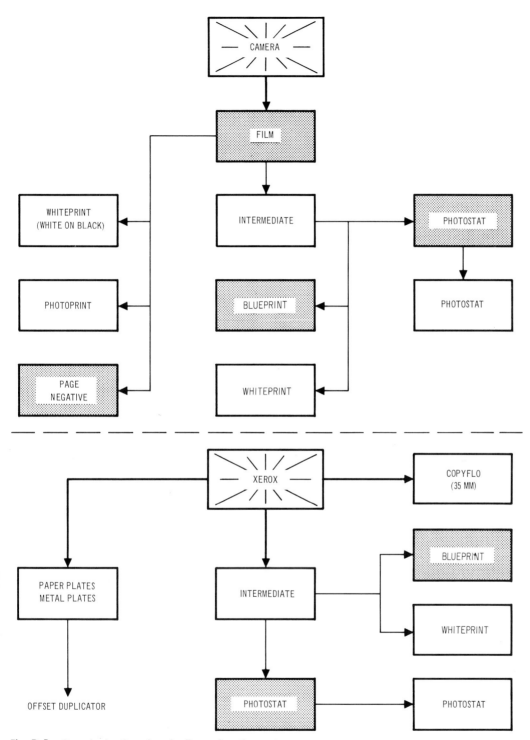

Fig. R-5 Reproduction flow chart for line and continuous-tone copy.

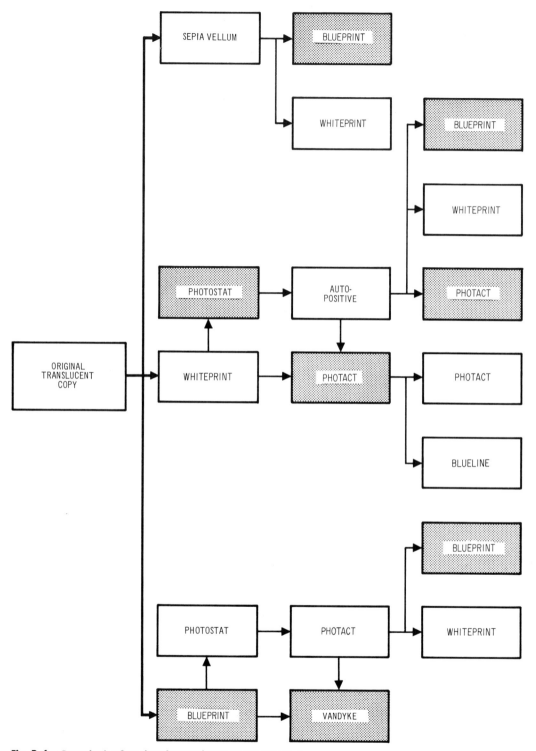

Fig. R-6   Reproduction flow chart for translucent or transparent copy.

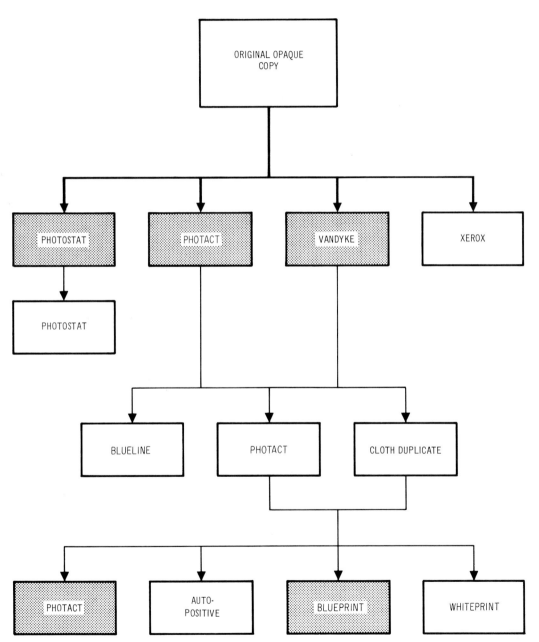

Fig. R-7   Reproduction flow chart for opaque line copy.

Reproduction paper for cold-composition copy, which is prepared by office composing machines such as IBM's Executive series of typewriters, the Justowriter, or the VariTyper, should be chosen not only for its image-accepting characteristics but for its erasing and mortising qualities. This stock should be coated and have a glossy finish. It should be surface-sized, that is, coated with a gelatin (animal) or starch (mineral) sizing. Gelatin sizing is desirable when erasing qualities are being considered. It is obvious that when a sized surface receives a typed image, the image is produced on the sizing because the paper is serving merely as a base. When the sizing is removed by erasing, the image is also removed. A surface-sized paper can be detected by scraping it with a knife. If the residue is fine and powdery, the paper will have good erasing qualities. If the residue is coarse and fibrous, wood sulfite and starch are evident and the paper will erase poorly.

A paper should not be used for reproduction typing unless it has been surface-sized. Some papers with a high gloss or a semigloss give the illusion of good reproduction tendencies. These papers, however, possess a glossy finish merely because they have been supercalendered by being passed many times through the calender rolls of the papermaking machine.

reproduction photostat (abbreviated **reprostat**)   High-quality glossy Photostat used for reproduction.

reproduction proof (etch proof; black and white)   Letterpress copy, composed either by machine or by hand, that is subsequently photographed for plate making and printing by the photo-offset or gravure processes. It is not a proof in the sense that an advance copy is printed for inspection and approval before the pressrun. Copy composed on an office composing machine is not a reproduction proof but is termed "reproduction copy."

reproduction typing   Production by a typist of composition copy that is ultimately printed. Technical reports, proposals, manuals, brochures, and house organs are among the kinds of publications that the reproduction typist may be called upon to type. The degree of skill required varies from simple typing to complete production, including typing prejustified and justified copy, proofreading, sizing and proportioning art and nomenclature, window masking for halftones, mortising, stripping, ruling, and page layout. Very few reproduction typists can accomplish all these tasks. These are, however, occupational skills for which a strong demand exists and which must be acquired on the job. The VariTyper, the IBM Executive typewriters, and the Justowriter are examples of cold-composition machines used for typing reproduction copy. (*See also* LAYOUT TYPING.)

reprographics Branch of the graphic arts that is concerned with the reproduction of images and especially with copying machines and their methods and processes.

reprostat Abbreviation for reproduction Photostat.

resist Enameled or bichromated coating that remains on a relief or offset plate after "burning" in and development and protects the printing area from the acid etch.

resolving power Ability of a photographic emulsion or lens to record fine detail, usually expressed in lines per millimeter.

retarder Mechanical device attached to a sheet-fed printing press to stop a sheet of paper and knock it down so that the next sheet falls into place in the stack.

reticulation Molecular conversion of a gelatin emulsion into a fine pattern of lines caused by changes in temperature between solutions. (*See also* PHOTOGELATIN PROCESS.)

retouching *See* AIRBRUSHING.

reversal generation Reproduction in which the original image has been reversed by a negative-working process.

reverse bluelines (also called **white on black; whiteline print**) Copy made from a photolithographic negative by running the negative through the whiteprint machine. During exposure, light penetrates the translucent image of the negative but cannot penetrate the opaque background. A white image is therefore produced on a black or dark blue background. Reverse bluelines of illustrations are excellent for check-out and approval before printing, and they are also useful as reference copies. An 8- by 10-inch negative should be specified for an illustration. The negative is placed over the copy paper so as to preserve white space for binding and identification.

reverse plate Plate on which line copy is reversed, the image being white and the background black. Reverse plates are common with logotypes and imprints.

reverse-reading (negative-reading; wrong-reading) Designating text material or copy that reads backward. It is the opposite of "right-reading."

reverse-reading intermediate Image imposed on a translucent

A

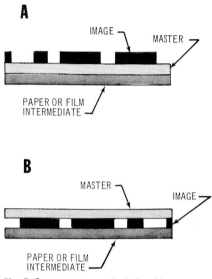

IMAGE

MASTER

PAPER OR FILM
INTERMEDIATE

B

MASTER

IMAGE

PAPER OR FILM
INTERMEDIATE

**Fig. R-8   Exposure method of making
reverse-reading intermediates.**

material that offers greater contrast on the opposite side of the sheet when the sheet is held for right reading. When extra-thin and thin paper or film intermediates are used, a more clearly defined image is obtained by reversing the master so that the dense side of the image on the master is in direct contact with the copy paper or film. Figure R-8A is grossly exaggerated to show the master placed on the paper or film faceup. View B shows the master in reverse with the image facedown. The better contact thus produced between image and copy paper or film results in high-fidelity reproduction. Prints made from reverse-reading intermediates are, of course, right-reading. Pencil or ink revisions are made easily on these intermediates.

rewinder   Device on a web-fed printing press that rewinds the printed web when sheeting and folding are not required.

ribbon copy   Copy made with a typewriter or other machine in which keys are struck against a ribbon to form the impression. The ribbon may be of paper or of fabric.

ribbons, typewriter   There are two kinds of typewriter ribbons, fabric and paper ribbons. The fabric ribbons, which are those commonly used in ordinary typewriters, may be made of cotton, silk, or nylon. All are preinked and are used repeatedly until the ink wears off. The highly absorbent cotton fabric ribbon retains a good ink content. The silk ribbon, which has excellent tensile strength and resists blows, produces the sharpest image of the fabric ribbons. The nylon ribbon produces a sharp, strong image and resists abrasion. Paper ribbons resemble carbon paper; they are used once and then discarded. The acetate paper ribbon, which has a high-quality coat of carbon, produces an exceptionally sharp black image and is used for reproduction copy. Some carbon paper ribbons are manufactured especially for typing on vellum. While the image is not so sharply defined as that on coated stock, the carbon produces a dense image for whiteprint production.

rider   Provision added to and made part of a document such as an insurance policy.

rider roller   Cylinder, such as an inking roller in a printing press, that rotates by friction with another roller instead of meshing gears directly with a driving force. In a web printing press, the rider roller is referred to as a "dancer roll." It rides on the paper roll between the latter and the metering unit to take up slack and to keep the paper under a uniform tension. The rider roller is interlocked with a brake to control paper unwinding.

right-angle fold   *See* CHOPPER FOLD.

right-hand page   *See* PAGE NUMBERING.

right-reading (positive-reading)   Designating text material or copy that reads in normal fashion. It is the opposite of reverse-reading.

ripple finish   Paper finish with a wavy appearance. It is produced by embossing or by using a plater, a calender in the papermaking machine.

river   Effect of open space or a stream of "air" running through a type mass, caused by excessive spacing between words. A river may be detected by scanning the length of a page with the eyes slightly squinted.

roll-size drawings   Large engineering drawings that, because of their length, are filed in rolls and do not usually have a printed format.

roll stand   In a web-fed printing press, the frame that supports the web (paper roll) as the web unwinds and feeds into the press. (*See also* AUXILIARY ROLL STAND.)

roman numerals   Numerals i, ii, iii, iv, or I, II, III, IV, etc., as distinguished from arabic numerals. Lowercase roman numerals are used to number front-matter pages. Uppercase roman numerals may be used for numbering chapters, parts, and sections.

ROP   Abbreviation for run-of-press.

rotary press   Printing press in which the printing material is locked on a rotating cylinder. The material must therefore be on a curved plate, either an electrotype or a stereotype. Presses of this type produce either one-color or multicolored work with fine register and speed. In a sheet-fed rotary press, the paper is fed from a pile, printed, and delivered in a pile. In contrast, a web perfecting rotary press prints from a continuous roll of paper called a web, which is printed and folded as a unit. A newspaper is an example of work produced on this type of rotary press. Units may be added to some rotary presses to increase their capacity. Single presses combined with additional units are called "quadruple," "sextuple," etc., an octuple press being composed of four units. (*See also* WEB OFFSET PRINTING.)

Rotofilm   Photographic resist on a Cronar polyester film base. It is designed for use in intaglio printing. The base can be stripped from the emulsion after the film has been placed either on a plate or cylinder.

rotogravure Print made by intaglio printing on a rotary press; also, the intaglio rotary printing process. (*See also* PRINTING METHODS.)

rotogravure paper Book paper manufactured especially for intaglio (gravure) printing. It has an English finish and is supercalendered to produce a smooth, even surface on both sides of the sheet. Rotogravure paper is used for magazines, catalogs, advertising pieces, labels, etc. Basic weights are 35, 40, and 45 pounds for 500 sheets of the basic size of 25 by 38 inches.

rough draft Text material that requires editing and possibly reworking before it becomes a final draft.

routing Cutting away nonprinting surfaces of a plate with a machine; also, removing unwanted background in a metal form or wooden block by drilling or gouging.

royal Paper size measuring 19 by 24 inches.

royalty Compensation paid for the use of property; hence, in publishing, money paid to an author as his share of the profits from the sale of copies of his work.

rubbing Impression taken from a stone inscription. While inscriptions cut in stone cannot be considered printing, reproductions from such inscriptions are deemed to have led directly to making books by means of inked impressions from wood and, from that method, to printing from movable type. The earliest-known dated rubbing is from the T'ang dynasty of China. Found at Tunhuang by Paul Pelliot, it bears a date equivalent to 653–654.

The rubbing process is as follows: A piece of felt is laid on the stone inscription, and a thin, tough, moistened sheet of paper is applied to the felt. The paper, with the felt behind it, is then hammered with a mallet and rubbed with a brush until it fits every depression and crevice of the stone. As soon as the paper is dry, a stuffed pad of silk or cotton is dipped in sized ink and passed lightly and evenly over it. When the paper is finally peeled off, it bears a durable impression of the inscription, which appears in white on a black background.

Rubylith Hand-cut red masking and stripping film laminated on a Mylar backing sheet. Rubylith is a trade name owned by Ulano.

The film, which photographs black, is used for masking windows in negatives, for dropouts and masks, for combining benday and texture sheets with open-window negatives in plate making, and for color overlays. The film is transferred to film negatives, positives, or glass negatives.

An adhesive holds the red film to the backing sheet and permits it to be cut and stripped from the sheet. The film should be cut with a sharp frisket or stencil knife. Selected portions of the image are cut and peeled from the backing sheet to form an open window, dropout, mask, or overlay. Rubylith is light-safe: a suitable light source passes through the cutout portions only and not through the red film. The film can be fastened to card stock and original artwork by a thin coat of rubber cement. The procedure for using Rubylith film is as follows:

1. Cut a piece of the desired film to the size of the areas to be masked and tape it down firmly at the top with the dull side up.

2. Cut out the image areas to be masked with a sharp blade, making certain that the backing sheet is not cut through.

3. Using the tip of the blade, lift a corner of the film, thus separating the film from the backing sheet.

4. Carefully peel off the film as outlined with the blade, leaving a completed positive or negative mask that corresponds to the desired pattern.

5. To transfer large pieces of Rubylith to the area to be masked, cover all but 1 inch of the area with a piece of paper.

T A B L E R-1   **Characteristics of Rubylith Masking Films**

Rubylith	Thickness, in.	Adhesiveness	Application
M3 . . .	0.003 (milky)	Very tacky.	General use and with Ortho M film*
D3R . . .	0.003 (clear)	Less tacky than M3 and DM3.	General use (not recommended for Ortho M film)*
DM3 . .	0.003 (clear)	Very tacky.	General use and with Ortho M film*
RA5 . . .	0.005 (milky)	Less tacky than M3 and DM3.	General use (not recommended for Ortho M film)*
5DR . . .	0.005 (clear)	Less tacky than M3 and DM3.	General use (not recommended for Ortho M film)*

*Ortho M film has a Cronar polyester base.

6. Strip the film from the backing sheet. Then place the stripped film, adhesive side down, on the paper with about 1 inch touching the area. Move the paper about 1 inch at a time and rub the film until the entire film adheres to the area. Using the paper in this manner prevents the film from forming many air bubbles.

Rubylith M3 was the first grade of masking film to be introduced. It is used in one of two ways: (1) The red film is cut and peeled and remains on the stable Mylar base; (2) When close contact between the red film and the film positive is important, the red film is peeled from the Mylar base and transferred to the film positive. Cutting and peeling are then done directly on the film positive. Table R-1 shows the various grades of Rubylith masking films and the characteristics of each.

Ulano's Plasti-Cut No. 25 Fotomask, while not belonging to the family of Rubylith films, is also red and photographs black. This film is coated on a vinyl backing sheet 0.005 inch thick. Since vinyl has image-adhering qualities, crayon and brush work can be done after open windows have been made.

rule In letterpress printing, a strip of metal that prints a line. Rules are measured in points (*See* Figure R-9).

run *See* PRESSRUN.

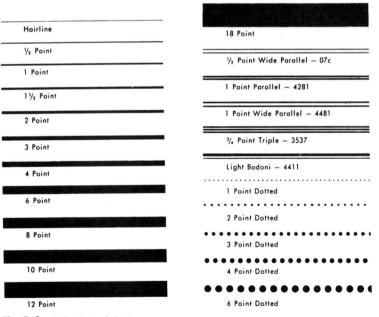

Fig. R-9   Rules (actual size).

run in Notation to set copy in the same paragraph although a break is shown. A line is drawn from the last word of the sentence before the break to the first word of the following sentence.

run-in heading Heading appearing on the same line with the text that follows it.

run-of-press Designating color work offered by a publisher, such as one who publishes a trade journal. The color work is regularly offered and printed as stock-in-trade. The term is also applied to multicolored printing in newspapers during high-speed pressruns.

run ragged To be uneven, or unjustified. The right margin in type-written text is not justified.

runaround Arrangement of text copy around an illustration of less than column or page width. A right runaround places the text copy to the right of the illustration; a left runaround, to the left. The use of runarounds often involves resetting text to a shorter measure after the position of the illustrations has been determined.

running foot Any symbol, number, or term that is repeated at the bottom of each page of a publication. Examples are a security classi-fication and a company logotype or address.

running head Heading that runs across the top of a page, giving the title of the publication or the chapter title. (*See also* PAGE-CONTENT HEADING.)

running text *See* STRAIGHT MATTER.

S

saddle stitching (sometimes called **saddle-wire stitching**) Method of mechanical binding that permits a book or magazine to be opened to its full extent. The book or magazine is opened to the center spread and wire-stapled or cord-stitched through the saddle in two or three places. The *Saturday Evening Post* and *Look Magazine,* for example, are both saddle-wired in three places. (*See also* BINDING, MECHANICAL.)

safelight In photomechanics, a filtered darkroom lamp that will not affect photographic material in a reasonable length of time. Different photographic materials require different safelight filters.

safety paper Sensitized paper on which it is impossible to erase or make changes without detection.

sans serif Without serifs, said of a letter that does not have a finishing stroke or line projecting from the end of the main stroke. Modern gothic faces are typical of typefaces without serifs. Figure S-1 compares gothic sans-serif type and a face with serifs.

satin finish Smooth paper finish that resembles satin.

satin white Coating mixture for quality coated and enameled papers, consisting of calcium sulfate and aluminum hydroxide.

Gothics

SANS SERIF

Modern

WITH SERIFS

Fig. S-1 Sans-serif typeface and a type-face with serifs.

scale drawing   Drawing such as a map, profile, or plan that shows relative sizes and proportions.

scale: engineering drawings   When practicable, engineering drawings should show an object or an assembly in full size. If a full-size view is not practicable, drawings may be made to reduced or enlarged scales. An enlarged scale is used when an object is so small that full-size representation will not clearly show its features. A reduced scale is employed to facilitate presentation of an object or an arrangement of such size that it exceeds the drawing space available, but such a scale should be used only if clarity can be maintained. In the selection of a reduced scale it may also be necessary to consider the degree of reduction contemplated in making a reproduction. Wherever practicable, detail drawings should be prepared to the same scale as the pertinent subassembly and assembly drawings, but this is not mandatory.

Three methods may be used in preparing drawings to scale: the fractional method (engineering), the equation method (engineering and architectural), and the graphic method. The first expresses, in the form of a common fraction, the ratio of the size of the object drawn to its true scale. This method is used on drawings for which the equation method is not appropriate. The scales commonly used are full size (1/1), enlarged (10/1, 4/1, 2/1), and reduced (1/2, 1/4, 1/10, 1/20, 1/30, 1/40, 1/50, 1/60, 1/100).

The equation method expresses, in the form of an equation, the relationship of the size of the object drawn to its true dimensions. This method is generally used on drawings where dimensions are expressed in feet and inches. The scales most commonly used are as follows:

Full size	*Reduced*	*Enlarged*
12 in. = 1 ft 0 in.		
	$\frac{1}{8}$ in. = 1 ft 0 in.	24 in. = 1 ft 0 in.
	$\frac{1}{4}$ in. = 1 ft 0 in.	48 in. = 1 ft 0 in.
	$\frac{3}{8}$ in. = 1 ft 0 in.	72 in. = 1 ft 0 in.
	$\frac{1}{2}$ in. = 1 ft 0 in.	
	$\frac{3}{4}$ in. = 1 ft 0 in.	
	1 in. = 1 ft 0 in.	
	$1\frac{1}{2}$ in. = 1 ft 0 in.	
	3 in. = 1 ft 0 in.	
	6 in. = 1 ft 0 in.	
	1 in. = 10 ft 0 in.	
	1 in. = 20 ft 0 in.	
	1 in. = 30 ft 0 in.	

In the graphic method, an actual measuring scale is shown on the drawing. This scale permits the approximate dimensions of the object in an enlarged or reduced reproduction to be determined.

scaling (dimensioning; sizing) Determining the proper dimensions for an image that is to be reduced or enlarged to occupy a given area when printed. In order to delineate fine details, most art is

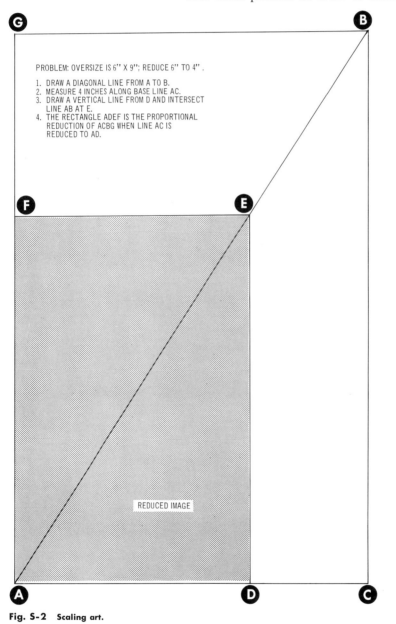

PROBLEM: OVERSIZE IS 6'' X 9''; REDUCE 6'' TO 4''.

1. DRAW A DIAGONAL LINE FROM A TO B.
2. MEASURE 4 INCHES ALONG BASE LINE AC.
3. DRAW A VERTICAL LINE FROM D AND INTERSECT LINE AB AT E.
4. THE RECTANGLE ADEF IS THE PROPORTIONAL REDUCTION OF ACBG WHEN LINE AC IS REDUCED TO AD.

REDUCED IMAGE

Fig. S-2 Scaling art.

drawn in a size larger than the final reproduction or page size. Oversize art may be drawn once and a half up, twice up, or larger.
The oversize measurements are determined from the final page size.
If the final page size is 42 picas, or 7 inches, wide and the art is
to be drawn once and a half up, the width of the oversize art is
$10\frac{1}{2}$ inches. Twice-up art would have a width of 14 inches. If the
art is to be boxed, a small area around the image is defined by
crop marks for this purpose. The lines of the box are drawn on
the basic reproduction page after the art has been pasted or mortised in position rather than on the art itself.

Only two dimensions are considered in art: the width, or horizontal dimension, and the height, or vertical dimension. The width
should always be stated first. The controlling dimension for scaling
art may be either the width or the height, but in most cases it is
the width. When a rectangle must be enlarged or reduced to fit
a given area, the width and height must be enlarged or reduced
in proportion to that area. If the oversize height of the art comes
within the limits of the required size, the width is the controlling
dimension. If the oversize height of the art is out of proportion to
the area the width must occupy, then the height is the controlling
dimension.

Several systems are used to determine the proportions to which
a rectangle can be reduced or enlarged. Proportional wheels and
slide rules are commonly employed. A simple formula may also be
used. For example, if a piece of art 14 inches wide and 20 inches
high must be reduced to a page width of 7 inches, three dimensions
are known and the fourth, the height of the reduced art, must be
found. Since 14 inches is to 20 inches as 7 inches is to X, $14X = 140$,
or $X = 10$.

Figure S-2 illustrates another method of scaling art.

In technical illustrating, scaling is drawing an object in proportion
to the area it will occupy without either congestion or excessive open
space. Figure S-3 is out of proportion for the object illustrated. The
object should be larger, and there should be less emphasis on the
hand that is holding it. Only a sufficient portion of the hand to
identify it as such is necessary. The object should always predominate.

scanning engraver   Automatic mechanical photoengraver that
scans continuous-tone and line art, both horizontally and vertically,
while activating a stylus that engraves halftone dots and lines on
a plate. (*See also* ELECTRONIC ENGRAVING.)

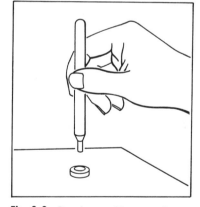

Fig. S-3   *Drawing an object to scale.*

schematic   Drawing that shows the layout of a system. It may be
a pneumatic or hydraulic flow diagram that shows the relationship
and flow between components in the system. Schematics are classed

as electrical, pneumatic, plumbing, hydraulic, and the like. (*See also* FLOW DIAGRAM.)

schoolbook perforating *See* PERFORATING, SCHOOLBOOK.

scissors editing Cutting out unwanted copy. Scissors editing is particularly adaptable to the whiteprint process, in which light penetrates a translucent or transparent master, leaving a white background. Light will penetrate the cutout portion of the master as well as any translucent or transparent area. The cutout portion should terminate with the apex or a V pointing toward the edge of the master that enters the whiteprint machine first. This precaution avoids fouling the master and copy paper between the rollers in the machine. Cutting across lines that have already been cut should be avoided, as should ragged edges. Depending on the size of the master and the capacity of the machine, it is sometimes possible to run the original through the machine so as to accommodate large cutouts.

scoring Making a partial cut in stock to facilitate folding. Cartons and boxes for display are scored.

Screen-process film Du Pont camera-speed stencil film. It has an orthochromatic emulsion on a stable supporting base. After the processed emulsion has adhered firmly to the silk screen, the base is stripped away, leaving the emulsion on the silk as the actual stencil for screen printing.

screen-process printing Form of stencil printing that utilizes a silk, nylon, or metal screen containing the image. A squeegee implement forces the ink through the screen to form the image on paper or other material. Early screens were made by painting the image on silk with a fluid resistant to ink. Masking materials were used to block out unwanted printing areas. Hand-cut stencils and photo-mechanical means may both be used in screen-process work. One technique involves coating the material with a light-sensitive emulsion. Exposure is made through a photographic film positive placed in contact with the screen. The surface of the screen is hardened in proportion to the degree of penetration of light; the hardened areas are then made insoluble to water, but the image is made soluble.

Thick deposits of ink compounds and paint make a wide variety of printing possible. Fabrics, plastics, metal, heavy card stock, and paper are only a few of the materials that are receptive to the screen process. (*See also* SERIGRAPH.)

screen ruling Number of lines per inch on a contact screen or ruled glass halftone screen.

screen tint *See* FLAT TONE.

screened paper print Halftone illustration made on photographic paper. It can be mounted with line copy on a page layout so that the entire page can be photographed at the same time as line copy for reproduction.

screened print Print made from continuous-tone copy and screened during photographic exposure. A Velox is a screened print. It is not necessary to screen the print again for reproduction printing; only a line shot is used. (*See also* VELOX.)

screening *See* HALFTONE SCREENING.

scriber (colloquial name **bug**) Device used in conjunction with a template to form characters, symbols, and the like. (*See also* PENS, TECHNICAL.)

script Type characters that resemble handwritten copy.

scumming In photomechanical plate making, an unfavorable condition in which the printing plate picks up ink in the clear areas and transfers it to nonimage areas of the sheet. The nonimage areas of the plate may not be desensitized properly to resist ink. Either the plate should be reetched or a new plate made. The entire plate, including nonimage as well as image areas, should always be worked with gum and developer. Scumming may also be caused by soiled damping rollers or other press problems, such as skidding from the roller, a loose blanket, or by an improperly balanced fountain solution.

second chopper fold (mail fold) Fold made in a web-fed printing press in the same manner as the first chopper fold. It immediately follows the first chopper fold and is parallel to it. Long narrow signatures that are 32-page multiples of the number of webs in the press are produced. The signature size is one-half of the web width by one-fourth of the cutoff length. (*See also* CHOPPER FOLD.)

second cover Inside surface of the front cover of a publication, usually identified as such for advertising purposes. The third cover is the inside surface of the back cover.

second parallel fold In a web-fed press, a paper fold made in the jaw folder immediately after the first parallel fold and parallel to it. The second parallel fold results in 16-page signatures of multiples of the number of webs used during the printing operation. The signature size is one-half of the width of the web by one-fourth of the cutoff length.

secondary colors   In printing, orange, green, and magenta. They are obtained by overprinting on primary colors. The primary colors for printing inks are yellow, red, and blue.

section   Usually, part of a chapter of a publication. Sometimes, however, sections may replace chapters as the highest divisions of a publication.

sectional view   View obtained by cutting away part of an object in an illustration or engineering drawing in order to show the shape and construction of the interior. (*See* SECTIONS: ENGINEERING DRAWINGS.)

sectionalizing   Arranging a technical publication in sections. Each section begins with a right-hand page, and paragraphs, pages, illustrations, and tables may be double-numbered within the section. The first number of the paragraph, page, illustration, or table represents the section. If the section number is in roman capital numerals, the number here should be converted to arabic. The second number represents the paragraph, page, illustration, or table within the particular section. For example, the third page of section IV is numbered 4-3, the fifth illustration of section VI is numbered 6-5, etc. Small publications should not be sectionalized. (*See also* PAGE NUMBERING.)

sectioning lines   In engineering and mechanical drawings, lines used in orthographic projection to indicate exposed surfaces of an object in a sectional view. They are generally thin, full lines but may vary with the material shown in the section. Sectioning lines are uniformly spaced lines drawn at an angle of 45 degrees to the base line of a section. On adjacent parts, the 45-degree angles are drawn in opposite directions. On a third part adjacent to two other parts, the sectioning lines may be drawn at an angle of 30 to 60 degrees. When the 45-degree sectioning lines are parallel or nearly parallel to the outline of an object, another angle should be selected. (*See also* LINE CONVENTIONS: ENGINEERING DRAWINGS; SECTIONS: ENGINEERING DRAWINGS.)

sections; engineering drawings   A section, or sectional view, is obtained by cutting away part of an object to show the shape and construction at the cutting plane. Such a view is used when the interior construction or hidden features of an object cannot be shown clearly by an outside view. Hidden lines and details beyond the cutting plane may be omitted unless they are necessary to portray the object adequately. A sectional view is made through an outside view and not through another sectional view unless such a procedure would clarify a drawing. A view may be rotated if an explanatory note, such as "Section *A-A* rotated 45 degrees clockwise," is shown next to it.

The cutting-plane lines described in LINE CONVENTIONS: ENGINEERING DRAWINGS, together with arrows and letters, make up the cutting-plane indication. The arrows at the ends of the lines show the direction in which the sections are viewed. The cutting plane may be a single continuous plane, or it may be offset if details can thus be shown to better advantage. In simple views, the cutting plane is indicated as in Figure S-4*A*. In complex views or views

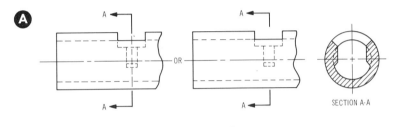

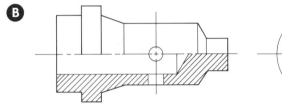

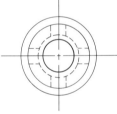

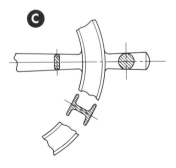

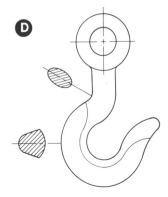

Fig. S-4   Sections and sectioning used on engineering drawings.

in which the cutting plane is offset, the cutting plane is shown as in Figure S-5*A*.

Viewing planes are indicated in a similar manner, except that they are placed outside the object to indicate the surfaces shown in the auxiliary views. All cutting-plane indications are identified by reference letters placed near the ends of the arrowheads. When a change in the direction of the cutting plane is not clear, reference letters may be placed at each change of direction. If more than one sectional view appears on a drawing, the cutting-plane indications are identified in alphabetical series. The letters identifying the cutting plane appear as part of the title under the sectional view, as in "Section *A-A*," "Section *B-B*." When the alphabet is exhausted, double letters may be used, as in "Section *AA-AA*," "Section *BB-BB*."

If possible, sectional views should appear on the same sheet as the subassembly, assembly, or detail drawings from which they have been taken. When sectional views must be drawn on a separate

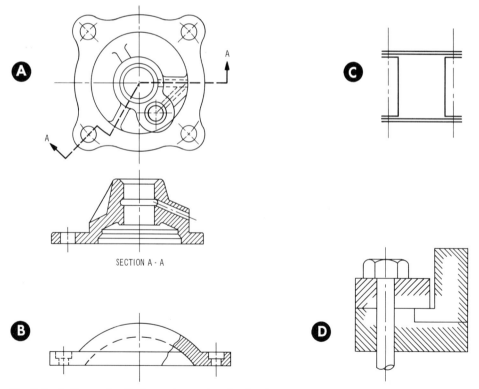

SECTION A - A

Fig. S-5 **Sections and sectioning used on engineering drawings.**

sheet, they are arranged from left to right in alphabetical order or with suitable cross-references by zone designations. If a sectional view appears on a sheet separated from the sheet containing the cutting-plane indication, the number of the latter is entered with the section title thus: "Section *B-B*, Sheet No. 3."

A full section is a view obtained when the cutting plane extends entirely across an object, as in Figure S-4*A*. For sections taken on the center line of a symmetrical view, the cutting-plane indications and the section title may be omitted if the section view is in correct orthographic projection. In all other cases, the section title and projection cutting-plane indications are shown.

A half section of a symmetrical object shows internal and external features by passing two cutting planes at right angles to each other along the center lines or symmetrical axes. One-quarter of the object is considered to have been removed and the interior exposed to view Cutting-plane indications and section titles are omitted (*see* Figure S-4*B*).

A revolved section drawn directly on an exterior view shows the shape of the cross section of a part, such as the spoke of a wheel. The cutting plane is passed perpendicular to the center line or axis of the part to be sectioned, and the resulting section is rotated into place. Cutting-plane indications are omitted (*see* Figure S-4*C*).

Removed sections may be used to illustrate particular features of an object; they are drawn in the same manner as revolved sections. They are placed to one side and are often drawn to a larger scale to bring out details (*see* Figure S-4*D*). If the cutting plane is not continuous, the resulting section is an offset section (*see* Figure S-5*A*). When a sectional view of only part of an object is needed, broken-out sections may be used. The break-line convention is employed to separate the sectional view, as in Figure S-5*B*.

When the true projection of a piece may be misleading, parts such as ribs or spokes are drawn as if they were rotated into or out of the cutting plane. The method of representing the lower spoke shown in Figure S-6*A* is preferred to the true projection. When the cutting plane passes through the rib, web, or similar element, sectioning lines may be omitted from these parts (see Figure S-5*A*).

Structural shapes, sheet metal, packing, gaskets, and the like that are too thin for section lining may be shown solid. If solid lines are used and two or more thicknesses are shown, a space as narrow as possible is left between them (*see* Figure S-5*C*). Shafts, bolts, nuts, rods, rivets, keys, pins, and similar parts whose axes lie in the cutting plane are not sectioned (*see* Figure S-5*D*). When the cutting plane passes at right angles to the axis of such parts, however, they are sectioned.

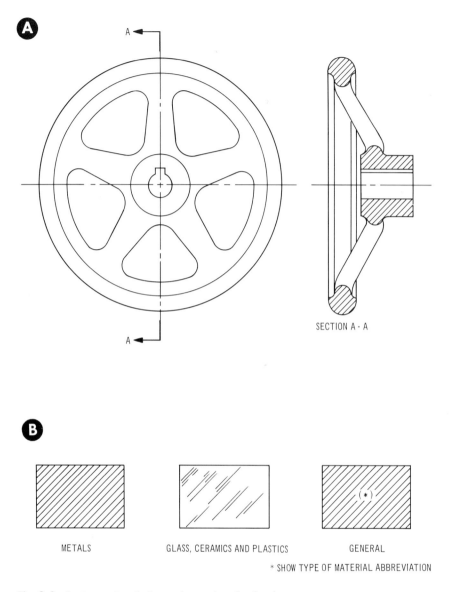

SECTION A-A

METALS

GLASS, CERAMICS AND PLASTICS

GENERAL

* SHOW TYPE OF MATERIAL ABBREVIATION

Fig. S-6 Sections and sectioning used on engineering drawings.

It is preferable to draw sectional views to the same scale as the outside views from which they were taken. When a different scale is used, the procedure is as outlined in SCALE: ENGINEERING DRAWINGS. In addition to showing shape and construction, sectional views may be used to distinguish individual components of an assembly or subassembly (*see* Figure S-5*D*). This is done by arranging these lines in section conventions on the exposed surfaces of the sectional view. Section conventions (*see* Figure S-6*B*) must not cross dimensions or obscure other conventions. When clarity is not thereby sacrificed, section conventions may be shown along the borders of a part. In section views, the metals symbol (Figure S-6*B*) is used to indicate other materials. Section lining is composed of uniformly spaced lines at an angle of 45 degrees to the base line of the section. On adjacent parts, the 45-degree angles are drawn in opposite directions. On a third part adjacent to two other parts, the section lining is drawn at an angle of 30 to 60 degrees (*see* Figure S-5*D*). When a 45-degree section lining is parallel or nearly parallel to the outline of an object, another angle is chosen.

see-through   *See* SHOW THROUGH.

self-cover   Cover of the same stock as the inside pages of a publication. The self-cover is printed at the same time as the inside pages.

self-mailer   Folder, broadside, or other mailing piece on which the address is printed directly, without use of an envelope.

self-quadder   Automatic quadder mechanism in Linotype machines. It consists of space matrices used in conjunction with spacebands. The quadder mechanism in Intertypes is called an "autospacer."

semilogarithmic grid   Grid composed of equal abscissa (horizontal) and ordinate (vertical) divisions laid out in a logarithmic ratio. A graph drawn on such a grid shows rate of change and changes in ratios or percentages.

sensitive material   Any material—diazo paper, plastic plate, photographic film—which is coated with diazo salts, bichromate solutions, or other chemicals that render its surface sensitive to light.

sensitivity, color   *See* FILMS AND PLATES.

sensitometry   Science of measuring the sensitivity and other photographic characteristics of photographic materials.

sepia   Dark yellowish-brown color of low brilliance.

sepia intermediate   Intermediate used in making duplicate transparencies by the whiteprint process. The original may be filed and the sepia intermediate revised and used to produce copies. When

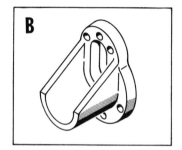

Fig. S-7   Shading on drawings.

sepia intermediates are made, exposure should be approximately one-third slower than for ordinary blueline or blackline papers. Normally, they should be made in reverse. Rather than placing the master over the treated paper with image side up, the master is placed facedown with the image in direct contact with the copy paper. (*See also* REVERSE-READING INTERMEDIATE.)

sequential-card camera   *See* CAMERA, SEQUENTIAL-CARD

serif   Finishing stroke or line projecting from the end of the main stroke of many letters in some typefaces. Letters that do not have such terminal strokes are said to be sans serif. Text typefaces have serifs, while gothic and similar faces are sans serif. The latter are generally used for forms, tabulated text matter, directories, headings, and display advertising. (*See also* SANS SERIF.)

serigraph   Color print made by the silk-screen process and executed by the artist himself. The production of serigraphs by either amateurs or accomplished artists can be a stimulating hobby or a profitable undertaking.

set solid   To set type without leading. (*See* LEADING.)

shading: drawings   Shading may be added to drawings with ink or pencil or by affixing preprints and hand-cut screening materials of various patterns. In an exploded view, shading effects on the various parts should indicate that the light is coming from the same source. If, for example, the light is coming from the upper right corner of the drawing, the shading should be applied to the opposite side of the parts. An area should not be shaded when it appears that the source light will strike the part. In Figure S-7*A*, light is coming from the upper right corner; in Figure S-7*B*, from the upper left corner. View *A* is an example of excessive shading. Shading in both cases was applied with preprinted patterns having an adhesive back, cut to the appropriate size, and burnished down. (*See also* SHADING MEDIUMS.)

Figure S-8 is an exploded view showing proper use of shading. The light source is coming from the upper left corner. Note the shading in the interior of housing 44. Note also that parts 4, 15, 22, 27, and 28 are filled in solidly except for highlights, which indicates that these parts are nonmetallic. Heavier lines are used to delineate the larger parts.

shading mediums   Sheets of preprinted tones and patterns with adhesive or developing characteristics that are used to improve the appearance of copy, especially artwork. The Craftint Manufacturing

Company's Craf-Tone sheets are available in approximately three hundred shadings and tones with patterns on thin adhesive-backed matte acetate. Some of the patterns are shown in Figure S-9. These shading mediums are used for borders, unusual lettering effects, maps, graphs, catalogs, yearbooks, posters, brochures, letterheads, technical illustrations, and other printed matter.

In applying Craf-Tone, remove sufficient shading from the sheet to cover the area to be shaded. Place the shading over the copy and flatten it by using mild pressure. It is better to start at the bottom and rub from left to right, working upward as the pattern adheres to the copy. Remove excess or unwanted shading by cutting it with a sharp frisket knife, but be careful to cut only the shading. After the excess shading has been removed, place a sheet of tissue over the area and burnish the shading through the overlay.

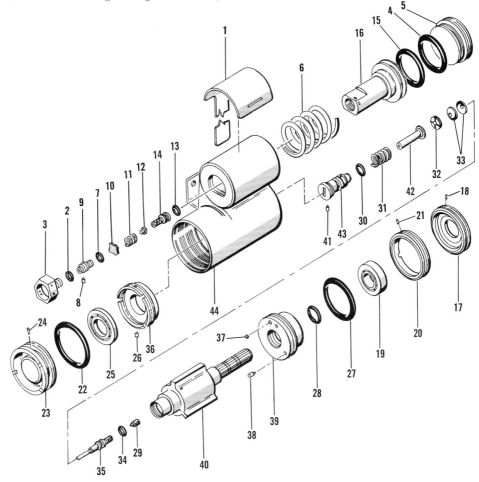

Fig. S-8   Shading on an exploded-view illustration.

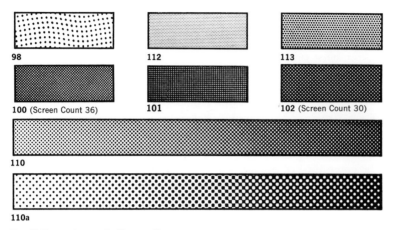

Fig. S-9 Craf-Tone shading-medium patterns.

Craftint has developed a process in which shadings of various styles and tones are applied by the artist directly on the drawing. Doubletone drawing paper, which resembles ordinary high-grade bristol board, has two hidden patterns. The Doubletone sheet is processed with two invisible shading screens, one having a light tone and the other a dark tone. By the application of two different developers, either the light or the dark tone is caused to appear on the drawing. Singletone drawing paper has one latent screen. The drawing is first outlined in pencil on the Singletone sheet. Ink is then used to make permanent lines. Developer is applied with pen or brush to the areas where the tone is desired and blotted immediately

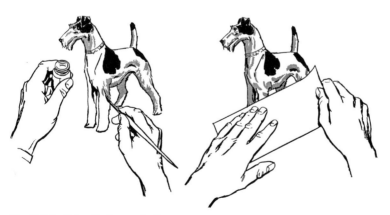

Fig. S-10 Using Singletone shading.

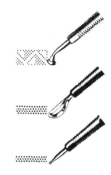

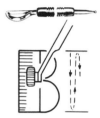

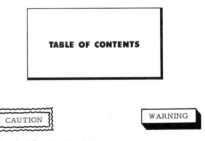

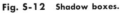

Fig. S-11 Stencil shading plates and styli.

(*see* Figure S-10). Both Doubletone and Singletone sheets are available in various patterns.

Craftint also produces engraver's top-sheet shading film with opaque patterns. The top sheet is placed over artwork or negatives to break up black solids. A white top-sheet dot can be made black by applying a developer. The white sheet breaks up solid black, whereas a black top sheet shades black on white.

shading: stenciling Producing a shading effect on a stencil by means of a transparent plastic plate with a raised pattern and a stylus. Shading is transferred to the stencil by placing it between the screen plate and a screen-plate stylus (*see* Figure S-11). With the stencil mounted on the duplicating machine (mimeograph), ink passes through openings in the stencil, thus transferring the image to paper. (*See also* MIMEOGRAPH; MIMEOSCOPE; STYLUS.)

shadow Darkest portion of a picture or image. In a negative, the low-density areas are called the shadow areas because they correspond to the high-density (dark) portions of the original copy.

shadow box Frame drawn around copy to give the illusion of a shadow. The lines of the box may be straight or wavy or be drawn heavier on one side (*see* Figure S-12).

TABLE OF CONTENTS

CAUTION

WARNING

Fig. S-12 Shadow boxes.

sharpness   In photographic material, the ability to reproduce the sharp edge of a line.

sheet   Piece of paper with or without copy. A page is one side of a sheet.

sheet-fed   Designating a printing press to which paper is fed in sheets rather than in rolls, or webs.

sheeter   Rotary device employed at the end of the last printing unit of a web-fed printing press. The web passes over the sheeter, which cuts individual sheets for stacking in a delivery pile.

shelf life   Length of time before sensitized materials such as diazo copy paper, film, and chemicals deteriorate with age. These materials have a limited use because their chemical properties are gradually lost.

shelf talker   Any printed sales message used to attract attention and describe merchandise on display. The material, which is pressure-sensitive, is affixed above or below the shelf on which the merchandise rests.

shelfback   *See* BACKBONE.

shop print   Engineering, construction, or architectural blueprint used in the shop or field. Shop prints are produced from original drawings made on vellum, tracing paper, cloth, or film. Blueprints, which have a white image on a black or dark blue background, can withstand hard usage and are impervious to grease and dirt. Even though they are exposed to sunlight, they will not fade for a reasonable length of time. (*See also* BLUEPRINT.)

short page   Page having fewer lines of text than are normally allocated to the pages of a publication. One or two lines may sometimes be omitted from a page to improve page makeup.

short title page   *See* HALF TITLE.

shoulder   In photomechanics, the portion of a characteristic curve above the straight-line section; in printing type, the portion of the surface on which the typeface rests.

show-through (see-through)   Visibility of printed matter on the opposite side of a sheet. The effect is due largely to a poor choice of paper, but it may also be caused by excessive ink penetration of the paper or too heavy an impression between the printing plate and the impression cylinder.

side roll stand　Roll stand for holding a web (paper roll) that is located to the side rather than in a direct line with the press. This arrangement is used when space is not available in line. The paper is turned and guided into line with angle bars.

sidehead　Caption or title that appears at the side (generally the left side) of a page or column. It may be flush or indented.

sidestitching (side-wire stitching)　Method of mechanical binding in which a booklet or a signature is stitched at the sides. "At the sides" means that the booklet or signature is stitched in the closed position. The pages therefore cannot be opened to their full width. (*See also* BINDING, MECHANICAL.)

sign paper　Paper used for indoor and outdoor advertising signs and posters. The back of the paper readily accepts paste for mounting, and the face is receptive to printer's ink. Sign paper comes in various colors and in sheets as well as in rolls as long as 1,000 feet.

signature　Sheet of paper printed on both sides and folded to make up part of a publication. For example, a sheet of paper with 2 printed pages on each side is folded once to form a 4-page signature. One with 4 pages on each side is folded twice to form an 8-page signature, and so on up to a 64-page signature with 32 pages on each side of the sheet. A 16-page signature is ideally suited to bookbinding machines. The proper arrangement of pages in signatures is called "imposition." (*See also* IMPOSITION.)

silhouette　Outline of an object, especially a portrait profile, filled in with black or another solid color. Silhouettes are often cut from black or colored construction paper and mounted on a white background. (*See* Figure S-13.)

Fig. S-13　**Silhouette.**

silhouetted halftone　Halftone from which the background has been deleted entirely or in part so that the image is silhouetted.

silk-screen printing process　*See* SCREEN-PROCESS PRINTING.

silver-generated　Designating a reproduction made from a silver image.

silver halide   A halide is a binary chemical compound formed by the direct union of a halogen, such as chlorine, iodine, or bromine, with another element or radical. Silver nitrate, one of the silver salts, is obtained by treating silver with nitric acid. It appears as colorless crystals on white fused or molded masses. A silver halide results from the union of silver salts with, usually, the halogen bromine. A remarkable susceptibility to light makes silver halides useful in photography and in graphic arts reproduction and photomechanical work.

silver print   *See* BROMIDE PRINT; BROWNLINE PRINT.

silver salts   *See* SILVER HALIDE.

single-coated paper   Coated or enameled paper to which only one coat has been applied.

single-color press   Printing press that is capable of printing only one color at a time. To produce multicolor work, various color plates are used and the sheet is run through the press for each color.

single printing   Printing first on one side of a sheet and then on the reverse side by either the work-and-turn or the work-and-tumble method. The process is the opposite of perfector printing, in which both sides of a sheet are printed in one run through the press. (*See also* PERFECTING PRESS.)

singletone   Sheet of high-grade board stock processed with an invisible shading screen. The artist applies a developer to bring out the tone desired on the drawing. (*See also* SHADING MEDIUMS.)

sinkage   Distance below the top margin of a page at which chapter openings and similar material are set.

size (also called **sizing**)   Any of various gelatinous materials made from starch, clay, glue, casein, and the like and used for glazing or coating papers and cloths during the manufacturing process. Size is also used in the tempera process of painting (*See* TEMPERA).

In printing, a clear size may be laid on stock by preprinting to seal the surface against ink penetration. Sizing is used especially in color work for better definition of the image when a porous stock is desired.

sizes: engineering drawings   The sizes of engineering drawings as set forth in military specifications are accepted as standard by almost all the concerns that make or reproduce such drawings. Flat-size drawings, which are relatively small, usually have a printed format and may be filed flat. Roll-size drawings, because of their length, are filed in rolls and usually do not have a printed format. The finished-sheet size of drawings refers to overall dimensions of drawing forms and of full-size reproductions made from them. As shown in the table below, sizes are designated by letters. To provide protection for roll-size drawings, a 4-inch margin should be added to the right end of the minimum lengths specified. When practicable, the maximum length of roll drawings should be 144 inches. The table shows finished-sheet sizes of the various drawings.

Size	Flat sizes, in.	Size	Roll sizes, in.
A.	8½ by 11	G	11 by 42
B.	11 by 17	H	28 by 48
C.	17 by 22	J	34 by 48
D.	22 by 34	K	40 by 48
E.	34 by 44		
F.	28 by 40		

sizing *See* SCALING; SIZE.

slide making Polaroid Land transparency films may be used with the Polaroid MP-3 camera to make lantern slides for projection. Two special-purpose films are available: one for line copy, such as charts, text matter, and line drawings, with a development time of ten seconds; and the other for continuous-tone copy, such as actual objects, pictures, and wash drawings, with a development time of two minutes. The finished transparency snaps into a Polaroid slide mount that may be used in a standard lantern-slide projector. Slides can also be made in 2¼- by 2¼-inch and 35-millimeter sizes. The 35-millimeter slides can be made four up on a 3¼- by 4¼-inch frame and then trimmed and mounted for projection. (*See also* POLAROID MP-3 INDUSTRIAL-VIEW LAND CAMERA.)

slip-sheet (interleave) To insert paper or other material between printed sheets in order to avoid offsetting an image on one sheet onto the back of the next sheet. In the preparation of copy, the term "slip-sheet" means to insert pages in proper sequence to designate the placement of illustrations that are still being prepared. Each such page identifies its particular illustration with a notation as to whether the illustration is line or halftone, foldout or horizontal, as well as the size, the negative or art file number, the figure number and title, and any other information that serves to key the illustration to its proper page for printing or collating.

slip-tracing   Tracing an object by shifting its position under a translucent paper on which the tracing is made. A different configuration can thus be drawn or the layout improved over the original.

slug (slugline)   Line of type cast by a linecasting machine; also, a metal strip wider than leading used for spacing between lines.

slugcasting machine   *See* LINECASTING MACHINE.

slugline   *See* SLUG.

small capital letters   (abbreviated **small caps**)   Capital letters set in a size smaller than regular capitals of the same font. A double underline is used to direct the printer to set words in small capital letters.

small pica   Old type size. The nearest equivalent in the point system is 11 point.

soft copy   Text copy typed on vellum or other paper, as opposed to camera-ready copy. It is provided for check-out and approval of the style and accuracy of the text. Soft copy is not final copy.

soft cover   Any book cover other than a hard cover or a self-cover. It may consist of any type of stock as long as the stock is not the same as that on which the pages are printed. (*See also* SELF-COVER.)

soft-roll   To roll a typewriter platen by hand above or below the normal line of typing in order to type superscripts or subscripts. If the typewriter is already equipped with a half-ratchet spacer, there is no need to soft-roll. To avoid soft-rolling, which requires estimating the space needed, ratchets can be installed to accommodate half spacing. Superscripts and subscripts can thus be accurately aligned.

solid copy   *See* STRAIGHT MATTER.

sorts   Symbols, designs, braces, stars, and the like that are not included in a regular font of type characters. (*See* Figure S-14 for an example of miscellaneous sorts.)

source-control drawing   Engineering drawing that specifies the source that exclusively provides the performance, installation, and interchangeability characteristics of an item selected and tested for specific application by a design activity. The drawing is identified by the contractor design group's name and number and shows the vendor's name, address, and part number. When the source-control drawing number is used as the identifying number on an assembly drawing or list, however, a note such as the following is placed on the drawing or list: "For procurement or part number, see source-control drawing."

A source-control drawing is identified by the words "Source-control drawing" adjacent to the title block. It also contains the following notice: "Only the item listed on this drawing and identified by vendor's name, address, and part number has been tested and approved by [name of the equipment design activity] for use in [name of item]. A substitute item must not be used without prior testing and approval by [name of equipment design activity]."

specification-control drawing Engineering drawing that discloses the configuration, design, and test requirements for the items (other than military standard items) designed and manufactured by vendors. Vendors' part numbers and names and addresses are included

6 POINT

8 POINT

10 POINT

12 POINT

14 POINT

Fig. S-14 Miscellaneous sorts (actual size).

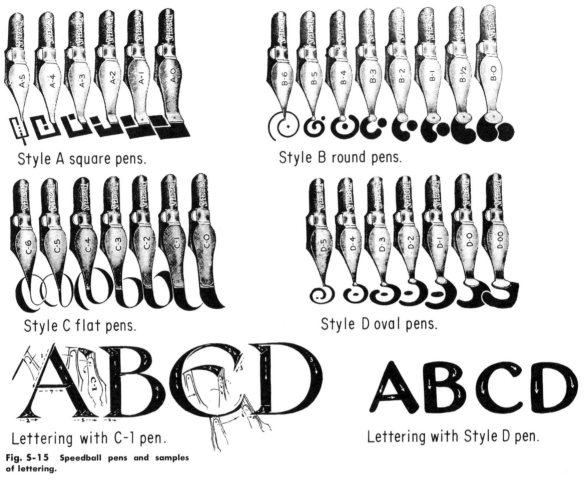

Style A square pens.

Style B round pens.

Style C flat pens.

Style D oval pens.

Lettering with C-1 pen.

Lettering with Style D pen.

Fig. S-15 Speedball pens and samples of lettering.

Fig. S-16 Speedball flicker pen.

in the drawing. A specification-control drawing number is not considered a part number. When the number is used as the identifying number on an assembly drawing or list, however, a note such as the following is placed on the drawing or list: "For procurement or part number, *see* specification-control drawing." A specification-control drawing must be identified by the words "Specification-control drawing" adjacent to the title block.

specification tree *See* CHECK-OUT CHART.

speedball pens Lettering and drawing pens manufactured by the Hunt Manufacturing Company, of which Speedball is a registered trademark. Five styles of Speedball pens, together with samples of lettering, are illustrated in Figures S-15 and S-16. The flicker lettering pens break open for easy cleaning and maintenance.

SPH Abbreviation for sheets per hour.

spine *See* BACKBONE

spiral binding *See* BINDING, MECHANICAL.

spirit duplicating (fluid duplicating) Direct-image duplicating process in which the image is typed, written, or drawn on a master that is backed by an aniline-dye carbon sheet. A deposit of dye is transferred to the back of the master, where it forms the image in reverse reading. When placed on the spirit duplicator, the copy paper comes in direct contact with the master. As the paper goes through the machine, it is moistened with the vapor of a duplicating fluid and a small amount of carbon dissolves to produce the image. The carbon paper is obtainable in purple, red, and green. Paper or card stock from a minimum size of 3 by 5 inches can be handled by various models of spirit duplicators. Masters are provided in grades designed for maximum performance and long runs as well as in economy grades for low cost and short runs.

The Ditto Masterset may be employed to prepare masters. It consists of a master and a carbon assembled for use. The master sheet is protected by a tissue until the set is used. To make a handwritten or drawn original image, the carbon is used as a typewritten original. The uncarbonized side of the carbon paper is placed on a hard, smooth surface, preferably glass. The blank master is then laid on the carbonized side, and writing or drawing is done directly on this sheet. A hard lead pencil, ballpoint pen, or stylus should be used, and just enough pressure to produce the desired thickness of line should be applied.

An ink eraser and an eraser shield to isolate the error are used to make corrections. When the error is erased, a purple smudge appears, but it will not be reproduced on the copies. An unused corner can be torn from the carbon paper and placed over the error when the correction is made. For faithful reproduction of the correction, a type key should be struck two or three times. Corrections may also be made by using a razor blade or sharp knife, an art-gum eraser, and an eraser shield. First, the error is isolated with the shield and scraped away with the blade or knife, care being taken not to damage the master paper. The remaining carbon can be removed with the art-gum eraser and the correction typed in.

Ditto's Model 18D-75 spirit duplicator produces a maximum of 110 copies per minute. The operator sits at the machine and operates it by a foot pedal. The copying surface is $17\frac{1}{2}$ by $13\frac{11}{16}$ inches for automatic feed and accommodates paper measuring 18 by 14 inches for hand and automatic feed, with a copy margin of $\frac{5}{16}$ inch.

Figure S-17 illustrates the Ditto Model D-31 spirit duplicator. An automatic motor-driven machine, it is $44\frac{1}{2}$ inches high with its cabinet. The copying surface is $8\frac{1}{2}$ by $13\frac{5}{8}$ inches, the maximum

Fig. S-17   Ditto's Model D-31 spirit duplicator.

Fig. S-18   A. B. Dick Company's Model 227 spirit duplicator.

paper size is 9 by 14 inches, and the copy margin is $\frac{3}{8}$ inch with automatic feed.

The A. B. Dick Model 227 spirit duplicator (Figure S-18) handles masters in sizes as large as 12 by 14 inches and paper ranging from 3 by 4 to 11 by 15 inches. Five colors can be produced in one operation. Masters can be prepared with a ballpoint pen, typewriter, tabulating machine, or other office equipment. The duplicator can produce 100 copies per minute and has a feed-table capacity of 500 sheets of 20-pound paper.

spot (locator)   In technical illustrating, an object that forms part of an assembly and is drawn in solid black in a small drawing adjacent to the drawing of the complete assembly. The spot indicates origin only and is used as a reference point. The part or section indicated by the spot constitutes the main illustration. The spot in the aircraft in Figure S-19 shows a portion of the inboard nacelle.

spotting   Painting out small defects on a negative or other material by using opaquing fluid or white paint.

spread   In advertising, two facing pages in a publication, with or without a gutter. (*See also* CENTER SPREAD.)

sprocketed film   Roll film with sprocket holes that engage sprocket wheels so that the film may be guided and controlled as it passes between reels.

square grid (cross-section grid)   Grid ruled in squares and designated by the number of lines per inch. A 4-by-4 grid, for example, has four lines per inch in both directions, usually with every fourth line

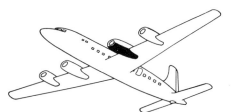

Fig. S-19   Using a spot in technical illustrating.

heavier than the others; a 5-by-5 grid has five lines per inch in both directions, with every fifth line heavier; and so forth. The basic unit is not always an inch, however, and a 10-by-10 grid may have a $2\frac{1}{2}$-inch grid. Because the square-ruled sheet can represent any assigned dimension or value, a square grid is frequently used for engineering sketches, block diagrams, and plant or office layouts.

S/S or **ss.** Abbreviation for same size, indicating that the copy is not to be enlarged or reduced.

stabilene film Tear-resistant film made by the Keuffel and Esser Company in thicknesses of 0.003, 0.005, and 0.0075 inch. It is available in various coatings, surfaces, and colors and may be opaque or translucent. Stabilene films are manufactured for map making, drafting, illustrating, and the drawing of printed circuits as well as for certain mechanical applications.

stabilization reproduction *See* PROCESSING, STABILIZATION.

stacker Device attached to a delivery conveyor that collects, compresses, and bundles signatures.

stacking In technical illustrating, placing nomenclature on an illustration so that a vertical line drawn through it shows balanced copy. Lines are neither flush right nor flush left but are centered on the first line of copy.

standing form Printing form that will be used repeatedly and therefore will not be disassembled or melted down.

steelfaced plate *See* NICKELTYPE.

stencil sheet Sheet of fine paper backed with heavier material on which an impression can be cut by typewriter percussion or by a stylus. When the stencil is mounted on the duplicator cylinder, fast-drying ink penetrates the cut impression. The ink is thus transferred to paper to form the image. This type of stencil is used in mimeographing.

step-and-repeat machine Machine that repeats a series of operations to produce multiple images from negatives or positives in register on photosensitive materials. The materials include metal plates and photographic glass or film for photo-offset, photogravure, silk-screen printing, printed-circuit production, and other industrial applications. The carriages of the machines may operate vertically or horizontally.

Figure S-20 illustrates the Model M-H 4 vertical photocomposer machine, which is capable of high-speed production of both single exposures and finished plates. It occupies floor space measuring 72 by 122 inches, requires headroom of 8 feet 5¼ inches, and weighs 4,200 pounds. The machine's specifications include a press-plate platen of 70 by 80 inches, a maximum press plate of 55 by 69 inches, and a maximum work area of 50 by 68 inches. (Five other models are available.)

With the lamp in position for exposure, the hood of the machine prevents light from reaching any portion of the plate except that under the negative. The vacuum is automatically connected through the saddle seating the negative holder. After each exposure, the lamp is pushed out of the way to permit a change to the next exposure position. The negative holder may be moved horizontally or vertically. It is locked in inch positions by means of horizontal and vertical notch bars and locking studs and is then moved to its final position by micrometer adjusting screws that operate on measurement units accurate to 0.001 inch.

Fig. S-20 Lanston vertical photocomposer machine, Model M-H 4.

stereotype mat Matrix into which molten metal is poured to produce a stereotype plate. (*See* MATRIX.)

stereotype plate Duplicate printing plate made from a type image. The face of the type or engraving is pressed into pulp material by a molding press. The stereotype matrix is then filled with molten metal and becomes a new printing surface that can be mounted on wood to the conventional height of type. Less expensive than electrotypes, stereotypes are popular in newspaper printing. They are curved and mounted on the plate cylinder of the newspaper press.

stet Latin word meaning "let it stand," used to indicate that a change is not to be made and that copy should remain as it was originally written. A row of dots placed beneath the copy is the proofreader's instruction not to make the change. The word "stet" is written in the margin.

stickup initial *See* INITIAL.

sticky back *See* AVERY.

stippling Drawing, engraving, or painting by means of dots or small, short touches that together produce a softly graded tone, instead of using continuous lines and solid areas.

stitch line In orthographic engineering and mechanical drawings, a line used to indicate sewing. Designated as a "medium" line, it consists of a series of evenly spaced short dashes. (*See also* LINE CONVENTIONS: ENGINEERING DRAWINGS.)

stock Paper, paperboard, or other paper product on which an image is printed, copied, or duplicated.

stomp Soft pencil made of paper or other soft material. Artists use stomp for blending chalks, pastels, or pencil graphite to produce shading and graded tones on drawings.

storyboard Panel presentation of rough sketches of a proposed series of views such as may be used on film slides or transparencies for overhead projection. Storyboards are also used in cartoon animation.

straight-line portion In photomechanics, the section of a characteristic curve that is essentially a straight line. It represents the range of exposure in which an increase in density is proportional to an increase in the logarithm of the exposure.

straight matter (running text; solid copy) Text that is not interrupted by headings, tables, illustrations, or displayed equations.

straightedge Instrument with one or more straight long edges, particularly a ruler having measured increments, used in artwork. The C-Thru ruler is a transparent straightedge that is popular with technical illustrators, layout personnel, and artists. It is inscribed with grid divisions for the alignment copy and has a beveled edge that prevents ink from smearing.

Figure S-21 shows Jacob's parallel straightedge. A straightedge of this type has three advantages over a T square: it is supported on both ends and affixed to the drafting board, it maintains parallel motion automatically, and it may be moved up or down the board by exerting pressure at any point along its length. This straightedge is $3\frac{1}{4}$ inches wide and $\frac{3}{8}$ inch thick and is available in lengths ranging from 3 to 8 feet. The edges are beveled for accurate, visible line work.

Fig. S-21 Jacob's parallel straightedge. (Courtesy of Keuffel and Esser Co.)

stripping Cutting out and placing in position, particularly with reference to arranging a photolithographic negative in masking paper for a plate. Stripping also means removing all or part of text copy or an illustration by mortising and replacing the material with something else, particularly with reference to reproduction copy. A screened halftone negative stripped in a line negative is a "strip-in"; the combination is called a "composite."

stripping film Film having a light-sensitive emulsion laid on a membrane 0.0005 inch thick. The membrane is bonded to a thicker base material. After the film has been developed, the base can be stripped away, leaving the membrane to hold the photographic image. With stripping film, wrong- or right-reading copy can be produced by placing the image between a light-sensitive coated material and a source of light. Close contact is achieved by using a vacuum frame. A disadvantage of stripping film is that the membrane is usually unstable because of shrinkage and stretching. These characteristics must be calculated and allowed for in planning.

stripping table *See* LIGHT TABLE.

stub List of subjects in the left-hand column of a table.

stuffer Printed circular enclosed in an envelope with regularly mailed material, such as an invoice.

style Uniform spelling, punctuation, abbreviation, capitalization, ruling, headings, typography, and the like used throughout a publication.

stylus Precision-made penlike instrument used for drawing, tracing, lettering, shading, ruling, and writing on stencil sheets for mimeographing; also, such an instrument used for engraving or etching.

subscript *See* INFERIOR.

suction feed Method of employing air suction to pick up paper and start to feed it through a printing press or similar machine. An automatic device introduces the air suction to pick up the paper and then cuts off the air at the proper instant to release the paper, which is caught between feed rollers. Suction feed may be distinguished from friction feed.

summary Supplement to the abstract of a publication, usually consisting of technical data. It precedes the body of the text. A summary is included only when a publication is lengthy or complicated. It should state concisely the reason for the publication, the matter covered, results and how they were obtained, and conclusions. The reader should be able to determine from it if the subject matter is of interest to him. A summary is written last, after the author has a complete grasp of the subject.

supercalendered finish Glossy finish applied to paper by passing it repeatedly through the calendar rolls of a papermaking machine.

superfine Designating high-grade writing paper.

superior Superscript or exponent; a letter, numeral, or symbol written above and to the right of another character, in contrast to an inferior, or subscript. It is set in a type size smaller than the text size. (*See also* INFERIOR.)

supplement Addition to a book or a newspaper or other periodical, intended to supply deficiencies or add special interest to a subject. It can be a separate publication printed to augment or change an original publication. A good example of a supplement is *Parade*, which is added to many large Sunday newspapers and bears the imprint (the name and sometimes the logotype) of the newspaper subscribing to it.

surface chart Graphical representation with plotted points moving across it from left to right in a logical sequence. The pattern thus reflected is extended to the base of the chart by shading or cross-hatching. The shaded area is the predominant feature of the chart. The vertical scale may indicate quantities, while the base may reflect periods of time, expressed in hours, days, weeks, months, or years. An example of a surface chart is shown in Figure S-22. (*See also* BAR CHART; COLUMN CHART; CURVE CHART; PIE CHART.)

surface sizing Sizing applied to paper by spraying it on both sides before it has run over the last series of dryer rolls in the papermaking machine. A sealed surface, such as that found on rag-content bond papers, is provided for ruling, typing, and printing.

surprinting Imposing unscreened line art on a plate on which half-tone art has already been printed. In this procedure, the continuous-tone art has become a halftone by prior screening, but the line art remains unscreened and therefore presents a better definition without a dot formation. The term "surprinting" may also mean printing over copy that has already been printed.

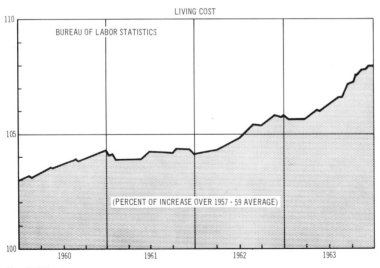

Fig. S-22 Surface chart.

swatch In printing, a color sample. When a printing color that may prove difficult to reproduce is desired, a swatch should be given to the printer. The printer will furnish a color proof if so requested.

symbol Any character, letter, or drawn configuration that is identified with or serves to explain the meaning of something. Unless a symbol is universally understood, a key or legend should be furnished to explain its intent.

symmetrical Designating an object whose parts are in balanced proportions on either side of a dividing line. Examples are cylinders, butterfly or airplane wings, and revolving doors.

T

tab *See* INDEX GUIDE.

table of contents *See* CONTENTS.

tabloid Newspaper about half the size of a regular newspaper. Text matter is compressed, and emphasis is placed on photographs.

tabloid fold *See* FIRST PARALLEL FOLD.

tabulated drawing Engineering drawing that depicts fixed characteristics only once but shows all differences in characteristics, dimensions, materials, finishes, or other requirements. Another drawing number or a double number is used to identify the difference. Since such a drawing may show many deviations from the basic characteristics of an item, it is unnecessary to make an individual drawing for each difference.

tailpiece Decorative design employed at the end of a chapter or section to mark the conclusion of the chapter or section.

tandem roll stand Dual or single roll stand located at the front of a web-fed press that permits multiple webs (rolled stock) to be fed to the press at the same time.

tape converter Device that converts press-wire tape for photomechanical typesetting. Figure T-1 shows the ATF press-wire tape converter. Source material, in the form of standard six-channel coded tape from the AP or UPI wire service, is fed directly into the converter, where it is converted automatically to ATF typesetter tape at a rate as high as 30 standard press-wire newspaper lines per minute. Wire-service tapes containing stock quotations, solid text, box scores, syndicated features, and other news are fed to the converter through the tape interpreter, or reader. Line measures and justification codes are programmed into the unit by setting dials, and stop codes are inserted in the tape.

The coded ATF tape is produced by the punch mounted on the converter and is ready for editing or for typesetting. If editing is required, the tape is inserted in the ATF typesetter keyboard unit (*see* Figure T-19), where corrections, deletions, and insertions are made. The corrected tape is then inserted in the ATF photographic unit (*see* Figure T-20), and the copy is set photographically and automatically justified on photographic paper that is developed and ready for paste-up.

tape interpreter *See* READER.

tape perforator Machine designed to punch holes in coded tape for subsequent translation. It is used in conjunction with linecast-

Fig. T-1 American Type Founders' tape converter.

ing-control typesetters such as the Linotype and the Intertype to compose news text, editorial and market matter, box scores, and classified ads. Tape perforators have a standard keyboard arrangement, which is supplemented by additional keys and controls. An operator types the information in much the same manner as he would operate a typewriter. As a character or functional key is struck, not only is a visual copy produced but the coded character or function is simultaneously punched in the tape. The tape then contains information in the form of text matter. When it is fed into another machine, such as an interpreter, or reader, the device senses the code, automatically translates, or "reads," the coded characters and functions, and thus actuates the movements of the linecasting machine. (*See also* READER.)

target date   Date set for completing a task that presumably will allow ample time for quality control before the deadline.

teacher's manual (teacher's key)   Guide for use by teachers in classroom instruction. Such a manual supplements a specific textbook but is printed and bound separately. Suggested elements for inclusion in a manual are instructions in how to use it, instructions in how to use the textbook to which it pertains, recommended questions and answers, methods of reviewing the subject matter, student problem areas, practice sheets, examination questions or suggestions, time schedules for assignments, study periods, and recommendations that will enable the teacher to conduct the course in accordance with good teaching practices.

tear sheet   Sheet extracted from a publication that contains an advertisement or other matter. Tear sheets may be distributed to a select group or to an interested individual. A tearsheet containing an advertisement is usually furnished free to the advertiser on request.

technical illustration   Graphic arts profession that embraces the art of making drawings for technical reports, proposals, manuals, and catalogs, as well as visual aids such as briefing charts, projecturals, slides, posters, and the like. Technical illustrations include wiring diagrams, cutaways, electrical schematics, pneumatic and hydraulic schematics, organization charts, graphs, pictorial and functional flow diagrams, and assembled and exploded views. Crayon, pastel, airbrush, pen and ink, pencil, oils, watercolors, and other equipment are utilized to produce images. A good knowledge of paper, types, paste-up, and reproduction equipment is required.

Technical illustrating did not come into its own as a professional field until World War II, when United States government agencies began to require instruction, maintenance, service, operation, flight, and other handbooks and manuals for use in maintaining and operating the equipment which they requisitioned. The field may now be divided into two main divisions, military illustrating for government agencies and commercial illustrating for private industry. On the military side, the art is created solely to serve as guidance, instruction, and planning material. Government standards and specifications must be followed. Sources of information for technical illustrators include engineering drawings whose orthographic projections must be converted to isometrics or perspectives, photographs, catalogs showing components and parts, observation of the equipment itself if it has been manufactured, and discussion of the equipment with engineers and others.

Not until the latter part of 1939 and the early part of 1940 were the first exploded views of an object photographed. The parts of the article were disassembled and placed in sequence on a flat surface, small parts being held in position with putty. An alternative method involved hanging the parts with string or wire against a bulkhead. These methods proved expensive and inadequate because airbrushing was required to remove the marks of the putty and strings. Moreover, it was practically impossible to obtain good perspective because flow lines were not exact. The next step was to trace the photograph of an exploded view in ink and so to improve its perspective and layout, but this method was time-consuming and expensive. The obvious answer to the problem was to draw exploded views directly from available information. Orthographic, isometric, perspective, and trimetric methods of projection are now used for exploded views. Figure T-2 illustrates the flow of art in a technical art department.

technical pens *See* PENS, TECHNICAL.

Teletypesetter Tape-controlled operating unit for automatic linecasting control. Teletypesetter is a trademark of the Fairchild Graphic Equipment Corporation. The device is used extensively in newspaper work and in industry generally. The reader is attached to a slugcasting machine, such as the Linotype or the Intertype, to control keyboard operation.

tempera Painting process in which the color is bound either with a size such as starch, glue, or casein or, especially, with egg instead of oil. The yolk or white of egg may be employed in combination or separately. Tempera was the most widespread method of painting among the early Egyptians, Babylonians, and Italians, who used such ingredients as fish oil, milk, and honey for painting on mummy cases, the walls of tombs, papyrus, parchment rolls, and panels. In modern usage, tempera is known as "distemper."

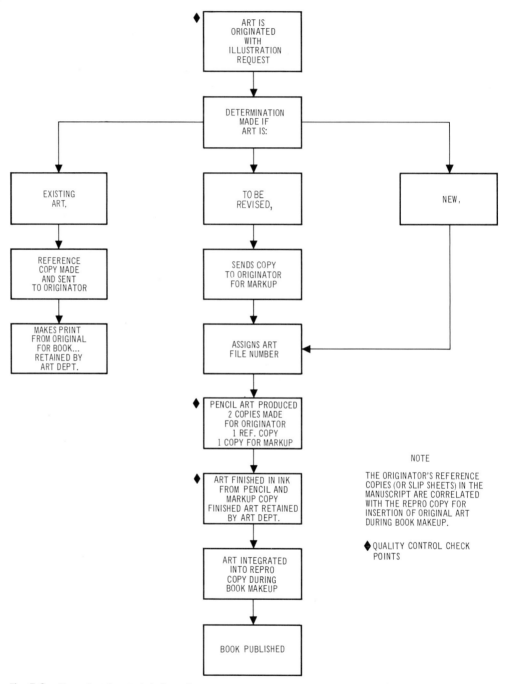

◆ ART IS ORIGINATED WITH ILLUSTRATION REQUEST

DETERMINATION MADE IF ART IS:

EXISTING ART,

TO BE REVISED,

NEW,

REFERENCE COPY MADE AND SENT TO ORIGINATOR

SENDS COPY TO ORIGINATOR FOR MARKUP

MAKES PRINT FROM ORIGINAL FOR BOOK... RETAINED BY ART DEPT.

ASSIGNS ART FILE NUMBER

◆ PENCIL ART PRODUCED 2 COPIES MADE FOR ORIGINATOR 1 REF. COPY 1 COPY FOR MARKUP

◆ ART FINISHED IN INK FROM PENCIL AND MARKUP COPY FINISHED ART RETAINED BY ART DEPT.

ART INTEGRATED INTO REPRO COPY DURING BOOK MAKEUP

BOOK PUBLISHED

NOTE

THE ORIGINATOR'S REFERENCE COPIES (OR SLIP SHEETS) IN THE MANUSCRIPT ARE CORRELATED WITH THE REPRO COPY FOR INSERTION OF ORIGINAL ART DURING BOOK MAKEUP.

◆ QUALITY CONTROL CHECK POINTS

Fig. T-2   Flow of art in a technical art department.

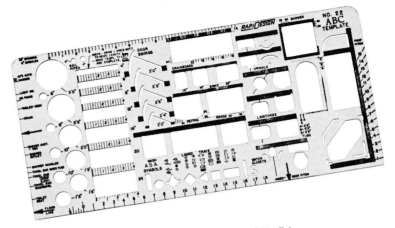

Fig. T-3　**Rapidesign drawing template.** *(Courtesy of Keuffel and Esser Co.)*

template　Guide made of highly polished transparent or translucent plastic material, containing patterns for use in pencil and ink work (*see* Figure T-3). Edges and shapes are designed to suit requirements. The use of color makes templates easy to identify as work progresses and also prevents glare. Templates increase drawing and drafting output because shapes may thus be drawn quickly and accurately.

test setup　Type of technical illustration used in a manual. It may be an orthographic drawing, as in Figure T-4, or a drawing showing components in either isometric or perspective projection. The iso-

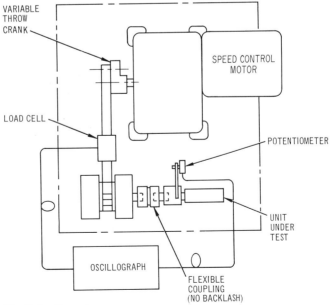

Fig. T-4　**Test setup.**

metric and perspective drawings present a true likeness of the components, whereas the orthographic presentation is symbolic. Illustrations of test setups are supported in the text of the manual with instructions on conducting the test.

text Typewritten or printed matter forming the main body of a work, as opposed to front and back matter, illustrative material, tables, extracts, and so on.

text finish Paper finish that is smoother than antique finish but not so smooth as machine finish.

text paper High-quality uncoated paper of good appearance used for books, booklets, brochures, programs, and the like. It may be obtained in various colors. The basic weight is 60 pounds for 500 sheets of the basic size of 25 by 38 inches.

text type *See* BODY TYPE.

thermographic copying Dry heat-transfer process of producing copies from an original. The image is heated with infrared radiation and transferred to copy paper that is sensitive to light.

thermography Inexpensive method of imitating engraved printing by the use of heat. While the printing ink is still moist, the sheets are conveyed to a machine that dusts the image with a powdered compound. Surplus powder is vacuumed off, and the sheets are conveyed through an oven to fix the powder. When the sheets are cooled, the result is raised lettering. Colors include copper, gold, silver, and white. The finish may be dull or glossy.

thin space Thin piece of type metal used to insert space between characters.

third-angle projection *See* ORTHOGRAPHIC PROJECTION: ENGINEERING DRAWINGS.

third cover *See* SECOND COVER.

third-dimension printing System of producing the illusion of depth in an image by adding a third dimension to width and height. One method involves coating a printed surface with plastic. Three-dimensional printing promises to be a factor in display work, packaging, and point-of-sale advertising.

three-view drawing *See* ORTHOGRAPHIC PROJECTION: ENGINEERING DRAWINGS.

thumb indexing *See* INDEX GUIDE.

thumbnail sketch Very small, concise sketch used particularly as an initial presentation but also for other purposes. Such a sketch is almost always intended to be finished and reproduced in a much larger size, but the term may be used to indicate a small sketch whether finished or not.

tick marks Short, fine lines imposed on a chart or graph to represent evenly spaced points on a scale between the vertical or horizontal division lines.

time card, illustration Card used in an illustration department for the record control of a piece of art. Figure T-5 shows a typical card. In a technical publications department, the technical writer requests the illustration, but time estimates are entered by the art director or art supervisor because time and costs are the responsibility of the art department. The director or supervisor assigns the job and enters pertinent instructions for the illustrator on the card. The card is retained by the illustrator until the assignment has been completed. It is then returned to the director or supervisor with the completed art.

ART WORK TIME CARD

ART SIZE _____

REDUCTION _____

OVER SIZE _____

REPRO SIZE _____

NOMENCLATURE _____

JOB NO. _____

CODE NO. _____

PUB. NO. _____

FIG. NO. _____

DATE OF ISSUE _____

ISSUED BY _____

ENGINEERING & PENCIL LAYOUT			INKING			OPAQUING			RETOUCHING			NOMENCLATURE		
DATE	TIME	INIT.	DATE	TIME	INIT.	DATE	TIME	INIT.	DATE	TIME	INIT.	DATE	TIME	INIT.
EST.			EST.			EST.			EST.			EST.		

NOTES: _____

_____

_____

_____

_____

Fig. T-5 **Typical illustration time card.**

time-gamma curve In photography, a curve that indicates the development times necessary at various temperatures to produce approximately the same degree of contrast as is given by the recommended times at 68° F. The chart on which the curve is shown is called a time-temperature chart.

tint block Cut processed to print a panel of color. One or more tint blocks may be printed on a sheet. For example, if a color is to be printed at the top and bottom of a leaflet, tint blocks are used to print the colors and the colors are then overprinted with text or other line copy. Tint blocks are also often used behind halftones to produce an economical pseudoduotone effect.

tint plate Printing plate with an image bearing a tint block.

tip-in Separate page or other printed matter, such as postage-paid inquiry card, pasted in a publication. (*See also* INSERT.)

tip-on Object or material glued, stapled, or otherwise fastened to an advertising display or other printed matter. Tip-ons are used extensively in greeting cards.

tissue overlay Thin, translucent paper placed over artwork for protection and correction. Register marks are used on the overlay to assure proper register for corrections. Overlays may also be placed over reproduction copy to mark corrections and to protect the copy while paste-ups are being burnished. Any light, inexpensive onionskin that does not have oily characteristics may serve as an overlay. Overlays should be retained on artwork or copy until all indicated corrections have been made. (*See also* MOUNTING AND FLAPPING.)

tissue proof Additional proof printed on tissue by some typesetters and furnished to a customer as an act of courtesy with a regular order for reproduction proofs. It can be used as a file copy.

title page Page of a book or other publication containing the full title and other information deemed necessary by the publisher, such as a brief synopsis, the author's name, the edition number, the name of the publisher, and the publisher's address. A half title precedes the full title page and is generally the first printed page of the book.

Various United States government agencies issue specifications that set forth requirements for full- and half-title pages. Type sizes and faces, spacing, and the inclusion of information on contents are specified. These pages are typeset as reproduction proofs and are usually printed by photo-offset. (*See also* HALF TITLE.)

toe In photomechanics, the portion of the characteristic curve below the straight-line section. It represents the area of minimum useful exposure.

tone art   Abbreviation for halftone art.

tone-line process   Method of converting continuous-tone art to line art. A continuous-tone negative and a film positive are made of the subject in equal tone values. The two are then placed in precise register. They cancel each other out except at the edges of contrasting tones, where sufficient light penetrates to form a line rendering during exposure for plate making.

toner   *See* DRY INK.

tooth   Ability of paper to take printing ink, drawing ink, pencil, and the like. If paper readily accepts these materials, it is said to have "tooth."

tracing cloth   Duplicate drawing with a black image made on blue or white waterproof cloth. It is probably the longest-lasting type of duplicate. The tracing cloth may be produced from any negative and in widths as large as 54 inches by any length. Pencil or ink corrections are easily made, since the image may be removed with a dampened eraser tip. Rather than make an ink drawing, which requires expensive drawing time, it is advisable to make a good pencil drawing and have a duplicate tracing cloth made. The scale is fair to good.

tracing paper   *See* DRAFTING AND TRACING MATERIALS.

trademark   As defined in section 45 of the 1946 act (Trademark Act of 1946), a trademark includes any word, name, symbol, or device, or any combination thereof, adopted and used by a manufacturer or merchant to identify his goods and to distinguish them from those manufactured or sold by others. The primary function of a trademark is to indicate origin. However, trademarks also serve to identify the source and any related quality of the goods bearing the mark and, through advertising, to create and maintain a demand for the product. Rights in a trademark are acquired only by use, and the use must ordinarily continue if the rights so acquired are to be preserved. Registration of a trademark in the Patent Office does not in itself create or establish any exclusive rights but is recognition by the government of the right of the owner to use the mark in commerce to distinguish his goods from those of others.

In order to be eligible for registration, a mark must be in use in commerce which may lawfully be regulated by Congress, for example, interstate commerce, at the time the application is filed.

Trademarks differ from trade and commercial names which are used by manufacturers, industrialists, merchants, agriculturists, and others to identify their businesses, vocations, or occupations or the names or titles lawfully adopted by persons, firms, associations, companies, unions, and other organizations. Trade names of the latter type are not subject to registration unless they are actually used as trademarks.

A trademark cannot be registered if it

(1) Consists of or comprises immoral, deceptive, or scandalous matter or matter which may disparage or falsely suggest a connection with persons, living or dead, institutions, beliefs, or national symbols or bring them into contempt or disrepute;

(2) Consists of or comprises the flag or coat of arms or other insignia of the United States, or of any state or municipality, or of any foreign nation, or any simulation thereof;

(3) Consists of or comprises a name, portrait, or signature identifying a particular living individual except by his written consent or the name, signature, or portrait of a deceased president of the United States during the life of his widow, if any, except by the written consent of the widow;

(4) Consists of or comprises a mark which so resembles a mark registered in the Patent Office or a mark or trade name previously used in the United States by another and not abandoned as to be likely, when applied to the goods of another person, to cause confusion, or to cause a mistake, or to deceive; or

(5) Consists of a mark which is generic or so generally descriptive that it is not distinguishable (e.g., no trademark can be registered for "Chair" when applied to a chair).

The application for registration must be filed in the name of the owner of the mark. The owner may file and prosecute his own application for registration, or he may be represented by an attorney or agent authorized to practice in trademark cases. The Patent Office cannot aid in the selection of an attorney or agent. Application forms for corporations, individuals, and firms are available from the Patent Office on request. A complete application comprises (1) a written application, (2) a drawing of the mark, (3) five specimens or facsimiles, and (4) the required filing fee.

Further information on trademarks is obtainable from the Patent Office, U.S. Department of Commerce, Washington, D.C. 20231. One booklet is *General Information concerning Trademarks*, and another is *Trademark Rules of Practice with Forms and Statutes*, both procurable from the Superintendent of Documents.[1]

[1]The information in this article is presented to assist the reader in an understanding of current trademark laws. Because laws change, it is recommended that competent legal authority be consulted concerning these matters.

trailing edge Last portion of a moving object that follows the remaining portion. An example is the trailing edge of a web (paper roll). The term is opposed to "leading edge."

transfer Sheet or gelatinlike film containing the image that is to be transferred to a metal printing surface.

transfer sheet Sheet of clear acetate paper containing preprinted characters and symbols, used in preparing cold-composition, camera-ready reproduction copy. The character or symbol is placed over the desired position on the reproduction copy and is transferred in place by burnishing. The method differs from applying a wax-backed character or symbol in that it is not necessary to cut, paste, and burnish the character or symbol in place. An excellent application for this transfer method is copy in which equations and Greek letters predominate. The method is fast, economical, and accurate.

translucent Designating a material that permits the passage of light. Such a material is not transparent because the image is indistinct when viewed through it. Translucent materials such as cloths, films, drawing and tracing papers, and vellums are used as originals from which copies are made by whiteprint, blueprint, and other processes in which light penetration is required during exposure.

transmitted light Light that passes through a material.

transmitted-light exposure Method of making copies from originals during exposure by transmitted light, as opposed to exposure by the reflex method. As indicated in Figure T-6, the original *B* is placed with the copy faceup. The emulsion side of the sensitized material *A* is placed facedown over the original. Light rays pass through the original *B* at points indicated by the letters *d* and reach the emulsion side of the sensitized material *A*, but they are intercepted by the image area (dark areas) indicated by the letters *c*. Therefore, the parts of the sensitized material above the dark areas are not exposed to light and do not form the image (or blacken) during development.

Trans-Pak Trademark of a line of die-cut symbols used for printed-circuitry illustrations. (*See* CHART-PAK.)

transparent Designating a material such as clear glass or clear acetate that permits the passage of light so that objects behind it are completely visible. Materials such as drawing and tracing papers,

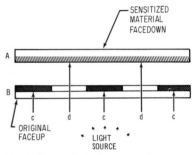

Fig. T-6 **Method of exposure by transmitted light.**

cloths, films, and vellums are not transparent; they are translucent. A distinct image must be seen through a material before it can be correctly termed "transparent."

triangular grid   Grid used for plotting the curves of three variables with a constant sum. Problems involving three elements that are expressed in percentages can thus be graphically portrayed for comparison.

trigonometry symbols   *See* TABLE 12.

trimetric projection   *See* AXONOMETRIC PROJECTION.

trimmed size   Size of a publication or a page after it has been trimmed to its final dimensions. Books are trimmed during the binding process.

tub sizing   In the manufacture of paper, immersing the paper in a solution of glue. Better grades of rag-content bond paper are tub-sized.

tucker blade   Reciprocating knifelike blade used in a web-fed printing press to form signatures into jaws when making a jaw fold or between rollers when making a chopper fold.

tucker fold   Fold made by a jaw folder.

tumble   *See* WORK AND TUMBLE.

turnaround   Time from the acceptance or beginning of a job until the completed job is delivered.

turning bar   *See* ANGLE BAR.

tusche   Solution resembling ink that is applied on a lithographic printing plate to produce a printed image.

TV screen   Shadow box used to frame an illustration, as in Figure T-7. A TV screen sets off an assembled view from the main illustration and, depending on company practice, may be inserted with the exploded view in the upper left- or right-hand corner of the main illustration. It should be a true rectangle or square with heavier lines opposite the assumed source of light. The lines must not be so heavy as to detract from the view they enclose. Note that in the illustration the base line is broken at one point.

twice up   In drawing, to a width twice that of artwork as it will

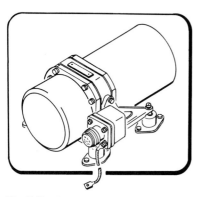

Fig. T-7   TV screen.

appear on the printed page. If the illustration is to have a printed-page width of 7 inches, it is drawn to a width of 14 inches. The height must be increased proportionately.

two-scale chart Column chart in which two values are compared. The vertical columns usually represent quantity, and the horizontal dimension represents time. Comparisons of salaries, employment, sales, progress rates, distances, growth, and the like may be charted. Such charts may be expanded to show many factors. (*See also* BAR CHART; COLUMN CHART; CURVE CHART; PIE CHART; SURFACE CHART.)

tympan Hard-surfaced material used to cover the impression cylinder of a printing press. It serves as a cushion behind the paper receiving the impression.

type description Typography is an extensive field. Knowledge of common typefaces, relative sizes, measurements, leading and spacing, and the elements that compose type is a basic requirement for graphic arts students. The size of the typeface does not indicate or determine the size of the type in points, which is the standard system used to measure type. Note in Figure T-8 that the point measurement is the depth of the point body, which includes the shoulder, and that it is greater than the depth of the typeface. The body must be large enough to accommodate the ascenders and descenders of the particular typeface. Type set without other spacing between lines than that furnished by the shoulders is said to be "set solid." Additional spacing is provided by leading. (*See also* LEADING; TYPE SPECIMENS; TYPEFACES.)

type-high Designating the measurement from the base of the type to the top of the typeface. This dimension, which measures 0.918 inch, was established as the standard by the Association of Type Founders of the United States.

type page Part of the page on which type is printed; the image area inside all margins.

type specimens Samples of type showing the various names, sizes, faces, and other information, offered for sale or available to the customer as a printing service. Figure T-9 shows examples of type specimens. Printers stock a variety of sizes and faces, and most have type books that show specimens available to users. Unless the customer is familiar with the type his printer stocks, he should order the desired face and size with the notation "or equivalent." This leaves the printer free to recommend and select an equivalent face and size carried in his stock.

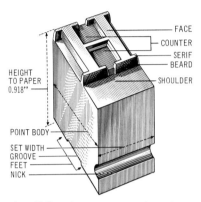

Fig. T-8 Elements composing type. (Courtesy of American Type Founders.)

Fig. T-9   Type specimens.
(Courtesy of American Type Founders.)

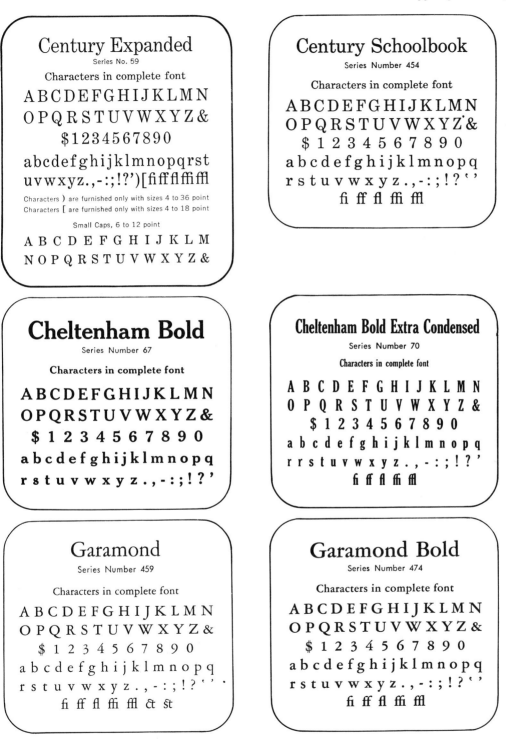

Century Expanded
Series No. 59

Characters in complete font

A B C D E F G H I J K L M N
O P Q R S T U V W X Y Z &
$1234567890
abcdefghijklmnopqrst
uvwxyz.,-:;!?')[fiff fl ffi ffl

Characters) are furnished only with sizes 4 to 36 point
Characters [are furnished only with sizes 4 to 18 point

Small Caps, 6 to 12 point

A B C D E F G H I J K L M
N O P Q R S T U V W X Y Z &

Century Schoolbook
Series Number 454

Characters in complete font

A B C D E F G H I J K L M N
O P Q R S T U V W X Y Z &
$ 1 2 3 4 5 6 7 8 9 0
a b c d e f g h i j k l m n o p q
r s t u v w x y z . , - : ; ! ? ' '
fi ff fl ffi ffl

Cheltenham Bold
Series Number 67

Characters in complete font

A B C D E F G H I J K L M N
O P Q R S T U V W X Y Z &
$ 1 2 3 4 5 6 7 8 9 0
a b c d e f g h i j k l m n o p q
r s t u v w x y z . , - : ; ! ? '

Cheltenham Bold Extra Condensed
Series Number 70

Characters in complete font

A B C D E F G H I J K L M N
O P Q R S T U V W X Y Z &
$ 1 2 3 4 5 6 7 8 9 0
a b c d e f g h i j k l m n o p q
r r s t u v w x y z . , - : ; ! ? '
fi ff fl ffi ffl

Garamond
Series Number 459

Characters in complete font

A B C D E F G H I J K L M N
O P Q R S T U V W X Y Z &
$ 1 2 3 4 5 6 7 8 9 0
a b c d e f g h i j k l m n o p q
r s t u v w x y z . , - : ; ! ? ' '
fi ff fl ffi ffl & st

Garamond Bold
Series Number 474

Characters in complete font

A B C D E F G H I J K L M N
O P Q R S T U V W X Y Z &
$ 1 2 3 4 5 6 7 8 9 0
a b c d e f g h i j k l m n o p q
r s t u v w x y z . , - : ; ! ? ' '
fi ff fl ffi ffl

Goudy Bold

Series Number 446

Characters in complete font

A B C D E F G H I J K L M N
O P Q R S T U V W X Y Z &
$ 1 2 3 4 5 6 7 8 9 0
a b c d e f g h i j k l m n o p q
r s t u v w x y z . , - : ; ! ? ' '
fi ff fl ffi ffl

Goudy Bold Italic

Series Number 464

Characters in complete font

A B C D E F G H I J K L M N
O P Q R S T U V W X Y Z &
$ 1 2 3 4 5 6 7 8 9 0
a b c d e f g h i j k l m n o p q
r s t u v w x y z . , - : ; ! ? ' '
fi ff fl ffi ffl ct

Spartan Book

Series No. 707

Characters in complete font

A B C D E F G H I J K L M N
O P Q R S T U V W X Y Z &
$ 1 2 3 4 5 6 7 8 9 0 * ¢ %
a b c d e f g h i j k l m n o p q
r s t u v w x y z . , - : ; ! ? ' ' " " ( )

Ligatures are included in fonts of 6 to 18 point
sizes, and are obtainable in 24 to 36 point sizes
in foundry lines.

ff fi fl ffi ffl

Spartan Medium

Series Number 680

Characters in complete font

A B C D E F G H I J K L M N
O P Q R S T U V W X Y Z &
$ 1 2 3 4 5 6 7 8 9 0 * ¢ %
a b c d e f g h i j k l m n o p q
r s t u v w x y z . , - : ; ! ? ' ' " " ( )

Ligatures are included in fonts of 6 to 18 point
sizes, and are obtainable in 24 to 120 point
sizes in foundry lines.

fi ff fl ffi ffl

Spartan Black

Series Number 683

Characters in complete font

A B C D E F G H I J K L M N
O P Q R S T U V W X Y Z &
$ 1 2 3 4 5 6 7 8 9 0 ¢ %
a b c d e f g h i j k l m n o p q
r s t u v w x y z . , - : ; ! ? ' ' " " ( )

Ligatures are included in fonts of 6 to 18 point
sizes, and are obtainable in 24 to 120 point
sizes in foundry lines.

fi ff fl ffi ffl

Spartan Black Condensed

Series Number 687

Characters in complete font

A B C D E F G H I J K L M N
O P Q R S T U V W X Y Z &
$ 1 2 3 4 5 6 7 8 9 0 ¢ %
a b c d e f g h i j k l m n o p q
r s t u v w x y z . , - : ; ! ? ' ' " " ( )

Ligatures are included in fonts of 10 to 18 point
sizes, and are obtainable in 24 to 120 point
sizes in foundry lines.

fi ff fl ffi ffl

Stymie Light

Series Number 553

Characters in complete font

A B C D E F G H I J K L M N
O P Q R S T U V W X Y Z &
$ 1 2 3 4 5 6 7 8 9 0
a b c d e f g h i j k l m n o p q
r s t u v w x y z . , - : ; ! ? ' ' « » ( ) § *

Superior $ furnished only with sizes 24 to 48 pt.

Stymie Medium

Series Number 552

Characters in complete font

A B C D E F G H I J K L M N
O P Q R S T U V W X Y Z &
$ 1 2 3 4 5 6 7 8 9 0
a b c d e f g h i j k l m n o p q
r s t u v w x y z . , - : ; ! ? ' ' ( )

Superior $ furnished with sizes 24 to 72/60 pt.

Franklin Gothic

Series Number 162

Characters in complete font

**A B C D E F G H I J K L M N
O P Q R S T U V W X Y Z &
$ 1 2 3 4 5 6 7 8 9 0
a b c d e f g h i j k l m n o p q
r s t u v w x y z . , - : ; ! ? '**

Franklin Gothic Wide

Series Number 701

Characters in complete font

**A B C D E F G H I J K L M N
O P Q R S T U V W X Y Z &
$ 1 2 3 4 5 6 7 8 9 0
a b c d e f g h i j k l m n o p q
r s t u v w x y z . , - : ; ! ? ' ' " "**

News Gothic

Series Number 338

Characters in complete font

A B C D E F G H I J K L M N
O P Q R S T U V W X Y Z &
$ 1 2 3 4 5 6 7 8 9 0
a b c d e f g h i j k l m n o p q
r s t u v w x y z . , - : ; ! ? '

News Gothic Extra Condensed

Series Number 340

Characters in complete font

A B C D E F G H I J K L M N
O P Q R S T U V W X Y Z &
$ 1 2 3 4 5 6 7 8 9 0
a b c d e f g h i j k l m n o p q
r s t u v w x y z . , - : ; ! ? '

Murray Hill Bold

24 pt. 5A 19a 8-1   L. c. alphabet 200 pts.   Char. per pica 1.7

Brazil and Colombia exported to Europe pottery impregnated with delicate perfumes. It shows civilizations at a time so remote

Bernhard Gothic Medium
Italic

24 pt. 6A 13a 5-1   Lower case alphabet 260 pts.   Characters per pica 1.3

BRAZIL AND THE OTHERS It shows that civilization at a time so remote could establish at that

Caslon 641

24 pt. 6A 12a 8-1   Lower case alphabet 323 pts.   Characters per pica 1.0

Rail and road transportation close at hand plus a network

Cooper Black

24 pt. 5A 10a 6-1   Lower case alphabet 376 pts.   Characters per pica .91

TO THE BUSY EXEC IN the hustle and bustle of

Craw Clarendon Condensed

24 pt. 9A 13a 7-1   L. c. alphabet 277 pts.   Char. per pica 1.2

GRAPHIC DESIGNER, RESPONSIVE to all the needs and requirements

Craw Modern Bold

24 pt. 5A 7a 4-1   L. c. alphabet 535 pts.   Char. per pica .64

LETTER FORMS
is truly excellent

Dom Bold

24 pt. 10A 18a 8-1   Lower case alphabet 202 pts.   Characters per pica 1.7

BRAZIL AND OTHER COUNTRIES ARE
It shows civilization at a time so remote

Franklin Gothic

24 pt. 6A 11a 5-1   Lower case alphabet 349 pts.   Characters per pica .98

Brazil and Peru export to

HEADLINE GOTHIC

48 pt. 4A 3-1

ZERO IS A MARK

Lydian Italic

30 pt. 7A 12a 5-1   Lower case alphabet 314 pts.   Characters per pica 1.1

JADE VARIES IN COLOR
It is used for jewelry or carve

New Caslon

24 pt.   5A 12a 7-1   Lower case alphabet 328 pts.   Characters per pica 1.0

BRAZIL AND OTHER
Shows civilization at a time
so remote that it is doubtful

UNIVERS 46

24-L pt. 6A 11a 6-1   Lower case alphabet 327 pts.   Characters per pica 1.0

| ABCDEFGHIJKLMNOPQR
| abcdefghijklmnopqrstuvw

News Gothic

30 pt.   6A 11a 5-1   Lower case alphabet 343 pts.   Characters per pica 1 0

JADE VARIES IN COLOR
It is used for jewelry and

UNIVERS 65

24-L pt. 5A 10a 5-1   Lower case alphabet 352 pts.   Characters per pica .97

| ABCDEFGHIJKLMNOP
| abcdefghijklmnopqrstuv

Type may be divided into two main divisions: text type, which is suited to solid blocks of text; and display type, which is used for display advertising, headings, and nomenclature applied to artwork and visual aids when large sizes are required.

Text type generally ranges from 8 to 10 points, although 12-point and even 14-point and larger type may be used for children's reading books and textbooks in the lower grades. An 8-point size is quite small, but dictionaries and similar publications may have text as small as 6 points. The ideal size for newspaper text is 9 points; 10-point type is popular for magazines, trade journals, typewritten matter, books, proposals, technical manuals, reports, and numerous other applications. Although 12-point type is too large for large blocks of text in conventional adult books, it is ideally suited for small blocks of text for mechanicals and for descriptive text in fine proposal work when used as a cutline with illustrative material. In general, there is a tendency to select type that is too small as text type.

Display typefaces are large faces that draw attention. A text type in 10 points can become a display type in 36 or 72 points. Typefaces have distinctive design characteristics that make them suitable for particular tasks. Type creates an illusion. Its appearance can suggest a thought, an idea, a statement, or a fact that it represents in copy. Type also conveys a mood or a condition, such as humor, happiness, gaiety, frivolity, anxiety, stateliness, solidarity, even sadness. Or, it can be feminine or masculine, soft or hard. It can whisper or shout and be bold or delicate. These illusions are the result of thick and thin lines, curves, boldfaces and heavy lines, solid masses of black and color, the presence or absence of serifs, and embellishments.

type writer, display Machine designed primarily for composing display type for posters, charts, bulletins, handbills, and advertising copy. Printasign (Figure T-10) is a trademark of the Reynolds Printasign Company for a machine that produces display type by the letterpress method. The machine cannot be classified as a typesetter, however, because it does not set type but makes an impression of the typeface from a relief matrix. A variety of faces in sizes ranging to 96 points are used.

typefaces The face of the type is the printing surface. A typeface may be judged by its design, printability, wearability, and position on the body. Past and present masters of the art of letter design and typographic layout have contributed much to the creation of artistic and practical type. Printability depends on deeply engraved matrices in hard nickel brass, from which the type is cast, on matrices made to provide crisp, clean edges on the finished product, on finish-

Fig. T-10   Printasign display type writer, Model HA.

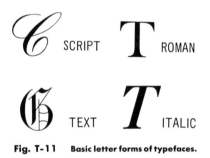

Fig. T-11   Basic letter forms of typefaces.

ing tools that produce sharp edges and well-incised crotches, and on matrices chromium-plated to impart a mirror-smooth printing surface to the type cast from them. Wearability depends on the use of high-quality metal cast at a high temperature under extreme pressure in a water-cooled mold. Type so made is tightly compressed and uniform in grain. It will print sharp images and last for a long time. The position of the face on the body is important for proper alignment and spacing. A strong and durable type results from the liberal use of tin, antimony, and copper, as well as from casting under rigidly controlled conditions.

Many faces and sizes of type have been manufactured since the first black-letter design, now sometimes used for German. This was the only design until roman and italic faces made their appearance. In the early eighteenth century, William Caslon of England designed the classic roman face. Later in the century, Giambattista Bodoni of Italy designed the first modern letter.

There are four basic forms of typefaces: text, roman, italic, and script (*see* Figure T-11). The roman faces, in one variation or another, make up the modern faces known today. All present-day type is based on these designs; it may be divided into two groups of faces, Old Style and modern. Figure T-12 shows the names used to describe the various lines of typefaces.

typescript   Typewritten text copy.

typeset matter, ordering of   Typesetting costs can be reduced and better quality assured when the printer is intelligently informed of all requirements. The printer's task is to follow copy, that is, to set copy exactly as it was submitted to him. Before ordering typeset matter, copy should be proofread for errors in spelling, punctuation, capitalization, and the like and checked for paragraph numbering (if any), indention, page numbering, and general format. Changes made to the typescript should be neat and legible and written in lowercase and capital letters as they are to be set. Copy should be

double-spaced, typed on one side of a sheet, and paginated in sequence, preferably in the upper right corner of each page. Long
tables should be typed on separate pages.

The following suggestions for ordering typeset matter should be
considered:

1. Specify the typefaces for text and headings and make certain
that the printer has the available faces and sizes. If this is not certain,
the notation "or equivalent" should be included on the purchase
order.

2. Specify the type size in points or request the printer to recommend a size.

3. For text copy, keep the line measure to approximately 39 characters ($1\frac{1}{2}$ alphabets is considered an ideal measure).

4. Give the line measure in picas, not in inches.

5. Specify copy that is to run ragged. Otherwise, the printer will
justify the lines.

6. Designate the leading desired (*see* LEADING).

7. If other than normal reproduction proofs are desired, specify
"Avery" for adhesive-backed paper, "dull seal" for transparent stock
with an adhesive back, and "cell" for transparent stock without an
adhesive back; or specify the particular paper desired.

typesetters, photographic   Photographic typesetters can be divided
into two broad classifications. The more sophisticated machines are
tape-controlled and computerized for the photographic typesetting
of text for newspapers, magazines, advertising copy, books, and stock
market quotations. Their output is on photographic paper or film.
Much less complicated in design and operation are the typesetters
whose primary purpose is to set display type. The fact that they
may also be operated to set text type is secondary to their primary
function. Their output is also on photographic paper or film. In
some cases the paper or film has an adhesive back and is ready for
paste-up.

Characters may be selected either by a keyboard or by a manual

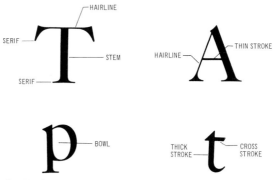

Fig. T-12   Typeface composition.

Fig. T-13 Friden's Typro photocomposing machine.

Fig. T-14 VariTyper's Headliner Model 860 photocomposing machine.

dial. They are then exposed by light onto photosensitive paper or film, and the image is developed by chemicals. The paper or film containing the image emerges from the machine ready for paste-up. Hand lettering, insignia, trademarks, and reverse images may be incorporated in the fonts.

Figure T-13 shows the Typro photocomposing machine, which is available in floor and desk models for either hand or continuous developing. A selector dial is turned to produce the desired character, which appears on a viewer, enlarged and illuminated, with composing targets to show proper spacing. A lever is raised to bring the sensitized paper or film into contact with the font during exposure. The copy is automatically developed, fixed, and dried and is ready for paste-up. Reverse images, justified letters, drop shadows, screen backgrounds, and more than one line can be composed on a strip. The Typro carries as many as 15 fonts on one reel. A selection from 1,800 fonts, ranging from 6 to 144 points, is available.

VariTyper's Headliner Model 860 (Figure T-14) composes one or more lines of type at the rate of 30 or more characters per minute. A wide assortment of type and other characters from 10 to 84 points may be selected. Each character is automatically letterspaced on 35-millimeter film or paper. The film may be used as a transparency for projection. Type is selected by placing the desired font, a plastic disk called a Typemaster, in operating position on the machine. A print key is pressed for each character in the copy. The Headliner automatically develops, fixes, and washes the type proof and delivers it ready for use in about ninety seconds.

The Filmotype phototypesetting and composing machine (Figure T-15) operates in conjunction with an automatic processor that develops, fixes, washes, and delivers copy set on the machine. Type sizes range from 12 to 144 points. Logotypes and trademarks may be produced. As many as 20 fonts may be inserted in the machine at one time. Since the fonts have a common base alignment, type styles may be intermixed. A vertically calibrated justification dial permits setting a word or line to the desired measure. A foot-switch control enables the operator to work with free hands, and an exposure control makes possible the reproduction of small, delicate type designs, fine screen patterns, and ornamental letters. In addition to standard fonts, fonts produced by hand lettering are available. These include formals, cursives, calligraphics, scripts, flat serifs, casuals, sans serifs, free styles, outlines, and novelties.

American Type Founders' Model KD-84 display typesetter (Figure T-16) is designed for headline composition. Display types in various sizes and faces ranging from 10 to 84 points are available as disks in standard font arrangements. Copy is set by operating keys that are almost identical with those of standard electric typewriters. When the desired typewriter key is struck, the disk, or font, responds and sets the copy photographically, fits it correctly, and spaces the lines on photographic film or paper. The KD-84T model allows unjustified display and headline copy to be set automatically from a coded punched tape prepared by an ATF Model A, AR, or B typesetter keyboard or by compatible tape-punching equipment. The copy may also be keyboarded directly.

Fig. T-15 Filmotype phototypsetting machine.

Fig. T-16 ATF's display and headline typesetter, Model KD-84.

Fig. T-17   **Photo-Typositor photographic typesetting machine.**

The Photo-Typositor (Figure T-17) is a product of the Visual Graphics Corporation. This machine projects typefaces from film fonts to either twice or one-fourth the size of the font face. Each of 600 available fonts can be used to set 2,800 variations of sizes, slants, and proportions. The Photo-Typositor can produce condensed, expanded, italicized, back-slanted, bouncing, and staggered characters; form interlocks; compose drop shadows; and make background tints. Copy is produced on photographic paper for paste-up or on clear acetate film. The machine can be operated in daylight, without need for a darkroom.

The Posteriter, also a product of the Visual Graphics Corporation, sets type from film fonts in sizes from $\frac{3}{4}$ to $3\frac{3}{4}$ inches high on clear acetate film or on photographic paper. Magazine loading of paper or film permits daylight operation. Continuous lines of copy as long as 100 feet are possible. Faces such as scripts, scrolls, border designs, interlocks, back slants, background tints, overlaps, and bounces, as well as a giant type for display purposes, may be produced.

The Harris-Intertype electronic photographic typesetting machine (Figure T-18) consists of two basic units, a keyboard console and a photographic printout. This kind of machine adapts the standard keyboard and the principle of circulating matrices to a camera device that replaces hot-metal casting elements. The keyboard console produces perforated tape that controls the operation of the printout unit as it produces justified text on film or photographic paper. Each unit has a built-in digital computer to control spacing and other functions. The keyboard console produces an eight-level perforated tape programmed with function codes to operate the printout unit automatically. At the same time, it produces hard copy for editing and correction.

A standard electric typewriter with 44 key buttons is used as the basic operating unit of the keyboard console. The operator may select 120 character positions. The eight-level input operates the printout unit with as many as 20 character exposures per second. It activates all functions, including positioning the correct typeface disk, selecting the proper character and point size from the disk, adjusting the lens system to one of 19 lens positions, adjusting the film-advance mechanism for proper line spacing, exposing characters in proper sequence with correct interletter and interword spacing to provide for accurate justification, tabulation, and quadding, and cutting photographic material on signal. The exposure speed in text sizes is 20 characters per second, which is comparable to 22 newspaper lines per minute or 22,000 ems per hour in book composition.

Fig. T-18   **Harris-Intertype electronic photographic typesetting machine, with keyboard console and photographic printout unit.**

Each type disk contains 240 characters, making 480 characters available for automatic selection and exposure. Disks rotate at 2,400 revolutions per minute. Type disks are made in the basic 10-point size, as well as in 15- and 20-point sizes. This system provides 19 point sizes for each disk in ranges as follows: 10-point disk, 5 through 36 points; 15-point disk, 7.5 through 54 points; and 20-point disk, 10 through 72 points.

American Type Founders' Model CS typesetter is designed for computerized typesetting. It will set photographically 12 standard newspaper lines per minute from a six-channel output tape of any computer programmed for this type of work. The Model CS is a computer slave unit. The production of composition is controlled automatically by tape from the computer. Unjustified composition can be keyboarded directly. Under computer control the typesetter can (1) word-space any line in the best combination of fixed units for justified or quadded composition, (2) letterspace a part of or an entire line in the best combination of fixed units down to $\frac{1}{18}$ em when bad hyphenation breaks occur, (3) mix signs and styles of specially designed faces to increase the speed of producing such copy as classified ads, and (4) word-space in a line with maximum and minimum limits as programmed in the computer. In operation, the machine reads the function and alphabetical codes contained in the computer-produced tape. Composition is accomplished photographically from a transparent type disk containing as many as 172 characters on film or photographic paper in widths of $2\frac{1}{2}$, $3\frac{3}{4}$, or $5\frac{3}{4}$ inches.

American Type Founders' Model B-8 keyboard unit (Figure T-19) is the production-control center of the Model B-8 photographic unit (Figure T-20). When the keyboard is operated, the keyboard unit

Fig. T-19   **ATF's Model B-8 keyboard unit.**

Fig. T-20   **ATF's Model B-8 photographic unit.**

punches coded tape that carries all the control data for automated typesetting. The manuscript copy is marked for type styles and sizes, line widths, leading, and other necessary instructions. The operator types until a panel light warns him that the justification zone has been reached. A switch justifies the line and returns the keyboard carriage. Errors are corrected by viewing the typed copy. The tape is then fed into the photographic unit, where the copy is produced on photographic paper for paste-up or on film for positive or negative plate making. In semiautomatic operation and at in-line speed, the keyboard unit can operate at a rate of 600 character and function codes per minute. At in-line photographic speed, the photographic unit can approximate 330 codes per minute, which is equivalent to ten 11-pica lines of $8\frac{1}{2}$-point Century Schoolbook straight matter, or about 155 ems per minute.

Figure T-21 is a photograph of the Monophoto filmsetter. The basic function of a filmsetter is to project character images directly onto a sheet of photosensitized film or paper and simultaneously compose them into justified lines of text. The filmsetter responds to perforated paper tape from a companion keyboard. As the paper unwinds and passes over the air tower for decoding, each successive step brings into alignment with the optical system one of a set of 272 characters and spaces held in the film matrix case for projection onto film. The selected character is held in a still position during an exposure of one-fiftieth of a second.

Film matrices are small photographic negatives having transparent characters on an opaque black background. Each negative is held in a protective plastic carrier, colored black for direct-reading or gray for reverse-reading matrices. In the film matrix case, the 272 characters are arranged in 16 rows of 17 matrices each. Each of the characters is separate and interchangeable. As a result, such sorts as accented letters, special signs, and fractions can be included in an original setting and patching can be avoided at the film makeup stage. Another advantage of separate film matrices is that they may be replaced inexpensively and conveniently if they are damaged despite the protection afforded by the plastic carrier.

Normally the size of the master images on the film matrices approximates 8 points, but a wide range of type sizes can be obtained by photographic enlargement or reduction. For most typefaces, one set of matrices covers all sizes from 8 to 24 points, with a second set for 6 and 7 points. There are exceptions to these groupings: all the sizes of Univers (6 to 22 points), for example, can be derived from one film matrix case, whereas three sets are recommended for Bembo. A change of face and size takes no longer than two minutes.

Once a film matrix has been aligned with the optical system according to response from the perforated tape, an exposure can be made. A projection lamp and a condenser lens are located above

Fig. T-21   Monotype's Monophoto filmsetter.

the selected matrix. The lens collects the divergent light and converts it into a parallel beam for illuminating all parts of the character equally. Under the film matrix, a shutter flashes the character for one-fiftieth of a second and the beam of light carrying the image is "folded up" by a pair of prisms. For the smaller type sizes (6 to 12 points) the light path continues through a projection lens onto a pair of mirrors inclined 45 degrees to the horizontal, which deflect the image toward the film. For the larger type sizes, the lens comes before the prisms. After each exposure, a lateral movement of the mirrors composes the characters into lines across the film. The use of prisms to bend the light beam saves space by keeping the machine within workable proportions and provides latitude for scaling all the intended type sizes. By means of a set of focusing bars and a control lever, the positions of the prisms and the projection lens can be altered to give the degree of magnification or reduction required (from 6 to 24 points), together with the correct focus. By adjusting the lens aperture to suit the type size being photographed, a constant exposure can be maintained throughout the range.

The drum on which the film is mounted automatically revolves for the required distance to the next line when the end of a line is reached. (The film itself does not move while a line is being exposed.) The movement of the drum is controlled by an adjustment on the drum driving unit, which has a scale graduated in $\frac{1}{2}$-point steps from 0 to 24 points. The equivalent of leading can therefore be incorporated in the setting of the film. Spacing takes no more time than is needed to give additional rotation to the drum. The film is secured to the surface of the drum with adhesive tape. Since the emulsion on the film does not come into moving contact with any other surface, scratching is avoided. Any convenient size of sheet film, to a maximum of 11 by 24 inches, can be loaded on the drum, permitting a maximum line measure of 60 ems. Litho-grade films and bromide papers commonly used in the printing industry are suitable for use with the filmsetter.

After a job has been completed, a gray scale is exposed at the head of the film to control development. The scale consists of nine squares of varying densities numbered 1 through 9. The No. 1 square is almost transparent, whereas No. 9 is very black. By observing these squares during development, the operator can recognize the point at which development should be stopped. Thus, when a particular square becomes visible, the operator knows that the image has reached a grade appropriate to the printing process being used.

Proofs of filmset matter are normally made in a whiteprint machine by exposing the positive over diazo-sensitized copy paper. The practice is to make house corrections on these proofs and to send them unrevised to the customer for checking. When the proofs are returned to the printer, both sets of corrections are made in a single operation.

typesetting Composing and setting type by hand, with hot-metal typecasting machines, or with photographic typesetters.

typewriter The history of the typewriter is one of slow progress to which many inventors have contributed. The original concept envisaged a device that would form a readable image faster than a person could write with a pen. However, the need for some means of enabling the blind to read by touch also played a large part in the development of the typewriter. Unlike a great number of inventions, the typewriter cannot be attributed to a single individual, although no doubt some inventors contributed more than others.

The accounts are replete with crude, slow devices that were unsuccessful, with trial and error, and with improvement from one device to the next.

The earliest recorded attempt to create a mechanical writing device was made in England in 1714. No drawings of this device are in existence. Seventy years later, in France, a device was constructed to emboss characters that could be translated by the blind. In 1829, the first United States patent was granted for a machine having type mounted on a disk. The disk was rotated to the desired character and a lever operated to impress the character on a surface. It was not until 1868 that a typewriter that could produce letters faster than a person could write was developed. Meanwhile, the platen had come into being as a means of holding paper.

The year 1873 is recognized as the beginning of the period when features were introduced to make the typewriter a workable machine. New developments were added to older models. The platen, the carriage return, typebars, and the advancing inked ribbon were either introduced or assembled as units. An escapement mechanism was devised that permitted the carriage to move to the next space. By providing corresponding capital and lowercase letters on a single typebar, the use of two keyboards, one for capital letters and one for lowercase, was eliminated. Mark Twain was the first author to use a typewriter for a book manuscript.

Development of a standard keyboard placed the most frequently used characters in positions where keys could be manipulated with the least effort and at the greatest speed. Thus, touch typing was introduced and schools were formed to give instruction in this new profession. Once having learned the technique of touch typing, operators were in demand and the profession was regarded as one of great skill. Operators were called typewriters because they wrote with type.

Manual percussion was used to force the relief image on the typebar against the ribbon and so to paper. It was not until 1920 that George Smathers produced a working model of an electric typewriter. A continuously revolving rubber power roller provides the force that propels the typebar of the electric typewriter against the ribbon. When a key is struck, a leg of the typebar is forced momentarily against the roller, which kicks it, thus forcing the typebar to strike the ribbon and form the impression. A subsequent advance in typing technology is represented by the IBM Selectric typewriter. A small interchangeable printing element containing characters in relief is used to form the typed image. During operation, the element moves across the paper typing the line of text. This principle has eliminated typebars and the moving paper carriage. (*See also* COLD COMPOSITION.)

It became apparent that typewriters could be used effectively to produce reproduction copy for offset printing. The VariTyper, the Justowriter, and the IBM Executive series are equipped for proportional spacing. Figure T-22 shows an Executive typewriter. All typewriters of the Executive series have various individual typefaces. Unlike the characters on standard typewriters, the characters on these typewriters have assigned unit values. It is this feature which makes them proportional-spacing machines and therefore highly suitable for preparing reproduction copy for offset printing.

Fig. T-22   IBM's Executive typewriter. (Courtesy of Office Products Division.)

Proportional spacing means that each typed character occupies a space equivalent to its width. Small letters such as i, l, j, and f have fewer units than such letters as m, w, and r. The smallest letter has 2 units; the largest, 5. Ordinary typewriters type all letters in the same amount of space (Figure T-23*A*), whereas with proportional spacing each letter is given its required space (Figure T-23 *B*).

Justification is made possible because spacing between words is also measured in units. Normal spacing between words has a value of 2 units, which is obtained by striking the 2-unit space bar once. It is thus possible not only to subtract 1 unit between words for long lines but to add 1 or more units for short lines. It is necessary to type the copy twice. The first typing, called "prejustifying," determines the line count, that is, the number of units to be added to or subtracted from each line. Actual justifying is accomplished in the second typing. It is possible to justify copy to any line measure. First, a series of M's is typed to the length of the desired measure.

iiiiiiiiiiiiiii

lllllllllllllll

mmmmmmmmmmmmmmm

wwwwwwwwwwwwwww

MMMMMMMMMMMMMMM

LLLLLLLLLLLLLLL

(All characters occupy
equivalent spaces)

- -

iiiiiiiiiiiiiii   (2 units each character)

lllllllllllllll   (2 units each character)

mmmmmmmmmmmmmmm   (5 units each character)

WWWWWWWWWWWWWWW   (5 units each character)

MMMMMMMMMMMMMMM   (5 units each character)

LLLLLLLLLLLLLLL   (4 units each character)

Fig. T-23   Ordinary and proportional spacing of letters.

When the operator strikes the last M, without striking the space bar again, he notes the position of the pointer on the right front paper scale. This is the reference point to which lines must be typed by adding or subtracting units. A tab is set to the right of the line for typing the number of units to be added or subtracted for each line.

For prejustifying copy, the operator types the text in normal fashion. When the end of the line approaches the reference point indicated by the pointer on the paper scale, he determines whether the line is long or short. If the pointer indicates that the line has been typed beyond the reference point, the backspace key, which has a value of 1 unit, is used to back up to the reference point. The number of units required to reach the reference point is typed at the tab and prefixed by a minus sign. If the typed line falls short of the reference point, the number of units to be added is found by striking the 2-unit space bar until the pointer rests on the reference point.

The number of units is then typed at the tab. When a period or a comma comes at the end of a line, it is necessary to backspace once and then count units to be added or subtracted. If a typed line ends exactly on the reference point, justification is not required and a zero is typed at the tab.

Once the unit count has been made for all lines of text, plus or minus marks are inserted between words as shown by the tab numbers. Each mark represents 1 unit. A red pencil is used to denote minus marks and a black pencil plus marks. After all plus and minus marks have been inserted and the copy proofread, it is ready for typing (justification) on reproducible paper. The text is typed exactly as in the first typing except where plus and minus marks have been inserted. The backspace key is used to delete units between words. The 3-unit space bar is used to add 1 unit between words, and the 2-unit space bar is used to add units as desired.

typewriter paper *See* BOND TYPEWRITER PAPER; BOXED PAPER.

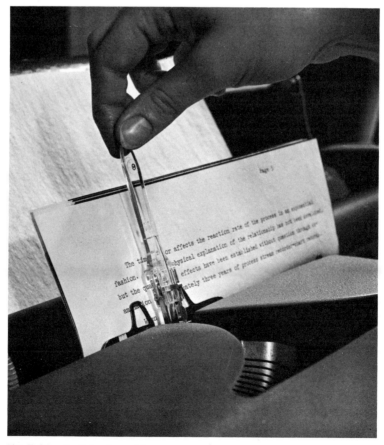

Fig. T-24   Typit typebar guide.

Typit Trade name of Mechanical Enterprises, Inc., for symbols used with typewriters for typing Greek letters, mathematical equations, diacritical marks, and many other miscellaneous symbols (*see* Figure T-24). Typits are used especially for technical publications. They are adaptable to various typewriter models. The typebar of the typewriter is replaced with a modified typebar guide to hold the symbol. When a symbol is desired, the corresponding Typit is inserted in the typebar holder. A key is struck, and the symbol is typed. The Typit is then removed and normal typing continued.

typographer One skilled in typography as a designer or as a printer.

typography Art and process of letterpress or similar printing, with reference to the style, format, and general appearance of the printed page.

Typro Trademark for a photocomposing machine (*See* TYPESETTERS, PHOTOGRAPHIC.)

U

uncoated book paper Paper used for the letterpress printing of catalogs, books, direct-mail pieces, folders, etc. It is manufactured in four finishes: machine, antique, English, and supercalendered. The antique finish, which is somewhat rough and reflects light, is used for catalogs, books, folders, and brochures for which bulk is not important. Because of its rough surface, antique finish is not recommended for halftones with screens of more than 85 lines. Standard weights are 30, 35, 40, 45, 50, 60, 70, 80, and 100 pounds for 500 sheets of the basic size of 25 by 38 inches.

The machine-finished uncoated book paper has a medium-smooth surface and is used for books, catalogs, direct-mail pieces, and broadsides in which line art is important. While the finish is smoother than antique, only halftones with 100-line or coarser screens are recommended. Standard basic weights are 30, 35, 40, 45, 50, 60, 70, 80, and 100 pounds for 500 sheets of the basic size of 25 by 38 inches.

The supercalendered finish is the smoothest finish of uncoated book paper. Catalogs, books, pamphlets, and magazines are examples of its use. Halftones of 100- to 120-line screens may be employed, the best results being obtained from the 100-line screen. This finish is applied by the same process as the machine and English finishes for uncoated book paper, additional smoothness being obtained by further calendering. The standard basic weights are 30, 35, 40, 45,

50, 60, 70, 80, and 100 pounds for 500 sheets of the basic size of 25 by 38 inches.

undercut   In photoengraving, the effect produced by allowing acid to etch under the printing area and undermine it; in technical illustrating, a break in the outline of an object at the point where the flow line intersects the object.

underrun   Printed or duplicated copies of sheets or pages less than the specified number.

undimensioned drawing   Engineering drawing that does not show actual dimensions but depicts to scale the loft-line, template, pattern, and printed-circuit information necessary to produce such parts within the allowable manufacturing limits shown on other engineering drawings. Undimensioned drawings are shop accessory drawings used in conjunction with other drawings; as such, they do not show part requirements. They permit quality control of complex contours of templates or patterns that would be difficult to measure in any other way.

unglazed finish   Paper finish without luster.

unit: cold-composition copy   Measurement of width used in typing with proportional-spacing machines, particularly IBM Executive typewriters. (*See* PROPORTIONAL SPACING; TYPEWRITER.)

unit perfecting press   *See* BLANKET-TO-BLANKET PRESS.

unit: printing   Individual printing unit added to a web-fed press to increase its capacity. Each unit has its own inking and roller system and is installed in line with one or more other units. (*See also* OFFSET PRESS; WEB OFFSET PRINTING.)

unitized film   Filmstrip of individual microforms, each containing a related image or unit, as opposed to a roll of microfilm.

unretouched photograph   Photograph that has not been altered or improved by airbrushing, hand, or other means. It is therefore an exact facsimile of the original view.

unsharp premask   Photographic material exposed and printed from the original color transparency before color-separation negatives are made. It gives better registration with less probability of showing defects between the two films.

V

vacuum frame *See* COPYBOARD.

value Relative lightness and darkness of different areas of a picture as represented in tones, shading, line balance, layout, and the like. (*See also* DENSITY.)

vandyke Term often used to designate a brownprint negative and sometimes a brownline positive. (*See* BROWNLINE PRINT; BROWNPRINT.)

vanishing point Point at which parallel lines, receding from the observer, appear to come together in a perspective drawing or photograph.

Varigraph Cold-type nonphotographic headline composing machine. Varigraph is a registered trademark of Varigraph, Inc. The machine is capable of setting headlines on artwork, paper plates, or any other ink-accepting material. Advertisements, comprehensives, catalog sheets, brochures, silk-screen layouts, posters, and packages are examples of applications.

Figure V-1 shows the Varigraph Headwriter with its composing table. The table, which serves as a horizontal track, is calibrated on both the vertical and the horizontal dimensions. One table model provides a transparent top for use as a light table. Horizontal and vertical grids enable the operator to align stock or plates.

407

Fig. V-1   **Varigraph headline composing machine.**

The Varigraph is operated by moving a swivel handle which follows guide grooves in the selected matrix or template. A production pen of the desired line weight sets the image in response to the pattern followed on the matrix. Two controls are added features. One control establishes the width of individual characters and the other the height. These controls are calibrated in both points and inches in sizes from 14 to 72 points. The operator can select any desired intermediate size from one matrix. Different matrices are available for popular headline typefaces, any of which may be used as variations for intermediate sizes as well as providing condensed, open-faced, extended, shadow, dancing, reverse, and other effects. An italic model produces back-slanted and vertical or italic characters from any Varigraph matrix.

Vario-Klishograph   Trademark of an automatic electric scanner. (*See* ELECTRONIC ENGRAVING.)

VariTyper   Cold-composition machine manufactured by the Vari-Typer Corporation. (*See* COLD COMPOSITION.)

varnishing (**lacquering**)   Applying fixative to reproduction copy or to a completed printed sheet for protection or appearance.

vector-analysis symbols   *See* TABLE 12.

vellum Kind of fine paper resembling parchment that is used for duplicating copies made with a whiteprint machine. Vellum is translucent and consequently permits the passage of light during exposure in the whiteprint process. For typing, vellum is sometimes backed with orange carbon paper to make the image more pronounced when it is reproduced. The finish of the paper is of high quality, and the content is 100 percent rag.

vellum finish Paper finish similar to text finish. It is smooth and dull.

vellum master Original produced on vellum paper.

vellum transfer Master copy on vellum, taken from the original and used to make additional copies by the whiteprint process. It is actually an intermediate because it is made from an original to produce copies.

Velox Print of a photograph or other continuous-tone copy which has been prescreened before paste-up or plate making with line copy and which may be screened in any manner with or without a darkroom. The necessity of making a composite negative (halftone art stripped into line art) is eliminated because only a line shot is required.

verso *See* RECTO.

vertical column chart *See* COLUMN CHART.

vertical dimension Distance between the top and bottom of an image when the image is held in an upright, or reading, position. It is perpendicular to the horizontal dimension. The vertical dimension is also known as the height, regardless of its length with respect to the horizontal.

When oversize copy is prepared, both dimensions must be in proportion to the reduced image area. If the copy is not in proportion, either the width or the height must be used as the controlling dimension so that the reduced copy will fit the prescribed area.

vertical page Page that contains right-reading copy when it is held in a normal reading position. It is contrasted with a broadside page, which must be turned 90 degrees clockwise to be read.

vertical press Printing press with a flatbed that is held in a vertical position with the printing forms locked in place. A rotating cylinder draws the paper around itself as it revolves and moves from the top to the bottom of the printing form, thus causing the impression to be made on the paper.

vicinity plan drawing   Drawing or map used with construction drawings to show the relationship of a site to features of the surrounding area, such as towns, bodies of water, railroads, and highways.

viewer, microfilm   *See* MICROFILM READER.

viewing-plane line   *See* LINE CONVENTIONS: ENGINEERING DRAWINGS.

vignette   Halftone copy in which the background fades from heavier to lighter tones until it is completely absorbed by the color of the paper. The dots should be graduated beginning $\frac{1}{2}$ inch from the edge of the vignette until they seem to disappear.

vignetter   Device for printing photographic vignettes; also, one who produces vignettes.

visible line   In orthographic mechanical and engineering drawings, the outline line. An unbroken line, it is used for all the visible lines of an object. (*See also* LINE CONVENTIONS: ENGINEERING DRAWINGS.)

visual: art   Preliminary rough layout of artwork, usually produced by a visualizer to exploit the best layout and composition possibilities of the article to be illustrated. A visual is desirable when an article has a complicated or technical design or the layout of the illustration is difficult.

visual: overhead projection   *See* OVERHEAD PROJECTION; PROJECTURAL.

vu-graph   Projectural consisting of carbon-backed film, used in overhead projection. The communicator writes or draws with a pencil or stylus, producing a white image on a black background. The term "vu-graph" is often used erroneously for a transparent projectural, which produces a black or colored image on a white background. (*See also* OVERHEAD PROJECTION.)

W

wash drawing Watercolor painting in which the color is applied mainly by washes. A complete drawing should be made before the washes are applied. A first wash of clear water is spread over the drawing. The following washes, from the lightest to the heaviest tones, are applied successively over one another. In the process, white or light areas are passed over. Final touches are added for emphasis.

washed-out drawing (wiped-out drawing) Watercolor in which a portion of the image is washed out with a damp brush while the painting is damp. The technique is used to add soft color on a canvas-grained paper. Dramatic sky effects may be produced. Indelible inks may be used for tinting. When glycerin is mixed with the painting solution, the wash has a tendency to "float" on the surface rather than to penetrate the paper immediately, thus allowing time to apply the washing technique.

washout Washing, drying, and cleaning of negatives, plates, and the like during the developing and processing stage.

washup Process of cleaning the rollers of a printing press, particularly to prepare them for a different color run.

water finish   High-quality glossy paper finish, obtained by applying water to one or more calender rolls in the papermaking process.

watercolor printing   Printing process in which special watercolor inks and soft, porous stock are used. Unlike oil or varnish inks used in ordinary printing, which are laid for the most part on the surface of the stock, watercolor inks are immediately absorbed by the paper. The process therefore permits colors to overlap and hues to be blended. For certain types of posters for which brilliant contrasting colors are desired, the effect is excellent.

watermark   Design, trademark, name, logotype, or the like impressed on paper by the dandy roll or other rollers during the paper-manu-facturing process.

wax engraving   Method of reproducing forms such as graphs, maps, and charts by cutting lines in wax that is backed with a thin copper sheet. The impression is used as a mold for an electroplate.

web   Roll of printing paper formed in the manufacturing process. To the printer, the web is the continuous roll of paper as it is fed through the press. The web or webs are attached to roll stands, which may be installed in line with the printing press or on the side when space is limited. They are diverted to the printing unit by angle bars. A web has a center shaft, or core, around which the paper is wound. The core may be made of metal and intended to be reused or of paper and so be expendable.

web cleaner   Vacuum cleaner installed before the first printing unit of a web-fed press to remove foreign particles from stock.

web flow   Continuous feeding of a web (paper roll) through a print-ing press, as opposed to feeding single sheets to the press. The printing of continuous forms is an example.

web lead rollers (idler rollers)   Set of rollers located between print-ing units of a blanket-to-blanket press in line with the lower blanket cylinder. The rollers support the stock and prevent it from wrinkling between the units and also control the stock as it unrolls from the web.

web offset printing   Lithographic printing from rolled stock. The paper manufacturer refers to the roll as a web. The printer uses the term "web" not only for the roll but for the paper itself as it feeds through the press. The web is a continuous roll of paper formed during manufacture and used extensively in printing news-papers. In some offset presses the web is fed between the blanket cylinder and an impression cylinder. Other presses are manufactured with a blanket-to-blanket arrangement, the web being fed between two blanket cylinders, each of which serves as an impression cylinder for the other. A great advantage of blanket-to-blanket web presses is their speed and resulting high productivity. Speeds may be twice those of some other presses because both sides of the web are printed at the same time. They may attain 800 feet per minute, or approximately 25,000 impressions per hour. This rate of speed will account for more than nine miles of paper per hour. Most web offset presses have widths of 36 to 38 inches.

Web offset presses can be divided into two broad classifications: those that are designed for great productivity but without flexibility for long printing runs; and multipurpose flexible presses for handling many varied sizes of printed matter. They may be subdivided into categories by such design characteristics as cylinder-to-cylinder relationships and features peculiar to individual manufacturers.

Figure W-1 shows a Webendorfer publications press. With one pass of the web, the press prints, folds, imprints, perforates, slits, and glues. It can handle such material as magazines, catalogs, telephone directories, house organs, shopping guides, newspapers and newspaper supplements, textbooks, institution manuals, gift wrappings, and encyclopedias. Printing units, added as required, print on the blanket-to-blanket principle. Sizes range from $22\frac{3}{4}$ by 36 to $41\frac{5}{8}$ by 60 inches.

Fig. W-1   American Type Founders' Webendorfer publications press.

Fig. W-2 Cottrell Vanguard Model 22 newspaper web offset press. (Courtesy of Harris-Intertype Corporation.)

Figure W-2 shows the Cottrell Vanguard Model 22 newspaper web offset press. While only one printing unit and web are shown in the photograph, as many as six other units may be added, making the press capable of producing a 24-page newspaper (48-page tabloid) at a rate of 22,000 copies per hour. Units can be used to add color. The printing area is 22 by 36 inches, the plate size $23\frac{7}{16}$ by 36 inches, and the blanket size $25\frac{1}{2}$ by $36\frac{1}{2}$ inches.

The Harris-Cottrell 35- by 51-inch blanket-to-blanket web offset press is designed especially for high-speed production of catalogs, newspapers, and magazines. Approximately 25,000 folded signatures can be produced in an hour.

web perfecting press Press that performs on the rotary principle with curved plates locked on a plate cylinder. The paper is fed from a web. Units containing inking rollers, an impression cylinder, a plate cylinder, and cylinders for transferring paper, as well as separate ink fountains for various colors, may be added as required. The press will print one color on both sides of the sheet in one operation with one or more printing units.

wet stripping Removal of the stripping layer from a film after the film has been processed but while it is wet.

white-flame arc Arc light that uses carbon with a core of chemicals that burn to produce an intense white light.

white on black *See* REVERSE BLUELINE.

whiteline print *See* REVERSE BLUELINE.

whiteprint process (diazo process; diazotype process; direct-copy process) Reproduction process based on the use of light-sensitive dyes. Several features are peculiar to the process: (1) masters must be of translucent or transparent material, (2) all copies are of the same size as the original, (3) all copies are facsimiles of the original, and (4) white on the original stays white and black on the original stays black on the copies. Whiteprint machines range from small models accommodating $8\frac{1}{2}$- by 11-inch paper to large commercial machines that can handle copy paper up to 54 inches in width by any length.

The whiteprint process is comparatively simple. An original is placed over the sensitized copy faceup, and the two sheets are fed in contact into the machine by the operator. The sheets are conveyed around a high-pressure mercury lamp where ultraviolet light inactivates the dye in the copy paper that is not protected by the opaque image of the original. The original is returned automatically to the operator. Meanwhile, the copy paper, carrying the latent image, is conveyed across ammonia vapors (dry process) or through developer rolls (moist process) that develop the image. The copy emerges as a facsimile of the original. The image is permanent, and the copy is dry. (*See also* ANHYDROUS AMMONIA SYSTEM; AQUEOUS AMMONIA SYSTEM; DRY DIAZO PROCESS.)

Depending on the type of copy paper used, the image may have blue, black, red, or sepia lines when it has been developed. Copies may be made on several grades or weights of white paper, on blue, pink, yellow, green, or other colored paper, or on film, cloth, or plastic-coated paper. The image may also be produced on paper or thin flexible plates which are developed by applying a solution and made ready for offset printing.

Photolithographic negatives or any negatives having a translucent image are adaptable to the whiteprint process for obtaining check-out and proof copies. The black background remains black or dark blue, and the image remains white. This type of copy, which has been given the name "reverse blueline," has many advantages, since it withstands smudging and grease marks in the shop or field, may be used for editing and checking, and can serve as a reference copy in a special file. (*See also* REVERSE BLUELINE.)

In addition to translucent bond and writing paper, vegetable parchment, greaseproof paper, rag tracing paper, and onionskin may be used as masters. While vegetable parchment and greaseproof paper have a high reprint speed, they do not function as well as printing and writing paper because of instability and distortion due to changes in atmospheric conditions. Rag tracing papers, such as those commonly used for engineering drawing work, are satisfactory as whiteprint reproduction masters with pencil and ink work. Such papers that have been transparentized by the addition of resin during manufacture make excellent masters. Films and cloths also make excellent masters, as they are sturdy, handle well, and are easily filed.

In preparing masters, several factors are essential for good reproduction. A master must have a solid definition of the image, composed of hard, even lines. For typewritten material, small drawings, or hand-ruled forms, the master may be backed with orange carbon paper to obtain greater opacity. (*See also* ORANGE BACKING.)

widow   Short last line of a paragraph that is carried over to the top of the next column or page, where it stands alone. Widows should be avoided during layout or makeup of copy. (*See also* ORPHAN.)

width   In the graphic arts, the distance between two points along the horizontal dimension. With height it is one of the two dimensions that measure a plane. When measurements are given for line and continuous-tone copy, the width and the height should be stated in that order. (*See also* HORIZONTAL DIMENSION.)

wild copy   Text copy that has been typed or printed to be cut and pasted as callouts for illustrations or for use in the composition of graphs, charts, or mechanicals.

window   Die-cut opening on the front cover of a publication that reveals the title or other information printed on the title page; also, any such opening that reveals an image of any kind imposed on the succeeding page. The term "window" may also be used as an equivalent of black patch. (*See* BLACK PATCH.)

wipe-on plate   Offset printing plate that requires the application of a light-sensitive coating before exposure. When the plate is exposed to light through the coating, the exposed areas of the coating harden. Wipe-on plates are chemically or mechanically grained to make them receptive to water.

wiped-out drawing *See* WASHED-OUT DRAWING.

wire side In the manufacture of paper, the side of the paper next to the wire (the underside) as it is conveyed along a belt. It is the opposite of the felt side.

wiring diagram Diagram of an electrical or electronic system in which wire numbers, colors, and sizes are shown together with an orthographic pictorial drawing representing the parts of the system. The parts may also be shown by a listing. A wiring diagram is often used to give instructions or information on wiring functions for assembly, disassembly, repair or replacement, and connections of an electrical system. It may cover internal or external connections, or both, and usually shows the details needed to trace and make connections.

woodcut Engraving cut in a block of wood; also, the impression made from the engraving. The woodcut was an early form of block printing. The image is drawn or written on the block and the background removed with fine cutting tools. A raised surface, representing the image, thus becomes the printing surface, which is used to make a black or white impression. When lines are incised in solid black areas, a range of middle tones is introduced, and the resulting impression is a white-on-black representation. Because there is no perceptible gradation of tone, woodcuts are classified as line art. Fine lines may be so well defined that some objects are better illustrated by woodcuts than by halftones.

wood-pulp bond *See* BOND PAPER.

word spacing Adjustment of spacing between words, particularly to shorten or extend a line in order to achieve justification.

work and tumble (print and tumble) To print one side of a sheet of paper and then turn the sheet over from gripper to back while using the same side guide.

work and turn (print and turn) To print one side of a sheet of paper and then turn the sheet over from left to right and print on the opposite side. The same gripper edge is used for both sides of the sheet.

work-up Defect appearing on a printed impression because of leading, furniture, or a slug that has worked up to the surface of a printing form.

wove finish   Paper finish that has no visible laid lines. Antique wove is an example of such a finish.

wraparound   Cylindrical printing plate that wraps around a plate cylinder. It is used on a rotary printing press.

wraparound cover   Soft cover used to bind or hold a booklet, brochure, etc. It consists of one sheet of stock that forms both front and back covers. Any type of mechanical binding may be used.

Wrico pens   *See* PENS, TECHNICAL.

writing paper   Paper suitable for writing with pen and ink.

wrong-reading   *See* REVERSE-READING.

X,Y,Z

X Twenty-fourth letter of the alphabet, used in the graphic arts to denote magnification of an image such as that of a microfilm. For example, 14X means that an enlargement is 14 times the size of the image on the microfilm.

xerography Copying process that utilizes electrostatic forces to form an image. The word is taken from the Greek *xeros,* meaning "dry," and *graphos,* meaning "writing." Xerography is a clean, fast, dry direct-positive process. Two methods may be used to produce the image. In the first, which is based on the drum principle, the image is transferred from a selenium-coated drum to paper. In the second, the image is transferred from a flat photoconductive plate to paper. In the drum operation, the original is placed facedown on a scanning glass and a scanning light passed under the glass. The image is projected onto the selenium-coated photoconductive drum, where a pattern of electrically charged and discharged areas corresponding to the image and nonimage areas of the original is formed. The surface of the drum is positively charged as the drum rotates. The latent electrostatic image is developed by a cascade of powder over the drum, and the powdered image is transferred electrostatically from drum to stock. The image is fused by heat for permanence. The Xerox 813, 914, and 2400 machines employ the drum method of producing the image. (*See also* COPYING MACHINES.)

The plate method uses a thin selenium-coated photoconductive plate as a substitute for camera film. The xerographic camera is referred to by its maker, Xerox Corporation, as Standard Equipment (*see* Figure C-11). The camera enlarges or reduces originals and then makes copies. In operation, the photoconductive selenium-coated plate is electrically charged in the charging chamber of a processor. After being charged, the plate is placed in the camera, and the material to be copied is exposed directly to the charged plate. The plate is then placed in a tray assembly of the processor, and the latent image is developed. After development, the image is transferred electrostatically from the plate to ordinary paper, vellum, or a paper or metal offset duplicating plate. The paper, vellum, or offset plate is then placed in a heat fuser and "baked," or fused, to make the image permanent. (*See also* CAMERA, XEROGRAPHIC PROCESS.)

zinc etching   Zinc plate on which a photoengraved line image has been etched.

zinc finish   Paper finish obtained by using sheets of zinc in the manufacturing process.

zinc halftone   Zinc plate on which a halftone has been etched.

Bibliography

General

Anatomy of the nuArc Camera, nuArc Company, Inc., Chicago, 1966.

The Book of American Types, American Type Founders Co., Inc., Elizabeth, N.J. 1961.

Carter, John, *ABC for Book-collectors,* 3d ed., rev., Alfred A. Knopf, Inc., New York, 1963.

Catalog of Brushes, Colors, Artists' Materials, M. Grumbacher, Inc., New York, 1963.

Coffman, J. W., "The Role of Visual Communication," 75th Anniversary Conference, Photographers' Association of America, Chicago, Aug. 15, 1955.

————, *Technology of the Diazotype Process,* Technifax Corporation, Holyoke, Mass.

Converkal: A Metal Type Conversion Film, Kalvar Corporation, New Orleans.

Craftint Quik-Graphics Catalog, No. 5, Craftint Manufacturing Co., Cleveland.

Dentsman, Harold, and J. Morton Schultz, *Photographic Reproduction,* McGraw-Hill Book Company, New York, 1963.

Diazo Microfilm for Miniaturization Systems, 10th Annual Conference, National Microfilm Association, Chicago, April 4–6, 1961.

Diazochrome Projecturals for Instructional Purposes, Technifax Corporation, Holyoke, Mass., 1962.

Diazochrome Projecturals for Visual Communication, Technifax Corporation, Holyoke, Mass., 1963.

Engineering Reproduction Handbook, E. I. du Pont de Nemours and Co., Wilmington, Del.

Equipment for Graphic Data Reduction, Film Reduction, and Plotting, Gerber Scientific Instrument Co., Hartford, Conn., 1963.

Fotorite News, vol. 2, no. 1, Fotorite, Inc., Chicago, 1964.

Frankenfield, H., *Block Printing with Linoleum,* 5th ed., Hunt Manufacturing Co., Philadelphia, 1956.

————, *Printmaking,* 6th ed., Hunt Manufacturing Co., Philadelphia, 1964.

The Functions and Applications of Monophoto Filmsetters, Lanston Monotype Company, Philadelphia.

General Information concerning Trademarks, Government Printing Office, Washington, D.C., May 1963.

George, Ross F., *Speedball Textbook for Pen and Brush Drawing,* 18th ed., Hunt Manufacturing Co., Philadelphia, 1960.

Graphic Arts Background Memorandum, E. I. du Pont de Nemours and Co., Wilmington, Del.

Graphic Arts Handbook, E. I. du Pont de Nemours and Co., Wilmington, Del.

Handy One-line ATF Type Style Selector, American Type Founders Co., Inc., Elizabeth, N.J.

Hodge, Stan, "Techniques of Inexpensive but Effective Graphic Processes," *General Dynamics/Astronautics,* 1963.

How, When and Why to Use a Line-up Table, nuArc Company, Inc., Chicago, 1965.

IBM Electric Typewriter, International Business Machines Corp., Office Products Division, New York.

The Kalvar Handbook, Technical Bulletin 104, Kalvar Corporation, New Orleans.

Kodak Graphic Arts Films and Plates, Eastman Kodak Company, Rochester, N.Y.

Kodak Pamphlet P-21, Eastman Kodak Company, Rochester, N.Y.

Kodak Pamphlet Q-21, Eastman Kodak Company, Rochester, N.Y.

Kodak Pamphlet Q-23, Eastman Kodak Company, Rochester, N.Y.

Koh-I-Noor Catalog 63, Koh-I-Noor, Inc., Bloomsbury, N.J.

McCarty, Arthur L., *Make More Accurate Halftone and Line Negatives,* reprint from *In-plant Printer,* June 1, 1965.

The Makeup and Correction of Filmset Matter Preparatory to Printing, Lanston Monotype Company, Philadelphia.

Melcher, Daniel, and Nancy Larrick, *Printing and Promotion Handbook,* 3d ed., McGraw-Hill Book Company, New York, 1966.

Moore, N. O., *The History of Printing,* Polytechnic High School and Junior College, Riverside, Calif.

Offset Platemaking with the nuArc Flip-Top Platemaker, nuArc Company, Inc., Chicago.

Photographic and Graphic Arts Equipment, Calumet Manufacturing Co., Chicago, 1964.

Reproduction Equipment Catalog, Charles Bruning Company, Mount Prospect, Ill., 1965.

Sensitized Reproduction Materials, Charles Bruning Company, Mount Prospect, Ill., 1961.

Technical Manual for Friden Compos-O-Line System, Friden, Inc., San Leandro, Calif., 1962.

Technical Manual for Friden Justowriter, Friden, Inc., San Leandro, Calif., 1961.

Technical Manual for Friden LCC-S Justowriter, Friden, Inc., San Leandro, Calif., 1961.

Techniques of Mimeographing, A. B. Dick Company, Chicago, 1963.

Type Catalog and Production Handbook, Varigraph, Inc., Madison, Wis., 1963.

Visualization Made Easier with Chart-Pak, Chart-Pak, Inc., Leeds, Mass., 1958.

Visucom Equipment and Materials Catalog, Technifax Corporation, Holyoke, Mass., 1958.

Military Standards

MIL-STD-1, *General Drawing Practice.*

MIL-STD-2, *Drawing Sizes.*

MIL-STD-3, *Format for Production Drawings.*

MIL-STD-4, *Format for Construction Drawings.*

MIL-STD-7, *Types and Definitions of Engineering Drawings.*

MIL-STD-8, *Dimensioning and Tolerancing.*

MIL-STD-24, *Revision of Drawings.*

Military Specifications

MIL-D-5480, *Data, Engineering and Technical* (Reproduction Thereof).

MIL-D-8510, *Drawing Negative, Reproducible Photographic, Preparation of.*

Associations and Societies

American Association of Industrial Editors
1300 Arch Street
Philadelphia, Pennsylvania 19107

American Book Publishers Council
One Park Avenue
New York, New York 10016

American Booksellers Association
175 Fifth Avenue
New York, New York 10010

American Institute for Design and Drafting
18465 James Couzens
Detroit, Michigan 48235

American Institute of Graphic Arts
1059 Third Avenue
New York, New York 10021

American Library Association
50 East Huron Street
Chicago, Illinois 60611

American Newspapers Publishers Association
Easton, Pennsylvania 18042

American Paper and Pulp Association
122 East Forty-second Street
New York, New York 10017

American Photoengravers Association
166 West Van Buren Street
Chicago, Illinois 60604

American Records Management Association
738 Builders Exchange
Minneapolis, Minnesota 55402

American Textbook Publishers Institute
432 Park Avenue South
New York, New York 10016

Associated Business Publications
205 East Forty-second Street
New York, New York 10017

Association of American University Presses
20 West Forty-third Street
New York, New York 10036

Association of Jewish Book Publishers
838 Fifth Avenue
New York, New York 10021

Association of Publications Production Managers
Care of Conde Nast Publications, Inc.
420 Lexington Avenue
New York, New York 10017

Authors Guild, The
Six East Thirty-ninth Street
New York, New York 10016

Book Manufacturers Institute
25 West Forty-third Street
New York, New York 10036

Business Publications Audit of Circulation
420 Lexington Avenue
New York, New York 10017

Canadian Lithographers Association
Front Street West
Toronto 1, Ontario, Canada

Canadian Printing Ink Manufacturers Association
67 Honge Street
Toronto 1, Ontario, Canada

Catholic School Press Association
552 North Thirteenth Street
Milwaukee, Wisconsin 53233

Christian Booksellers Association
5609 West Chicago Avenue
Chicago, Illinois 60651

College Publishers Group
432 Park Avenue South
New York, New York 10016

Columbia Scholastic Press Advisers Association
Box 11, Low Memorial Library
Columbia University
New York, New York 10027

Education Press Association of America
Glassboro State College
Glassboro, New Jersey 08028

Educational Council of the Graphic Arts Industry
1141 K Street, N.W.
Washington, D.C. 20005

Flexographic Technical Association
157 West Fifty-seventh Street
New York, New York 10019

Graphic Arts Association Executives
321 Tower Building
Washington, D.C. 20005

Graphic Arts Research Foundation
13–19 Temple Street
Quincy, Massachusetts 02169

Graphic Arts Technical Foundation
131 East Thirty-ninth Street
New York, New York 10016

Gravure Engravers Association
2929 South Floyd
Louisville, Kentucky 40217

Gravure Technical Association
60 East Forty-second Street
New York, New York 10017

International Association of Blue Print and
  Allied Industries
33 East Congress Parkway
Chicago, Illinois 60605

International Association of Electrotypers and
  Stereotypers, Inc.
758 Leader Building
Cleveland, Ohio 44114

International Council of Industrial Editors
2108 Braewick Circle
Akron, Ohio 44313

International Graphic Arts Educational Association
1411 K Street, N.W.
Washington, D.C. 20005

International Graphic Arts Society
410 East Sixty-second Street
New York, New York 10021

International Screen Process Printing Association
5769 North Lincoln Avenue
Chicago, Illinois 60645

Jewish Publication Society of America
222 North Fifteenth Street
Philadelphia, Pennsylvania 19130

Lithographic Technical Foundation
1800 Prairie Avenue
Chicago, Illinois 60616

Magazine Publishers' Association
575 Lexington Avenue
New York, New York 10022

National Association of Blueprint and Diazotype Coaters
1925 K Street, N.W.
Washington, D.C. 20006

National Association of Book Editors
171 Madison Avenue
New York, New York 10016

National Association of Litho Clubs, Inc.
230 West Forty-first Street
New York, New York 10036

National Association of Photo-lithographers
230 West Forty-first Street
New York, New York 10036

National Association of Printing Ink Makers, Inc.
39 West Fifty-fifth Street
New York, New York 10019

National Association of Publishers
271 Madison Avenue
New York, New York 10016

National Business Publications
1913 Eye Street, N.W.
Washington, D.C. 20006

National Council of College Publications Advisers
205 Communications Center
State University of Iowa
Iowa City, Iowa 52240

National Printing Equipment Association
217 Broadway
New York, New York 10007

National Scholastic Press Association
18 Journalism Building
University of Minnesota
Minneapolis, Minnesota 55455

National Society of Art Directors
115 East 40th Street
New York, New York 10016

Periodical Publishers Association of America
575 Lexington Avenue
New York, New York 10022

Printing Estimators and Production Men's Club
461 Eighth Avenue
New York, New York 10001

Printing Industries of America, Inc.
20 Chevy Chase Circle, N.W.
Washington, D.C. 20015

Professional Bookmen of America
P.O. Box 1571
Indianapolis, Indiana 46206

Proofreaders' Club of New York
62 West Fourteenth Street
New York, New York 10011

Publishers' Library Promotion Group
Care of William R. Scott, Inc.
333 Avenue of the Americas
New York, New York 10014

Religious Publishers Group
One Park Avenue
New York, New York 10016

Research and Engineering Council of the Graphic
Arts Industry
1141 K Street, N.W.
Washington, D.C. 20005

Rotogravure Association
13 East Grand Avenue
Chicago, Illinois 60611

Society of American Graphic Artists
1083 Fifth Avenue
New York, New York 10028

Society of National Association Publications
610 Ring Building
Washington, D.C. 20036

Society of Technical Writers and Publishers, Inc.
Suite 421, Denrike Building
1110 Vermont Avenue, N.W.
Washington, D.C. 20005

Southern California Microfilm Association
5774 Rodeo Road
Los Angeles, California 90016

Technical Association of the Graphic Arts
P.O. Box 3064, Federal Station
Rochester, New York 14614

Technical Association of the Pulp and Paper Industry
360 Lexington Avenue
New York, New York 10017

Technical Illustrators Management Association
P.O. Box 1021
Inglewood, California 90308

Western Society of Business Publications
1872 West Fifty-fourth Street
Los Angeles, California 90062

Women's National Book Association
Route 1, Box 118, Suman Road
Valparaiso, Indiana 46383

Trade Journals

Advertising Age
740 North Rush Street
Chicago, Illinois 60611

ALA Bulletin
American Library Association
50 East Huron Street
Chicago, Illinois 60611

American Artist
165 West Forty-sixth Street
New York, New York 10036

American Ink Maker
National Association of Printing Ink Industry
254 West Thirty-first Street
New York, New York 10001

American Pressman
Pressmen's Home, Tennessee 37850

American Vocational Journal
1025 Fifteenth Street, N.W.
Washington, D.C. 20006

Art Direction
19 West Forty-fourth Street
New York, New York 10036

Art Education
1201 Sixteenth Street, N.W.
Washington, D.C. 20036

Audiovisual Instruction
1201 Sixteenth Street, N.W.
Washington, D.C. 20036

Australian Printer
49 Clarence Street
Sydney, New South Wales, Australia

Book Production Industry
1276 West Third Street
Cleveland, Ohio 44113

Book Production Magazine
Freund Publishing Company, Inc.
34 North Crystal
East Stroudsburg, Pennsylvania 18301

Book Review Digest
950 University Avenue
Bronx, New York 10452

Booklist and Subscription Books Bulletin
American Library Association
50 East Huron Street
Chicago, Illinois 60611

British Printer
30 Old Burlington Street
London W.1, England

Business Management
22 West Putnam Avenue
Greenwich, Connecticut 06830

CA Magazine
3975 East Bayshore
Palo Alto, California 94303

Canadian Printer and Publisher
Box 100
Toronto, Ontario, Canada

Editor and Publisher
850 Third Avenue
New York, New York 10022

El Arte Tipografico
61 Hilton Avenue
Garden City, New York 11534

Engineering Graphics
25 West Forty-fifth Street
New York, New York 10036

Flexography
Graphic Magazines, Inc.
61 Hilton Avenue
Garden City, New York 11534

Graphic Arts Buyer
Two North Riverside Plaza
Chicago, Illinois 60606

Graphic Arts Monthly
7373 North Lincoln Avenue
Chicago, Illinois 60646

Graphic Arts Progress
Rochester Institute of Technology
65 Plymouth Avenue South
Rochester, New York 14608

Graphic Arts Review
Denckler Building
Four North Eleventh Street
Philadelphia, Pennsylvania 19107

Graphic Purchasing
1605 North Cahuenga Boulevard
Los Angeles, California 90028

Graphic Science
Nine Maiden Lane
New York, New York 10038

Graphic Technology
58 Fifth Street
London W.1, England

Gravure Magazine
Graphic Magazines, Inc.
61 Hilton Avenue
Garden City, New York 11534

In-plant Printer
200 Madison Avenue
New York, New York 10016

Industrial Art Methods
25 West Forty-fifth Street
New York, New York 10036

Industrial Arts and Vocational Education
400 North Broadway
Milwaukee, Wisconsin 53201

Inland Printer/American Lithographer
300 West Adams Street
Chicago, Illinois 60606

Ireland's Press and Printing
Dame House, Dame Street
Dublin C.1, Ireland

Job Shopping Aids Journal
Box 322
Anaheim, California 92805

Jobbing Printer
29 Oakhill Road
Ashstead, Surrey, England

Library Journal
1180 Avenue of the Americas
New York, New York 10036

Lithographers' Journal
233 West Forty-ninth Street
New York, New York 10019

London Typographical Journal
3-7 New Street
London E.C.4, England

Micro Image News
5774 Rodeo Road
Los Angeles, California 90016

Mid-Atlantic Graphic Arts Review
134 North Thirteenth Street
Philadelphia, Pennsylvania 19107

Modern Lithography
Four Second Avenue
Denville, New Jersey 07834

Modern Office Procedures
812 Huron Road
Cleveland 15, Ohio 44115

Modern Stationer
One East First Street
Duluth, Minnesota 55802

New England Printer and Lithographer
470 Atlantic Avenue
Boston, Massachusetts 02210

Office Equipment and Methods
481 University Avenue
Toronto 2, Ontario, Canada

Office Publications, Inc.
73 Southfield Avenue
Stamford, Connecticut 06904

Offset Newspaper Production
1605 North Cahuenga Boulevard
Los Angeles, California 90028

Paper Industry
431 South Dearborn Street
Chicago, Illinois 60605

Paper Trade Journal
49 West Forty-fifth Street
New York, New York 10036

PD News
P.O. Box 371
Grand Prairie, Texas 75050

Photo Methods for Industry
33 West Sixtieth Street
New York, New York 10023

Plan and Print
33 East Congress Parkway
Chicago, Illinois 60605

Plating
443 Broad Street
Newark, New Jersey 07102

Print
527 Madison Avenue
New York, New York 10022

Printers' Digest
2335 Central Avenue
Minneapolis, Minnesota 55818

Printers' Ink
501 Madison Avenue
New York, New York 10022

Printing Impressions
134 North Thirteenth Street
Philadelphia, Pennsylvania 19107

Printing Magazine/National Lithographer
466 Kinderkamack Road
Oradell, New Jersey 07649

Printing Monthly
432 Mechanic
Detroit, Michigan 48226

Printing News
468 Park Avenue South
New York, New York 10016

Printing Plates Magazine
715 Leader Building
Cleveland, Ohio 44114

Printing Production
1213 West Third Street
Cleveland, Ohio 44113

Printing Review of Canada
1117 Catherine Street West
Montreal, Quebec, Canada

Printing World
296-302 High Holborn
London W.C.1, England

Productionwise
468 Park Avenue South
New York, New York 10016

Publishers' Weekly
1180 Avenue of the Americas
New York, New York 10036

Pulp and Paper
370 Lexington Avenue
New York, New York 10017

Reproduction Engineer
18465 James Couzens
Detroit, Michigan 48235

Reproductions Review
393 Seventh Avenue
New York, New York 10001

Reprographics
200 Madison Avenue
New York, New York 10016

RM—Reproduction Methods for Business
and Industry
33 West Sixtieth Street
New York, New York 10023

School Product News
812 Huron Road
Cleveland, Ohio 44115

Screen Process
407 Gilbert Avenue
Cincinnati, Ohio 45202

Share Your Knowledge Review
7599 Kenwood Road
Cincinnati, Ohio 45236

Special Libraries Association
31 East Tenth Street
New York, New York 10003

STWP Review
Society of Technical Writers and Publishers
Suite 421, Denrike Building
1110 Vermont Avenue, N.W.
Washington, D.C. 20005

Today's Art
25 West Forty-fifth Street
New York, New York 10036

Torch
740 North Plankinton
Milwaukee, Wisconsin 53203

Western Office Reproduction Digest
6425 Hollywood Boulevard
Hollywood, California 90028

Western Printer and Lithographer
1605 North Cahuenga Boulevard
Los Angeles, California 90028

Writer
Eight Arlington Street
Boston, Massachusetts 02116

Writer's Digest
22 East Twelfth Street
Cincinnati, Ohio 45210

Product Index[1]

Classification	Product	See	Manufacturer
Adhesive materials	Avery	AVERY	Avery Label Company
	Paste-ups and transfers	ARTISTS AID	Jay G. Lissner
	Paste-ups and transfers	CHART-PAK	Chart-Pak, Inc.
	Paste-ups and transfers	CRAFTINT	The Craftint Manufacturing Co.
Art brushes	Art brushes	BRUSHES, ART	M. Grumbacher, Inc.
Binding equipment	Automatic punch	BINDING, MECHANICAL	General Binding Corporation
	Combo punching-binding equipment	BINDING, MECHANICAL	General Binding Corporation
	Model 30 electric punch	BINDING, MECHANICAL	American Photocopy Equipment Co.
Block printing	Block-printing instruments	BLOCK PRINTING	Hunt Manufacturing Co.
Bookbinding equipment	Bookbinding equipment	BOOKBINDING	T. W. & C. B. Sheridan Company
Brushes, Art	Art brushes	BRUSHES, ART	M. Grumbacher, Inc.
Camera, Polaroid	Industrial-view Land camera MP-3	POLAROID MP-3 INDUSTRIAL-VIEW LAND CAMERA	Polaroid Corporation
Camera, Process; Paper plates	Platemaster	CAMERA, PROCESS: PAPER PLATES	Itek Business Products
Camera accessories	Transsuction copyboard	COPYBOARD	Robertson Photo-Mechanix, Inc.

[1]For complete address of manufacturer or distributor, *see* MANUFACTURERS' INDEX.

Classification	Product	See	Manufacturer
Cameras, Process	AC process camera	CAMERA, PROCESS	Robertson Photo-Mechanix, Inc.
	Jupiter process camera	CAMERA, PROCESS	Robertson Photo-Mechanix, Inc.
	Meteorite process camera	CAMERA, PROCESS	Robertson Photo-Mechanix, Inc.
	MH 40- by 48-inch over-head camera	CAMERA, PROCESS	Lanston Monotype Company
	Model S-R Compos-O-Line	CAMERA, SEQUENTIAL-CARD	Friden, Inc.
	Model SST-1418	CAMERA, PROCESS	nuArc Company, Inc.
	Model SST-2024	CAMERA, PROCESS	nuArc Company, Inc.
	Model 320 process camera	CAMERA, PROCESS	Robertson Photo-Mechanix, Inc.
	Model 400 process camera	CAMERA, PROCESS	Robertson Photo-Mechanix, Inc.
	Sprite process camera	CAMERA, PROCESS	Robertson Photo-Mechanix, Inc.
	Xerox (Standard Equipment)	CAMERA, XERO-GRAPHIC PROCESS	Xerox Corporation
Cold-composition machines	Justowriter	COLD COMPOSITION	Friden, Inc.
	Magnetic-tape Selectric typewriter	COLD COMPOSITION	IBM, Office Products Division
	Printasign display type writer	TYPE WRITER, DIS-PLAY	Reynolds Printasign Company
	VariTyper	COLD COMPOSITION	VariTyper Corporation
Collators	Automatic A-10 high-speed collator	COLLATING	Thomas Collators, Inc.
	Automatic 8 collator	COLLATING	General Binding Corporation
	50-station Rotomatic collator and stitcher	COLLATING	Thomas Collators, Inc.
Composing machines, Headline	Display and headline typesetter, Model KD-84	TYPESETTERS, PHOTO-GRAPHIC	American Type Founders Co., Inc.
	Filmotype phototype-setting machine	TYPESETTERS, PHOTO-GRAPHIC	Filmotype Corporation
	Model 860 photocompos-ing machine	TYPESETTERS, PHOTO-GRAPHIC	VariTyper Corporation
	Photo-Typositor	TYPESETTERS, PHOTO-GRAPHIC	Visual Graphics Corporation
	Posteriter photographic typesetter	TYPESETTERS, PHOTO-GRAPHIC	Visual Graphics Corporation
	Printasign display type writer	TYPE WRITER, DIS-PLAY	Reynolds Printasign Company
	Typro photocomposing machine	TYPESETTERS, PHOTO-GRAPHIC	Friden, Inc.
	Varigraph headline com-posing machine	VARIGRAPH	Varigraph, Inc.
Conversion equipment	Converkal	CONVERSION FILM PROCESS	Kalvar Corporation for Kal/Graphic, Inc.

Classification	Product	See	Manufacturer
Conversion equipment (*continued*)	Dycril Type C plate	DYCRIL TYPE C PRINTING PLATE	E. I. du Pont de Nemours & Co.
	Instant Negative Conversion	NEGATIVE CONVERSION	Printing Arts Research Laboratories, Inc.
	No. 100 clarifier	CRONAPRESS CONVERSION SYSTEM	E. I. du Pont de Nemours & Co.
Copying machines	Copyflex Model 255 automatic-feed copying machine	COPYING MACHINES	Charles Bruning Company
	Copyflex Model 675	COPYING MACHINES	Charles Bruning Company
	Dial-A-Copy copying machine	COPYING MACHINES	American Photocopy Equipment Co.
	Kodak Readyprint copier	COPYING MACHINES	Eastman Kodak Company
	Masterfax copying machine	COPYING MACHINES	Ditto, Inc.
	Model 120 photocopying machine	COPYING MACHINES	A. B. Dick Company
	Model 813 copier	COPYING MACHINES	Xerox Corporation
	Model 914 copier	COPYING MACHINES	Xerox Corporation
	Model 2000R electrostatic copier	COPYING MACHINES	Charles Bruning Company
	Model 2400 copier	COPYING MACHINES	Xerox Corporation
	Revolute Star whiteprint machine	COPYING MACHINES	Charles Bruning Company
	Systematic copying machine	COPYING MACHINES	American Photocopy Equipment Co.
	Verifax Bantam Model C-K copier	COPYING MACHINES	Eastman Kodak Company
	Verifax Calvacade copier	COPYING MACHINES	Eastman Kodak Company
Correction aids	Ko-Rec-Copy	KO-REC-COPY	Eaton Allen Corporation
Display typesetters	*See* classifications "Composing machines, Headline"; "Photolettering machines"		
Drafting equipment	Automatic drafting system	DRAFTING, AUTOMATED	Gerber Scientific Instrument Co.
	Jacob's parallel straightedge	STRAIGHTEDGE	Keuffel & Esser Company
	Paragon Auto-Flow drafting machine	DRAFTING MACHINE	Keuffel & Esser Company
	Photo-Draft system	PHOTO-DRAFT SYSTEM	American Type Founders Co., Inc.
	Rapidesign drawing templates	TEMPLATE	Keuffel & Esser Company
Drafting materials	Cronaflex drafting film	CRONAFLEX DRAFTING FILM	E. I. du Pont de Nemours & Co.

Classification	Product	See	Manufacturer
Drafting materials (continued)	Helios drafting papers and cloths	HELIOS	Keuffel & Esser Company
	Herculene drafting film	HERCULENE DRAFTING FILM	Keuffel & Esser Company
	Onyx papers and cloths	ONYX	Keuffel & Esser Company
	Ozalid opaque cloth	OZALID OPAQUE CLOTH	Ozalid Reproduction Products
Duplicators, Offset		OFFSET DUPLICATOR	
Duplicators, Plate		MULTILITH DUPLIMAT MASTERS	
Duplicators, Spirit		SPIRIT DUPLICATING	
Duplicators, Stencil		MIMEOGRAPH	
Electrostatic screen printing process	Pure-Foodmaker	ELECTROSTATIC SCREEN PRINTING PROCESS	Unimark Corporation
Engraving, Electronic	Vario-Klischograph electronic scanner and engraver	ELECTRONIC ENGRAVING	HCM Corporation
Envelopes	Envelopes	ENVELOPES	United States Envelope Co.
Film, Conversion	Cronapress conversion film	CRONAPRESS CONVERSION FILM	E. I. du Pont de Nemours & Co.
Film, Lithographic and Process	Acetate Ortho Litho film	ACETATE ORTHO LITHO FILM	E. I. du Pont de Nemours & Co.
	Clearback Ortho Litho film	CLEARBACK ORTHO LITHO FILM	E. I. du Pont de Nemours & Co.
	Clearbase film	CLEARBASE FILM	E. I. du Pont de Nemours & Co.
	Commercial S film	COMMERCIAL S FILM	E. I. du Pont de Nemours & Co.
	Direct Positive Clear film	DIRECT POSITIVE CLEAR FILM	E. I. du Pont de Nemours & Co.
	Direct Positive D film	DIRECT POSITIVE D FILM	E. I. du Pont de Nemours & Co.
	High Contrast Pan film	HIGH CONTRAST PAN FILM	E. I. du Pont de Nemours & Co.
	Kalvalith lithographic films	KALVALITH	Kalvar Corporation for Kal Graphic, Inc.
	Kalvatone	KALVATONE	Kalvar Corporation for Kal Graphic, Inc.
	Kodagraph Autopositive paper	KODAK AUTOPOSITIVE MATERIALS	Eastman Kodak Company
	Kodak Autopositive materials	KODAK AUTOPOSITIVE MATERIALS	Eastman Kodak Company
	Kodak gray contact screen	KODAK GRAY CONTACT SCREEN	Eastman Kodak Company
	Kodak magenta contact screen	KODAK MAGENTA CONTACT SCREEN	Eastman Kodak Company

Classification	Product	See	Manufacturer
Film, Lithographic and Process (continued)	Kodalith Autoscreen Ortho film	KODALITH AUTO- SCREEN ORTHO FILM	Eastman Kodak Company
	Lithofilm	LITHOFILM	Ozalid Reproduction Products
	Low Contrast Pan film	LOW CONTRAST PAN FILM	E. I. du Pont de Nemours & Co.
	Low Gamma Pan film	LOW GAMMA PAN FILM	E. I. du Pont de Nemours & Co.
	Masking (Blue-sensitive) film	MASKING (BLUE- SENSITIVE) FILM	E. I. du Pont de Nemours & Co.
	Ortho A film; Ortho D film; Ortho M film; Ortho S film	ORTHO A FILM; OR- THO D FILM; OR- THO M FILM; OR- THO S FILM	E. I. du Pont de Nemours & Co.
	Ozachromes	OZACHROME	Ozalid Reproduction Products
	Pan Litho film	PAN LITHO FILM	E. I. du Pont de Nemours & Co.
	Pan Masking film	PAN MASKING FILM	E. I. du Pont de Nemours & Co.
Film bases	Cronar	CRONAR	E. I. du Pont de Nemours & Co.
	Mylar	MYLAR	E. I. du Pont de Nemours & Co.
Film-processing equipment	LD-24 automatic film processor	PROCESSING, FILM	LogEtronics, Inc.
	Nitrogen-burst processing unit	PROCESSING, NITRO- GEN-BURST	Calumet Manufacturing Co.
Film: Visual aids	Diazochrome projecturals	DIAZOCHROME PRO- JECTURALS	Technifax Corporation
	Ozachrome view foils	OZACHROME VIEW FOIL	Ozalid Reproduction Products
	Ozalid Projecto-Foil	OZALID PROJECTO- FOIL	Ozalid Reproduction Products
	Ozalid Transferon	OZALID TRANSFERON	Ozalid Reproduction Products
Fixatives	Krylon	KRYLON	Krylon, Inc.
Jogging equipment	Model J-2 jogger	JOGGER	Syntron Company
	Model TJ-1 jogger	JOGGER	Syntron Company
Laminators	18-inch laminator	LAMINATION	General Binding Corporation
	Ply-On laminator	LAMINATION	American Photocopy Equipment Co.
Lamps	Arc lamp	ARC LAMP	nuArc Company, Inc.
Layout aids	Copy Block	COPY BLOCK	The Craftint Manufacturing Co.
	Lineup tables	LINEUP TABLE	nuArc Company, Inc.

Classification	Product	See	Manufacturer
Lettering guides: Ink	Leroy lettering guides and effects	PENS, TECHNICAL	Keuffel & Esser Company
	Wrico lettering effects	PENS, TECHNICAL	The Wood-Regan Instrument Co.
Lettering guides: Stencils	Lettering guides	LETTERING GUIDES	A. B. Dick Company
Light tables	Lineup tables	LINEUP TABLE	nuArc Company, Inc.
	Mimeoscope	MIMEOSCOPE	A. B. Dick Company
Line conversion	Photographic line conversion	LINE CONVERSION	Unigraf
Linecasting equipment	Computer and Intertype linecasting machine	LINECASTING MACHINE	Intertype Company
	Elektron Mixer Linotype	LINECASTING MACHINE	Mergenthaler Linotype Company
	Elektron tape-operated Linotype linecaster	LINECASTING MACHINE	Mergenthaler Linotype Company
	Elektron II Linotype	LINECASTING MACHINE	Mergenthaler Linotype Company
	Ludlow Model M caster	LUDLOW	Ludlow Typograph Company
	Model LCC-S tape perforator	LINECASTING MACHINE	Friden, Inc.
	Tape converter	TAPE CONVERTER	American Type Founders Co., Inc.
Masking and stripping films	Amberlith	AMBERLITH	Ulano Graphic Arts Supplies, Inc.
	Bourges	BOURGES	Bourges Color Corp.
	Rubylith	RUBYLITH	Ulano Graphic Arts Supplies, Inc.
Microfilm equipment	Copyflo 11 continuous printer, Models 1, 2, 3	PRINTER	Xerox Corporation
	Copyflo 24C continuous printer	PRINTER	Xerox Corporation
	1824 printer	PRINTER	Xerox Corporation
	Filmac 100 microfilm reader-printer	READER-PRINTER	Minnesota Mining and Mfg. Company
	Filmsort 1000d microfilm processor-camera	CAMERA, MICROFILM	Minnesota Mining and Mfg. Company
	Itek 18.24 Standard reader-printer	READER-PRINTER	Itek Business Products
	K-10 Colight printer	MICROFILM DUPLICATOR	Kalvar Corporation for Kal/Graphic, Inc.
	KalKard activator Model 240 aperture-card developing unit	MICROFILM DUPLICATOR	Kalvar Corporation for Kal/Graphic, Inc.
	KalKard exposer Model 200 aperture-card unit	MICROFILM DUPLICATOR	Kalvar Corporation for Kal/Graphic, Inc.
	Kalvar's instant developer	MICROFILM DUPLICATOR	Kalvar Corporation for Kal/Graphic, Inc.

Classification	Product	See	Manufacturer
Microfilm equipment (*continued*)	Microfiche reader Model 576-95	MICROFILM READER	DuKane Corporation
	Microphotograph reader Model 576-90	MICROFILM READER	DuKane Corporation
	Model DRS8514 portable microfilm camera	CAMERA, MICROFILM	Data Reproduction Systems
	Model 576-75 microfilm viewer	MICROFILM READER	DuKane Corporation
	MultiMode Reproducer Model 400 microfilm copier	MICROFILM DUPLICATOR	Kalvar Corporation for Kal/Graphic, Inc.
	Recordak Prostar microfilm processor	MICROFILM PROCESSOR	Recordak Corporation, subsidiary of Eastman Kodak Co.
Monotype casters and keyboards	Composition caster	MONOTYPE	Lanston Monotype Company
	Monomatic caster	MONOTYPE	Lanston Monotype Company
	Monomatic keyboard	MONOTYPE	Lanston Monotype Company
	Monomatic Style D keyboard	MONOTYPE	Lanston Monotype Company
Offset-duplicator plates	Multilith Duplimat masters	MULTILITH DUPLIMAT MASTERS	Addressograph-Multigraph Corp.
	Ozalith plates	OZALITH PLATE	Ozalid Reproduction Products
Offset duplicators	Model 360 offset duplicator	OFFSET DUPLICATOR	A. B. Dick Company
	Model 1250 offset duplicator	OFFSET DUPLICATOR	Addressograph-Multigraph Corp.
	Model L-16 offset duplicator	OFFSET DUPLICATOR	Ditto, Inc.
Overhead projection	Acto-O-Matic overhead projector	OVERHEAD PROJECTION	Technifax Corporation
	Deluxe pickle jar	PICKLE JAR	Technifax Corporation
	Diazochrome projecturals	DIAZOCHROME PROJECTURALS	Technifax Corporation
	Transpaque Junior overhead projector	OVERHEAD PROJECTION	Technifax Corporation
	Visucom diazo copier	OVERHEAD PROJECTION	Technifax Corporation
	Visucom overhead projector	OVERHEAD PROJECTION	Technifax Corporation
Papers, Photographic	Litho T photographic paper	LITHO T PHOTOGRAPHIC PAPER	E. I. du Pont de Nemours & Co.
Paste-ups and transfers	Adhesive materials	ARTIST AID	Jay G. Lissner
	Adhesive materials	AVERY	Avery Label Company
	Adhesive materials	CHART-PAK; TRANSPAK	Chart-Pak, Inc.
	Adhesive materials	CRAFTINT	The Craftint Manufacturing Co.

Classification	Product	See	Manufacturer
Pens, Lettering	Leroy	PENS, TECHNICAL	Keuffel & Esser Company
	Lettering pens	SPEEDBALL PENS	Hunt Manufacturing Co.
	Wrico	PENS, TECHNICAL	The Wood-Regan Instrument Co.
Pens, Steel-brush	Speedball steel-brush	PENS, STEEL-BRUSH	Hunt Manufacturing Co.
Pens, Technical	Koh-I-Noor Rapidograph pens	PENS, TECHNICAL	Koh-I-Noor, Inc.
	Leroy pen sets and scribers	PENS, TECHNICAL	Keuffel & Esser Company
	Wrico pens and scribers	PENS, TECHNICAL	The Wood-Regan Instrument Co.
Photolettering machines	Display and headline typesetter, Model KD-84	TYPESETTERS, PHOTOGRAPHIC	American Type Founders Co., Inc.
	Filmotype phototype-setting machine	TYPESETTERS, PHOTOGRAPHIC	Filmotype Corporation
	Model 860 photocomposing machine	TYPESETTERS, PHOTOGRAPHIC	VariTyper Corporation
	Photo-Typositor	TYPESETTERS, PHOTOGRAPHIC	Visual Graphics Corporation
	Posteriter photographic typesetter	TYPESETTERS, PHOTOGRAPHIC	Visual Graphics Corporation
	Typro photocomposing machine	TYPESETTERS, PHOTOGRAPHIC	Friden, Inc.
Plate-making equipment	Model FT-26 Flip-Top plate maker	PLATE-MAKING EQUIPMENT	nuArc Company, Inc.
	Model FT-40NS Flip-Top plate maker	PLATE-MAKING EQUIPMENT	nuArc Company, Inc.
	Model 106 plate exposure unit	PLATE-MAKING EQUIPMENT	A. B. Dick Company
	Platemaster	CAMERA, PROCESS: PAPER PLATES	Itek Business Products
Presses, Electrostatic printing	Pressureless printing machine	ELECTROSTATIC SCREEN PRINTING PROCESS	Unimark Corporation
Presses, Letterpress cylinder	Model 38 letterpress printing press	LETTERPRESS PRINTING	Mergenthaler Linotype Company
Presses, Offset: Sheet-fed	Champion single-color sheet-fed offset press	OFFSET PRINTING PRESS	HCM Corporation
	Chief 15-inch (11- by 15-inch) offset press	OFFSET PRINTING PRESS	HCM Corporation
	Mailander flatbed offset press	OFFSET PRINTING PRESS	HCM Corporation
	Media Master No. 29 single-color sheet-fed rotary offset press	OFFSET PRINTING PRESS	Mergenthaler Linotype Company
	Solna 24-inch perfector offset press	PERFECTING PRESS	American Type Founders Co., Inc.
	Solna 230 (23- by 30-inch) two-color offset press	OFFSET PRINTING PRESS	American Type Founders Co., Inc.

Classification	Product	See	Manufacturer
Presses, Offset: Sheet-fed (*cont.*)	29 single-color press	OFFSET PRINTING PRESS	The Miehle Company
Presses, Offset: Web-fed	Cottrell Vanguard Model 22 newspaper web off-set printing press	WEB OFFSET PRINT-ING	Harris-Intertype Corporation
	Harris-Cottrell 35- by 51-inch blanket-to-blanket web offset press	WEB OFFSET PRINT-ING	Harris-Intertype Corporation
	Kluge web-flow continu-ous-form press	CONTINUOUS-FORM PRESS	Brandtjen and Kluge, Inc.
	Webendorfer publications press	WEB OFFSET PRINT-ING	American Type Founders Co., Inc.
Presses, Offset: Web/sheet feeder	54/77 four-color offset press	OFFSET PRINTING PRESS	The Miehle Company
	54/77 six-color offset press	OFFSET PRINTING PRESS	The Miehle Company
Presses, Platen	Automatic die-cutting, embossing, and foil-stamping platen press	PLATEN PRESS	Brandtjen and Kluge, Inc.
	Kluge automatic platen press	PLATEN PRESS	Brandtjen and Kluge, Inc.
	Kluge Model 14- by 22-inch HD series	PLATEN PRESS	Brandtjen and Kluge, Inc.
Pressure-sensitive materials	Adhesive materials	CHART-PAK; TRANS-PAK	Chart-Pak, Inc.
	Artist Aid	ARTIST AID	Jay G. Lissner
	Avery	AVERY	Avery Label Company
	Paste-ups and transfers	CRAFTINT	The Craftint Manufac-turing Co.
Printing equipment, Direct	Photact	PHOTACT	Keuffel & Esser Company
Printing plates	Duplimat masters	MULTILITH DUPLI-MAT MASTERS	Addressograph-Multi-graph Corp.
	Dycril	CRONAPRESS CONVER-SION SYSTEM	E. I. du Pont de Nemours & Co.
	Dycril Type C plate	DYCRIL TYPE C PRINTING PLATE	E. I. du Pont de Nemours & Co.
	Ozalith plates	OZALITH PLATE	Ozalid Reproduction Products
Processing, Film	*See* classification "Film-processing equipment"		
Processors, Stabili-zation	Ilfoprint stabilization processor	PROCESSING, STA-BILIZATION	Ilford, Inc.
	Rapid-print processor	PROCESSING, STA-BILIZATION	Fotorite, Inc.
Proportional scales	Linkrule	LINKRULE	Linkrule Company
Shading mediums	Adhesive materials	CHART-PAK; TRANS-PAK	Chart-Pak, Inc.

Classification	Product	See	Manufacturer
Shading mediums (*continued*)	Artist Aid	ARTIST AID	Jay G. Lissner
	Contak	CHART-PAK	Chart-Pak, Inc.
	Craf-Tone shading mediums	SHADING MEDIUMS	The Craftint Manufacturing Co.
	Doubletone shading	SHADING MEDIUMS	The Craftint Manufacturing Co.
	Paste-ups and transfers	CRAFTINT	The Craftint Manufacturing Co.
	Singletone shading	SHADING MEDIUMS	The Craftint Manufacturing Co.
Spirit duplicating	Model D-31 spirit duplicator	SPIRIT DUPLICATING	Ditto, Inc.
	Model 18D-75 spirit duplicator	SPIRIT DUPLICATING	Ditto, Inc.
	Model 227 spirit duplicator	SPIRIT DUPLICATING	A. B. Dick Company
Stabilization processing	*See* classification "Processors, Stabilization"		
Step-and-repeat machines	Model M-H 4	STEP-AND-REPEAT MACHINE	Lanston Monotype Company
Tape converters	ATF tape converter	TAPE CONVERTER	American Type Founders Co., Inc.
Typesetters, Photographic	B-8 keyboard unit	TYPESETTERS, PHOTOGRAPHIC	American Type Founders Co., Inc.
	B-8 photographic unit	TYPESETTERS, PHOTOGRAPHIC	American Type Founders Co., Inc.
	Electronic photographic typesetting machine	TYPESETTERS, PHOTOGRAPHIC	Harris-Intertype Corporation
	Model CS typesetter	TYPESETTERS, PHOTOGRAPHIC	American Type Founders Co., Inc.
	Monophoto filmsetter	TYPESETTERS, PHOTOGRAPHIC	Lanston Monotype Company
Typewriters	IBM Executive typewriter	TYPEWRITER	IBM, Office Products Division
	IBM Selectric typewriter	COLD COMPOSITION	IBM, Office Products Division
Typing aids	Typit	TYPIT	Mechanical Enterprises, Inc.
Whiteprint machines	*See* classification "Copying machines"		
Whiteprint materials	Ozalid cloth-backed paper	OZALID CLOTH-BACKED PAPER	Ozalid Reproduction Products
	Ozalid gum-backed paper	OZALID GUM-BACKED PAPER	Ozalid Reproduction Products
	Ozalid papers	OZALID PAPERS	Ozalid Reproduction Products
	Ozalid reversal foil	OZALID REVERSAL FOIL	Ozalid Reproduction Products
	Ozaplastic	OZAPLASTIC	Ozalid Reproduction Products

Manufacturers'
Index

Manufacturer	Product	See
Addressograph-Multigraph Corp. 1200 Babbitt Road Cleveland, Ohio 44132	Model 1250 offset duplicator Multilith Duplimat masters	OFFSET DUPLICATOR MULTILITH DUPLIMAT MASTERS
American Photocopy Equipment Co. 2100 West Dempster Street Evanston, Illinois 60202	Dial-A-Copy copying machine Model 30 electric punch Ply-On laminator Systematic copying machine	COPYING MACHINES BINDING, MECHANICAL LAMINATION COPYING MACHINES
American Type Founders Co., Inc. 200 Elmora Avenue Elizabeth, New Jersey 07202	ATF tape converter B-8 keyboard unit B-8 photographic unit Chief 15-inch (11- by 15-inch) offset press Display and headline typesetter, Model KD-84 Model CS typesetter Photo-Draft system Solna 24-inch perfector offset press Solna 230 (23- by 30-inch) two-color offset press Tape converter Webendorfer publications press	TAPE CONVERTER TYPESETTERS, PHOTOGRAPHIC TYPESETTERS, PHOTOGRAPHIC OFFSET PRINTING PRESS TYPESETTERS, PHOTOGRAPHIC TYPESETTERS, PHOTOGRAPHIC PHOTO-DRAFT SYSTEM PERFECTING PRESS OFFSET PRINTING PRESS TAPE CONVERTER WEB OFFSET PRINTING
Avery Label Company 1616 South California Avenue Monrovia, California 91016	Paste-ups and transfers	AVERY
Bourges Color Corp. 80 Fifth Avenue New York, New York 10011	Masking and stripping films	BOURGES

Manufacturer	Product	See
Brandtjen and Kluge, Inc. 653 Galtier St. Paul, Minnesota 55103	Automatic die-cutting, emboss- ing, and foil-stamping press	PLATEN PRESS
	Kluge automatic platen press	PLATEN PRESS
	Kluge Model 14- by 22-inch HD series	PLATEN PRESS
	Kluge web-flow continuous-form press	CONTINUOUS-FORM PRESS
Bruning, Charles, Company 1800 West Central Road Mount Prospect, Illinois 60056	Copyflex Model 255 automatic- feed copying machine	COPYING MACHINES
	Copyflex Model 675	COPYING MACHINES
	Model 2000R electrostatic copier	COPYING MACHINES
	Revolute Star whiteprint machine	COPYING MACHINES
Calumet Manufacturing Co. 6550 North Clark Street Chicago, Illinois 60626	Nitrogen-burst processing unit	PROCESSING, NITROGEN-BURST
Chart-Pak, Inc. Leeds, Massachusetts 01053	Adhesive materials	CHART-PAK; TRANS-PAK
	Contak	CHART-PAK
Cottrell Company, The Division of Harris-Intertype Corporation Westerly, Rhode Island 02891	*See* Harris-Intertype Corporation	
Craftint Manufacturing Co., The 18501 Euclid Avenue Cleveland, Ohio 44112	Adhesive materials	CRAFTINT
	Copy Block	COPY BLOCK
	Craf-Tone shading mediums	SHADING MEDIUMS
	Doubletone shading	SHADING MEDIUMS
	Paste-ups and transfers	CRAFTINT
	Singletone shading	SHADING MEDIUMS
Data Reproduction Systems 300 East Beach Avenue Inglewood, California 90302	Model DRS8514 portable microfilm camera	CAMERA, MICROFILM
Dick, A. B., Company 5700 West Touhy Avenue Chicago, Illinois 60648	Lettering guides	LETTERING GUIDES
	Model 106 plate exposure unit	PLATE-MAKING EQUIPMENT
	Model 120 photocopying machine	COPYING MACHINES
	Model 277 spirit duplicator	SPIRIT DUPLICATING
	Model 360 offset duplicator	OFFSET DUPLICATOR
	Mimeoscope	MIMEOSCOPE
Ditto, Inc. 6800 McCormick Road Chicago, Illinois 60645	Masterfax copying machine	COPYING MACHINES
	Model D-31 spirit duplicator	SPIRIT DUPLICATING
	Model 18D-75 spirit duplicator	SPIRIT DUPLICATING
	Model L-16 offset duplicator	OFFSET DUPLICATOR
Dukane Corporation St. Charles, Illinois 60174	Microfiche reader Model 576-95	MICROFILM READER
	Microphotograph reader Model 576-90	MICROFILM READER
	Model 576-75 microfilm viewer	MICROFILM READER
Du Pont de Nemours, E. I., & Co. Wilmington, Delaware 19898	Acetate Ortho Litho film	ACETATE ORTHO LITHO FILM
	Clearback Ortho Litho film	CLEARBACK ORTHO LITHO FILM
	Clearbase film	CLEARBASE FILM

Manufacturer	Product	See
Du Pont de Nemours, E. I., & Co. (*continued*)	Commercial S film	COMMERCIAL S FILM
	Cronaflex drafting film	CRONAFLEX DRAFTING FILM
	Cronapress conversion film	CRONAPRESS CONVERSION FILM
	Cronar	CRONAR
	Direct Positive Clear film	DIRECT POSITIVE CLEAR FILM
	Direct Positive D film	DIRECT POSITIVE D FILM
	Dycril	CRONAPRESS CONVERSION SYSTEM
	Dycril Type C plate	DYCRIL TYPE C PRINTING PLATE
	High Contrast Pan film	HIGH CONTRAST PAN FILM
	Low Contrast Pan film	LOW CONTRAST PAN FILM
	Low Gamma Pan film	LOW GAMMA PAN FILM
	Litho T photographic paper	LITHO T PHOTOGRAPHIC PAPER
	Masking (Blue-sensitive) film	MASKING (BLUE-SENSITIVE) FILM
	Mylar	MYLAR
	No. 100 clarifier	CRONAPRESS CONVERSION SYSTEM
	Ortho A film	ORTHO A FILM
	Ortho D film	ORTHO D FILM
	Ortho M film	ORTHO M FILM
	Ortho S film	ORTHO S FILM
	Pan Litho film	PAN LITHO FILM
	Pan Masking film	PAN MASKING FILM
Eastman Kodak Company Rochester, New York 14604	Kodagraph Autopositive paper	KODAK AUTOPOSITIVE MATERIALS
	Kodak Autopositive materials	KODAK AUTOPOSITIVE MATERIALS
	Kodak gray contact screen	KODAK GRAY CONTACT SCREEN
	Kodak magenta contact screen	KODAK MAGENTA CONTACT SCREEN
	Kodak Readyprint copier	COPYING MACHINES
	Kodalith Autoscreen Ortho film	KODALITH AUTOSCREEN ORTHO FILM
	Verifax Bantam Model C-K copier	COPYING MACHINES
	Verifax Calvacade copier	COPYING MACHINES
Eaton Allen Corporation 67 Kent Avenue Brooklyn, New York 11211	Correction aids	KO-REC-COPY
Electrostatic Printing Corp. of America 254 Sutter Street San Francisco, California 94108	Electrostatic screen printing	ELECTROSTATIC SCREEN PRINTING PROCESS
	Pure-Foodmarker (Unimark)	ELECTROSTATIC SCREEN PRINTING PROCESS
Filmotype Corporation 7500 McCormick Boulevard Skokie, Illinois 60076	Filmotype phototypesetting machine	TYPESETTERS, PHOTOGRAPHIC
Fotorite, Inc. 6424 North Western Avenue Chicago, Illinois 60645	Rapid-print processor	PROCESSING, STABILIZATION
Friden, Inc. 2350 Washington Avenue San Leandro, California 94577	Justowriter	COLD COMPOSITION
	Model LCC-S tape perforator	LINECASTING MACHINE
	Model S-R Compos-O-Line	CAMERA, SEQUENTIAL-CARD
	Typro photocomposing machine	TYPESETTERS, PHOTOGRAPHIC

Manufacturer	Product	See
General Binding Corporation 1101 Skokie Boulevard Northbrook, Illinois 60062	Automatic 8 collator Automatic punch Combo punching-binding unit 18-inch laminator	COLLATING BINDING, MECHANICAL BINDING, MECHANICAL LAMINATION
Gerber Scientific Instrument Co. P.O. Box 305 Hartford, Connecticut 06101	Automatic drafting system	DRAFTING, AUTOMATED
Grumbacher, M., Inc. 460 West Thirty-fourth Street New York, New York 10001	Art brushes	BRUSHES, ART
Harris-Intertype Corporation 55 Public Square Cleveland, Ohio 44113	Cottrell Vanguard Model 22 newspaper web offset press Electronic photographic type-setting machine Harris-Cottrell 35- by 51-inch blanket-to-blanket web offset press	WEB OFFSET PRINTING TYPESETTERS, PHOTOGRAPHIC WEB OFFSET PRINTING
HCM Corporation 115 Cuttermill Road Great Neck, New York 11021	Champion single-color sheet-fed offset press Mailander flatbed offset press Vario-Klischograph electronic scanner and engraver	OFFSET PRINTING PRESS OFFSET PRINTING PRESS ELECTRONIC ENGRAVING
Hunt Manufacturing Co. 1405 Locust Street Philadelphia, Pennsylvania 19102	Block-printing instruments Speedball pens Speedball steel-brush pens	BLOCK PRINTING SPEEDBALL PENS PENS, STEEL-BRUSH
Ilford, Inc. 37 West Sixty-fifth Street New York, New York 10023	Ilfoprint stabilization processor	PROCESSING, STABILIZATION
International Business Machines Corp. Office Products Division 590 Madison Avenue New York, New York 10022	IBM Executive typewriter IBM Selective typewriter Magnetic-tape Selectric type-writer	TYPEWRITER COLD COMPOSITION COLD COMPOSITION
Intertype Company Division of Harris-Intertype Corporation 360 Furman Street Brooklyn, New York 11201	Computer and Intertype line-casting machine	LINECASTING MACHINE
Itek Business Products 1001 Jefferson Road Rochester, New York 14623	Itek 18.24 Standard reader-printer Platemaster	READER-PRINTER CAMERA, PROCESS: PAPER PLATES
Kalvar Corporation Kal/Graphic, Inc. 909 South Broad Street New Orleans, Louisiana 70125	Converkal K-10 Colight printer KalKard activator Model 240 aperture-card developing unit KalKard exposer Model 200 aperture-card unit Kalvalith lithographic films	CONVERSION FILM PROCESS MICROFILM DUPLICATOR MICROFILM DUPLICATOR MICROFILM DUPLICATOR KALVALITH

Manufactuer	*Product*	*See*
Kalvar Corporation	Kalvar's instant developer	MICROFILM DUPLICATOR
(*continued*)	Kalvatone	KALVATONE
	MultiMode Reproducer Model 400 microfilm copier	MICROFILM DUPLICATOR
Keuffel & Esser Company	Helios drafting papers and cloths	HELIOS
300 Adams Street		
Hoboken, New Jersey 07030	Herculene drafting film	HERCULENE DRAFTING FILM
	Jacob's parallel straightedge	STRAIGHTEDGE
	Leroy lettering guides and effects	PENS, TECHNICAL
	Leroy pen sets and scribers	PENS, TECHNICAL
	Onyx papers and cloths	ONYX
	Paragon Auto-Flow drafting machine	DRAFTING MACHINE
	Photact	PHOTACT
	Rapidesign drawing templates	TEMPLATE
Koh-I-Noor, Inc.	Koh-I-Noor Rapidograph pens	PENS, TECHNICAL
100 North Street		
Bloomsbury, New Jersey 08804		
Krylon, Inc.	Fixatives	KRYLON
Norristown, Pennsylvania 19401		
Lanston Monotype Company	Composition caster	MONOTYPE
Division of United States Banknote Corp.	MH 40- by 48-inch overhead camera	CAMERA, PROCESS
3620 G Street	Model M-H 4 step-and-repeat machine	STEP-AND-REPEAT MACHINE
Philadelphia, Pennsylvania 19134	Monomatic caster	MONOTYPE
	Monomatic keyboard	MONOTYPE
	Monomatic Style D keyboard	MONOTYPE
	Monophoto filmsetter	TYPESETTERS, PHOTOGRAPHIC
Linkrule Company	Proportional scales	LINKRULE
P.O. Box 34669		
Los Angeles, California 90034		
Lissner, Jay G.	Paste-ups and transfers	ARTIST AID
3417 West First Street		
Los Angeles, California 90004		
LogEtronics, Inc.	LD-24 automatic film processor	PROCESSING, FILM
500 East Monroe Avenue		
Alexandria, Virginia 22301		
Ludlow Typograph Company	Ludlow Model M caster	LUDLOW
2032 Clybourn Avenue		
Chicago, Illinois 60614		
Mechanical Enterprises, Inc.	Typing aids	TYPIT
3127 Colvin Street		
Alexandria, Virginia 22314		
Mergenthaler Linotype Company	Elektron Mixer Linotype	LINECASTING MACHINE
	Elektron tape-operated Linotype linecaster	LINECASTING MACHINE
29 Ryerson Street		
Brooklyn, New York 11205	Elektron II Linotype	LINECASTING MACHINE

Manufacturer	Product	See
Mergenthaler Linotype Company (*continued*)	Media Master No. 29 single-color sheet-fed rotary offset press	OFFSET PRINTING PRESS
	Model 38 letterpress printing press	LETTERPRESS PRINTING
Miehle Company, The 2011 Hastings Street Chicago, Illinois 60608	29 single-color press	OFFSET PRINTING PRESS
	54/77 four-color offset press	OFFSET PRINTING PRESS
	54/77 six-color offset press	OFFSET PRINTING PRESS
Minnesota Mining and Mfg. Company 2501 Hudson Road St. Paul, Minnesota 55119	Filmac 100 microfilm reader-printer	READER-PRINTER
	Filmsort 1000d microfilm processor-camera	CAMERA, MICROFILM
nuArc Company, Inc. 4110 West Grand Avenue Chicago, Illinois 60651	Arc lamp	ARC LAMP
	Lineup tables	LINEUP TABLE
	Model FT-26 Flip-Top plate maker	PLATE-MAKING EQUIPMENT
	Model FT-40NS Flip-Top plate maker	PLATE-MAKING EQUIPMENT
	Model SST-1418	CAMERA, PROCESS
	Model SST-2024	CAMERA, PROCESS
Ozalid Reproduction Products Division of General Aniline and Film Corporation 25 Ozalid Road Binghamton, New York 13903	Lithofilm	LITHOFILM
	Ozachrome view foils	OZACHROME VIEW FOIL
	Ozachromes	OZACHROME
	Ozalid cloth-backed paper	OZALID CLOTH-BACKED PAPER
	Ozalid gum-backed paper	OZALID GUM-BACKED PAPER
	Ozalid opaque cloth	OZALID OPAQUE CLOTH
	Ozalid papers	OZALID PAPERS
	Ozalid Projecto-Foil	OZALID PROJECTO-FOIL
	Ozalid reversal foil	OZALID REVERSAL FOIL
	Ozalid Transferon	OZALID TRANSFERON
	Ozalith plates	OZALITH PLATE
	Ozaplastic	OZAPLASTIC
Polaroid Corporation Cambridge, Massachusetts 02139	Industrial-view Land camera MP-3	POLAROID MP-3 INDUSTRIAL-VIEW LAND CAMERA
Printing Arts Research Laboratories, Inc. La Arcada Building Santa Barbara, California 93104	Instant Negative Conversion	NEGATIVE CONVERSION
Recordak Corporation Subsidiary of Eastman Kodak Company 770 Broadway New York, New York 10003	Recordak Prostar microfilm processor	MICROFILM PROCESSING
Reynolds Printasign Company 9830 San Fernando Road Pacoima, California 91331	Printasign display type writer	TYPE WRITER, DISPLAY

Manufacturer	Product	See
Robertson Photo-Mechanix, Inc. 250 West Wille Road Des Plaines, Illinois 60018	AC process camera	CAMERA, PROCESS
	Jupiter process camera	CAMERA, PROCESS
	Meteorite process camera	CAMERA, PROCESS
	Model 320 process camera	CAMERA, PROCESS
	Model 400 process camera	CAMERA, PROCESS
	Sprite process camera	CAMERA, PROCESS
	Transsuction copyboard	COPYBOARD
Sheridan, T. W. & C. B., Company Subsidiary of Harris-Intertype Corporation 220 Church Street New York, New York 10013	Bookbinding equipment	BOOKBINDING
Syntron Company Homer City, Pennsylvania 15748	Model J-2 jogger	JOGGER
	Model TJ-1 jogger	JOGGER
Technifax Corporation 195 Appleton Street Holyoke, Massachusetts 01040	Acto-O-Matic overhead projector	OVERHEAD PROJECTION
	Deluxe pickle jar	PICKLE JAR
	Diazochrome projecturals	DIAZOCHROME PROJECTURALS
	Transpaque Junior overhead projector	OVERHEAD PROJECTION
	Visucom diazo copier	OVERHEAD PROJECTION
	Visucom overhead projector	OVERHEAD PROJECTION
Thomas Collators, Inc. 100 Church Street New York, New York 10007	Automatic A-10 high-speed collator	COLLATING
	50-station Rotomatic collator and stitcher	COLLATING
Ulano Graphic Arts Supplies, Inc. 610 Dean Street Brooklyn, New York 11238	Masking and stripping films	AMBERLITH
	Masking and stripping films	RUBYLITH
Unigraf 4505 West First Street Los Angeles, California 90004	Photographic line conversion	LINE CONVERSION
	Special effects	LINE CONVERSION
Unimark Corporation Old Crow Canyon Road P.O. Box 197 San Ramon, California 94583	Pure-Foodmarker	ELECTROSTATIC SCREEN PRINTING PROCESS
United States Envelope Co. 21 Cypress Street Springfield, Massachusetts 01104	Envelopes	ENVELOPES
Varigraph, Inc. Madison, Wisconsin 53701	Varigraph headline composing machine	VARIGRAPH
VariTyper Corporation 720 Frelinghuysen Avenue Newark, New Jersey 07114	Model 860 photocomposing machine	TYPESETTERS, PHOTOGRAPHIC
	VariTyper	COLD COMPOSITION

Manufacturer	Product	See
Visual Graphics Corporation 1398 Northeast 125th Street North Miami, Florida 33161	Photo-Typositor Posteriter photographic type- setter	TYPESETTERS, PHOTOGRAPHIC TYPESETTERS, PHOTOGRAPHIC
Wood-Regan Instrument Co., The 184 Franklin Avenue Nutley, New Jersey 07110	Wrico lettering effects Wrico pens and scribers	PENS, TECHNICAL PENS, TECHNICAL
Xerox Corporation Rochester, New York 14603	Copyflo 11 continuous printer, Models 1, 2, 3 Copyflo 24C continuous printer 1824 printer Model 813 copier Model 914 copier Model 2400 copier Xerox (Standard Equipment)	PRINTER PRINTER PRINTER COPYING MACHINES COPYING MACHINES COPYING MACHINES CAMERA, XEROGRAPHIC PROCESS

Tables

TABLE 1 Comparing pen line weights

Pen No.	Leroy	Pen No.	Wrico	Pen No.	Koh-I-Noor Rapidograph
00	————	7T	————	00	————
0	————	7	————	0	————
1	————	6	————		
2	————	5	————	1	————
3	————	4	————	2	————
4	————			2½	————
		3	————	3	————
5	————			4	————

NOTE: Line weights are matched as closely as possible. Comparable line weights are not necessarily in 100 percent agreement. Worn pen points may produce heavier line weights than those rated on the chart.

448

T A B L E 2   Paper sizes

Type of paper	Standard size*	Standard weights, lb.
Bible	25 by 38	20
	28 by 42	24
	28 by 44	30
	32 by 44	35
	35 by 45	. . .
	38 by 50	. . .
Bond	17 by 22	9
	17 by 28	13
	19 by 24	16
	22 by 24	. . .
	24 by 38	20
	28 by 34	24
	34 by 44	. . .
Book (antique,	$22\frac{1}{2}$ by 35	30
eggshell, machine	24 by 36	35
finish, English finish,	25 by 38	40
supercalendered)	28 by 42	45
	28 by 44	50
	32 by 44	60
	35 by 45	70
	36 by 48	80
	38 by 50	80
Book (coated-two-sides,	$22\frac{1}{2}$ by 35	50
glossy or matte	24 by 36	60
finish)	25 by 38	70
	26 by 40	80
	28 by 42	90
	28 by 44	100
	32 by 44	120
	35 by 45	. . .
	36 by 48	. . .
	38 by 50	. . .
Book (coated-one-side,	20 by 26	50
glossy finish)	25 by 38	60
	26 by 40	70
	28 by 42	80
	28 by 44	. . .
	32 by 44	. . .
	35 by 45	. . .
	36 by 48	. . .
	38 by 50	. . .
	41 by 54	. . .

*Underscored size denotes basis weight.

T A B L E 2 **Paper sizes** *(Continued)*

Type of paper	Standard size*	Standard weights, lb
Book (process- coated)	24 by 36	45
	25 by 38	50
	28 by 42	60
	32 by 44	70
	35 by 45	. . .
	38 by 50	. . .
Cover (uncoated)	20 by 26	40
	23 by 35	50
	26 by 40	65
	35 by 46	80
	. . .	90
	. . .	100
	. . .	130
Cover (coated)	20 by 26	50
	23 by 35	60
	26 by 40	65
	35 by 46	80
	. . .	100
Ledger (regular and loose-leaf)	16 by 21	24
	17 by 22	28
	17 by 28	32
	19 by 24	36
	22 by 34	. . .
	24 by 38	. . .
	28 by 34	. . .
Newsprint	21 by 32	28
	22 by 34	
	24 by 36	to
	25 by 38	
	28 by 34	35
	28 by 42	28
	34 by 44	
	36 by 48	to
	38 by 50	35
Offset (uncoated and coated)	$22\frac{1}{2}$ by 35	50
	25 by 38	60
	28 by 42	70
	28 by 44	80
	32 by 44	100
	35 by 45	120
	36 by 48	150
	38 by 50	. . .
	38 by 52	. . .
	41 by 54	. . .
	44 by 64	. . .

*Underscored size denotes basis weight.

TABLE 2 (*Continued*)

Type of paper	Standard size*	Standard weights, lb
Onionskin and manifold	17 by 22	
	19 by 24	
	17 by 28	7
	21 by 32	
	22 by 34	to
	24 by 38	
	26 by 34	10
	28 by 34	
Opaque circular	17 by 22	16
	17 by 28	20
	22 by 34	24
	25 by 38	28
	28 by 34	. . .
	35 by 45	. . .
	38 by 50	. . .
Papeterie	17 by 22	16 to
	22 by 34	32
Gravure	25 by 38†	35
	28 by 42	40
	28 by 44	45
	32 by 44	50
	35 by 45	. . .
	38 by 50	. . .
Text	25 by 38	60
	26 by 40	70
	35 by 45	. . .
	38 by 50	. . .
Wedding	17 by 22	28
	22 by 34	32
	35 by 45	36
		40
Writing	17 by 22	13
	17 by 28	16
	19 by 24	20
	22 by 34	24
	24 by 38	. . .
	28 by 34	. . .

*Underscored size denotes basis weight.
†Supercalendered in this size only; weights 30, 35, and 40 lb.

T A B L E 3 **Paper-cutting chart for booklets**

Trimmed page size	Number of printed pages	Number from sheet	Standard paper size	Kinds of paper
$3\frac{1}{8}$ by $6\frac{1}{4}$	4	24	28 by 42	Bible; book; newsprint; offset; gravure
	6	16		
	8	12		
	12	8		
	16	6		
	24	4		
	48	2		
$3\frac{3}{8}$ by $6\frac{1}{4}$	4	24	28 by 42	Bible; book; newsprint; offset; gravure
	6	16		
	8	12		
	12	8		
	16	6		
	24	4		
	48	2		
$3\frac{3}{4}$ by $5\frac{1}{8}$	4	32	32 by 44	Bible; book; offset; gravure; text
	8	16		
	16	8		
	32	4		
	64	2		
$4\frac{1}{4}$ by $5\frac{3}{8}$	4	32	35 by 45	Bible; book; offset
	8	16		
	16	8		
	32	4		
	64	2		
$4\frac{1}{2}$ by 6	4	32	25 by 38	Opaque circular; gravure; text
	8	8		
	16	4		
	32	2		
4 by $9\frac{1}{8}$	4	12	25 by 38	Opaque circular; gravure; text
	6	8		
	12	4		
4 by $9\frac{1}{8}$	8	12	38 by 50	Bible; book; newsprint; offset; opaque circular; gravure; text
	16	6		
	48	2		
$5\frac{1}{4}$ by $7\frac{5}{8}$	4	16	32 by 44	Bible; book; offset; gravure; text
	8	8		
	16	4		
	32	2		

T A B L E 3 *(Continued)*

Trimmed page size	Number of printed pages	Number from sheet	Standard paper size	Kinds of paper
$5\frac{1}{2}$ by $8\frac{1}{2}$	4	16	35 by 45	Bible; book; offset; opaque circular; gravure; text; wedding
	8	8		
	16	4		
	32	2		
6 by $9\frac{1}{8}$	4	8	25 by 38	Opaque circular; gravure; text
	8	4		
	16	2		
$7\frac{3}{4}$ by $10\frac{5}{8}$	4	8	32 by 44	Bible; book; offset; gravure; text
	8	4		
	16	2		
$8\frac{1}{2}$ by 11	4	8	35 by 45	Bible; book; offset; gravure; text
	8	4		
	16	2		
$9\frac{1}{4}$ by $12\frac{1}{8}$	4	8	38 by 50	Bible; book; newsprint; offset; opaque circular; gravure; text
	8	4		
	16	2		

T A B L E 4 **Cover-paper cutting chart for booklets**

Trimmed Size of book	Cover-paper size without trim	Number from sheet	Cover-paper size with trim	Number from sheet
$3\frac{1}{8}$ by $6\frac{1}{4}$	20 by 26	12*	23 by 35	15
$3\frac{3}{8}$ by $6\frac{1}{4}$	. . .	. . .	23 by 35	15
$3\frac{3}{4}$ by $5\frac{1}{8}$	. . .	. . .	23 by 35	16
$4\frac{1}{4}$ by $5\frac{3}{8}$	23 by 35	16	20 by 26	8
$4\frac{1}{2}$ by 6	. . .	. . .	20 by 26	8
4 by $9\frac{1}{8}$	. . .	. . .	20 by 26	6
$5\frac{1}{4}$ by $7\frac{5}{8}$	. . .	. . .	23 by 35	8
$5\frac{1}{2}$ by $8\frac{1}{2}$	. . .	. . .	23 by 35	8
6 by $9\frac{1}{8}$	. . .	. . .	20 by 26	4
$7\frac{3}{4}$ by $10\frac{5}{8}$	. . .	. . .	23 by 35	4
$8\frac{1}{2}$ by 11	23 by 35	4*	20 by 26	2
$9\frac{1}{4}$ by $12\frac{1}{8}$	. . .	. . .	20 by 26	2

NOTE: Cover paper may also be obtained in other sizes.

*Close trim.

T A B L E 5 Greek alphabet

Name of Letter	English equivalent	Greek letters Capital	Small
alpha	a	A	α, a
beta	b	B	$\beta, \boldsymbol{6}$
gamma	g	Γ	γ
delta	d	Δ	δ, ∂
epsilon	e	E	ϵ
zeta	z	Z	ζ
eta	ē	H	η
theta	th	Θ	θ, ϑ
iota	i	I	ι
kappa	k	K	$\kappa, \varkappa$
lambda	l	Λ	λ
mu	m	M	μ
nu	n	N	ν
xi	x	Ξ	ξ
omicron	o	O	o
pi	p	Π	π
rho	r	P	ρ
sigma	s	Σ	σ, s
tau	t	T	τ
upsilon	y, u	Υ	υ
phi	ph	Φ	ϕ, φ
chi	ch	X	χ
psi	ps	Ψ	ψ
omega	ō	Ω	ω

T A B L E 6 Blotter-cutting chart

Standard type	Cut size, in.	Number from sheet	Standard sheet size, in.
No. 6	3 by 6	24	19 by 24
No. 9	$3\frac{5}{8}$ by $8\frac{5}{8}$	12	19 by 24
No. 10	$3\frac{5}{8}$ by $8\frac{5}{8}$	12	19 by 24
Checkbook	2 by 6	36	19 by 24

NOTE: Blotting paper may also be obtained in standard sheet size of 24 by 28 in. Basic weights for blotting papers range from 60 to 140 lb.

T A B L E 7 Inch-pica-point conversion chart

in.	Picas (approx.)	Points (approx.)	in.	Picas (approx.)	Points (approx.)
0.0625	0.3750	4.500	6.250	37.50	
0.1250	0.750	9	6.50	39	
0.250	1.50	18	6.750	40.50	
0.500	3	36	7	42	
0.750	4.50	54	7.250	43.50	
1	6	72	7.50	45	
1.250	7.50	90	7.750	46.50	
1.50	9	108	8	48	
1.750	10.50	126	8.250	49.50	
2	12	144	8.50	51	
2.250	13.50	162	8.750	52.50	
2.50	15	180	9	54	
2.750	16.50	198	9.250	55.50	
3	18	216	9.50	57	
3.250	19.50		9.750	58.50	
3.50	21		10	60	
3.750	22.50		10.250	61.50	
4	24		10.50	63	
4.250	25.50		10.750	64.50	
4.50	27		11	66	
4.750	28.50		11.250	67.50	
5	30		11.50	69	
5.250	31.50		11.750	70.50	
5.50	33		12	72	
5.750	34.50				
6	36				

T A B L E 8 Point-pica measurements

Points	in.	Picas	in.
1	0.01384	1	0.166
2	0.0277	2	0.332
3	0.0415	3	0.498
4	0.0553	4	0.664
5	0.0692	5	0.830
6	0.0830	6	0.996
7	0.9690	7	1.162
8	0.1107	8	1.328
9	0.1245	9	1.494
10	0.1384	10	1.660
11	0.1522	11	1.826
12	0.1660	12	1.993

NOTE: 12 points = 1 pica; 6 picas = 1 in. (approx.).

TABLE 9 Useful mathematical rules

To find circumference:
  Multiply diameter by..3.1416
  Or divide diameter by 0.3183

To find diameter:
  Multiply circumference by...0.3183
  Or divide circumference by 3.1416

To find radius:
  Multiply circumference by...0.15915
  Or divide circumference by 6.28318

To find side of an inscribed square:
  Multiply diameter by..0.7071
  Or multiply circumference by...0.2251
  Or divide circumference by 4.4428

To find side of an equal square:
  Multiply diameter by..0.8862
  Or divide diameter by 1.1284
  Or multiply circumference by...3.5450

TABLE 10 Constants and conversion factors

1 angstrom	=	10^{-8} centimeter
1 micron	=	0.001 millimeter
1 centimeter	=	0.39370 inch
1 inch	=	2.5400 centimeters
1 foot	=	30.480 centimeters
1 rad	=	57.2958 degrees
1 gram	=	15.432 grains
1 ounce	=	28.350 grams
1 pound	=	445,000 dynes
1 atmosphere	=	14.697 pounds per square inch
1 joule	=	10 million ergs
1 calorie	=	4.186 joules
1 coulomb	=	3 by 10^9 electrostatic units of charge
1 volt	=	1/300 ergs per electrostatic unit of charge
1 farad	=	9 by 10^{11} electrostatic units of capacitance
1 square inch	=	6.4516 square centimeters
1 square foot	=	929.03 square centimeters
1 cubic inch	=	16.387 cubic centimeters
1 liter	=	1,000 cubic centimeters
1 gallon	=	231 cubic inches
1 pound	=	453.59 grams
1 kilogram	=	2.2046 pounds
1 foot-pound	=	1.3549 joules
1 British thermal unit	=	252.00 calories
1 British thermal unit	=	778 foot-pounds
1 horsepower	=	746 watts
1 abampere	=	10 amperes
1 abvolt	=	10^{-8} volt
1 faraday	=	96,500 coulombs

$\pi = 3.1416 \qquad \varepsilon = 2.17183 \qquad \log_\varepsilon 10 = 2.3026$

T A B L E 10   **(Continued)**

$$
\begin{aligned}
\text{Charge of electron} &= 4.80 \times 10^{-10} \text{ electrostatic unit} \\
\text{Mass of electron (at rest)} &= 9.11 \times 10^{-28} \text{ gram} \\
\text{Avogadro's number} &= 6.02 \times 10^{23} \\
\text{Planck's constant} &= 6.63 \times 10^{-27} \text{ erg-second} \\
\text{Mass of hydrogen atom} &= 1.661 \times 10^{-24} \text{ gram} \\
\text{Velocity of light in vacuum} &= 299{,}776 \text{ kilometers per second}
\end{aligned}
$$

T A B L E 11   **Numerals**

Arabic	Greek	Roman
0		
1	α	I
2	β	II
3	γ	III
4	δ	IV
5	ϵ	V
6	$\digamma$	VI
7	ζ	VII
8	η	VIII
9	ϑ	IX
10	ι	X
11	$\iota\alpha$	XI
12	$\iota\beta$	XII
13	$\iota\gamma$	XIII
14	$\iota\delta$	XIV
15	$\iota\epsilon$	XV
16	$\iota\digamma$	XVI
17	$\iota\zeta$	XVII
18	$\iota\eta$	XVIII
19	$\iota\theta$	XIX
20	κ	XX
30	λ	XXX
40	μ	XL
50	ν	L
60	ξ	LX
70	o	LXX
80	π	LXXX
90	ϱ	XC
100	ρ	C
200	σ	CC
300	τ	CCC
400	υ	CD or CCCC
500	ϕ	D
600	χ	DC
700	ψ	DCC
800	ω	DCCC
900		CM
1,000		M
2,000		MM

T A B L E 12 **Mathematical symbols**

	Arithmetic and algebra
$+$	Addition; positive value; underestimation; approach through positive values.
$-$	Subtraction; negative value; overestimation; approach through negative values.
$\pm$	Add or subtract; plus-or-minus value.
$\mp$	Used where $\pm$ has appeared previously, as in $(a \pm b)$ $(a^2 \mp ab \pm b^2) = a^3 \pm b^3$; upper or lower signs are to be taken throughout.
$\cdot$	Multiplication (dot centered; $\times$ used in arithmetic).
$(\ )$	Parentheses; for grouping.
$[\ ]$	Brackets, for grouping.
$\{\ \}$	Braces; for grouping.
$^-$ (superscript)	Vinculum; for grouping.
$\%$	Percent.
$/$	Solidus, indicating division.
$-$	Horizontal rule, indicating division; fraction line.
$\div$	Division sign, used chiefly in arithmetic.
$:$	Ratio (in proportion).
$::$	Equals (in proportion).
$=$	Equivalent sign; is equal to.
$\neq$	[Is] not equal [to].
$\approx$	[Is] approximately equal [to].
$\equiv$	[Is] identical with; [is] identically equal [to].
$\equiv_x$	Indicates identity with all values of x for which both terms are defined.
$<$	[Is] less than.
$<\,<$	[Is] much less than.
$\leqq$ or $\leq$ or $\measuredangle$	Equal to or less than; not greater than.
$>$	[Is] greater than.
$>\,>$	[Is] much greater than.
$\geqq$ or $\geq$	Greater than or equal to; not less than.
$\propto$	Varies directly as.
$N!$	Factorial; continued product of all integral numbers from 1 to N, where N is an integral number.
^{n} (superscript numbers of letters)	Exponent; raised to the power of degree n (exponent indicates number of iterations).
$\sqrt[n]{}$	Radical sign; superscript n indicates index of degree of root; index omitted in case of square root.
$^{m/n}$ (superscript)	Fractional index; . . . raised to power of degree m/n.
$^{-n}$ (superscript)	Negative exponent; changes the term to its reciprocal.
$\exp f\,(x,\, y,\, \ldots)$	Functional symbol; exponential function.
$\exp u$	Functional symbol; exponential u.
i or j	Imaginary unit; j operator. $\sqrt{-1}$
$a\cdot 10^n$	Scientific notation; notation by powers of 10.
$\cdot$	Decimal point (placed on line); separates whole numbers from numerators of decimal fractions or is placed to the left of the numerator of a decimal fraction.
∞	Infinity symbol; algebraic number positively or negatively larger than any other number.
$\rightarrow$	Arrow; approaches as a limit.

TABLE 12 *(Continued)*

′ (superscript)	Prime; notational method of distinguishing between differing variables and constants.
″ (superscript)	Double prime; notational method of distinguishing between differing variables and constants.
‴ (superscript)	Triple prime; notational method of distinguishing between differing variables and constants.
. . .	Three dots; dots of omission, meaning "and so forth."
$\log_a X$	Logarithm of X to base a.
$\log X$	Logarithm of X to base 10 (common system of logarithms).
$\ln X$	Logarithm of X to base e (Napierian system, or natural logarithms).
e	Base of Napierian (natural) logarithms (2.7182—).
$P\ (n,\ r)$	Permutations of n things taken r at a time.
$C\ (n,\ r)$	Combinations of n things taken r at a time.
$\|\ \|$	Vertical bars; indicates absolute value of the quantity inside the bars; vector magnitude; determinant.
$\|\|\ \|\|$	Double vertical bars; indicates a matrix; set of quantities written in specific order of rows and columns.
a_{ij}	Element in row i, column j, of determinant or matrix.
$\det\ (a_{ij})$	Determinant with elements a_{ij} [or determinant of matrix (a_{ij})].
space or half space	Used instead of commas to separate convenient groups of digits.
subscript number or letter	Notational method of indicating differing values in a set or series.

Elementary Geometry

$\angle$, $\angle_s$	Angle(s).
$\perp$, $\perp_s$	Perpendicular(s); perpendicular to.
$\|$, $\|_s$	Parallel(s), parallel to.
$\triangle$, $\triangle_s$	Triangle(s).
$\bigcirc$, $\bigcirc_s$	Circle(s).
$\Box$, $\Box_s$	Parallelogram(s).
$\Box$, $\Box_s$	Square(s). (Do not use symbols for any other types of polygon.)
$\Box$, $\Box_s$	Trapezoid(s).
$\cong$	[Is] congruent [to].
$\sim$	[Is] similar [to].
$\overline{\wedge}$	[Is] equiangular.
$\therefore$	Three dots; hence; therefore.
$\overline{AB}$	Vinculum; chord AB of a circle; length of line segment between A and B.
$\overleftarrow{AB}$	Directed segment B to A.
$\overset{\frown}{AB}$	Arc AB of a circle.
π	Pi; constant ratio of circumference of a circle to its diameter.

Analytic geometry

x, y, z	Rectangular (Cartesian) coordinates of a point in space.
x, y	Rectangular coordinates of a point in a plane.
α	Alpha; indicates direction angle with x axis.

TABLE 12 *(Continued)*

l	Indicates directional cosine (with x axis).
β	Beta; indicates direction angle with y axis.
m	Indicates directional cosine (with y axis).
γ	Gamma; indicates direction angle with z axis.
n	Indicates directional cosine (with z axis).
r, θ, ϕ	Spherical coordinates of a point in space.
r, θ	Polar coordinates of a point in a plane.
ψ	Psi; indicates angle from radius vector to tangent of plane curve.
r, θ, z	Cylindrical coordinates of a point in space.
p, s	Indicates intrinsic coordinates.
e	Eccentricity of a conic.
p	Semilatus rectum.
m	Slope of a curve or line.
C	Circumference of a circle.
r	Radius of a circle.
D	Diameter of a circle.
ρ	Radius of curvature.
d	Perpendicular distance from a point to a line (length of normal).

Trigonometry	
° (superscript)	Indicates degree(s).
θ	Angle measured in rads.
′ (superscript)	Prime; indicates minutes.
″ (superscript)	Double prime; indicates seconds.
sin	Sine of angle.
cos	Cosine of angle.
tan	Tangent of angle.
cot	Cotangent of angle.
sec	Secant of angle.
csc	Cosecant of angle.
vers	Versed sine of angle; $1 - \cos\theta$.
covers	Coversed sine of angle.
hav	Haversine of angle; $\frac{1}{2}(1 - \cos\theta)$.
cis θ	$\cos\theta + 1\sin\theta$.
arc sin or $\sin^{-1}$	Inverse sine [of]; angle whose sine is.
arc cos or $\cos^{-1}$	Inverse cosine [of]; angle whose cosine is.
$[\sin f(x)]^n$	The nth power [of].

Hyperbolic functions	
sinh	Hyperbolic sine.
cosh	Hyperbolic cosine, etc.
arc sinh or $\sinh^{-1}$	Inverse hyperbolic function [of]; angle whose hyperbolic sine is.
arc cosh or $\cosh^{-1}$	Inverse hyperbolic function [of]; angle whose hyperbolic cosine is, etc.
$[\sinh f(x)]^n$	nth power [of].
$[\cosh f(x)]^n$	nth power [of], etc.

T A B L E   12 *(Continued)*

Calculus

d	Differential operator.
d^n	Differential operator of nth order.
$\dfrac{d}{dx}$	Derivative operator of first order.
$\dfrac{d^n}{dx}$	Derivative operator of nth order.
∂	Curly d; indicates partial differentiation.
D	Differential operator.
D^n	Differential operator of nth order.
$\dot{x}, \ddot{x}$	Indicates first and second derivatives with respect to time (Newton's notation).
$d^n y/dx^n$	Derivative of nth order.
$''$ (superscript)	Double prime; order of differentiation.
$'''$ (superscript)	Triple prime; order of differentiation.
$\int, \iint, \iiint$	Integral signs.
$\int_i^m, \int_a^b, \int_a^b, \int_c^d$	Integral signs, indicating index and limits.
$\oint$	Integral around a closed path.
Δ	Delta; indicates increment.
$\sum\limits_i$	Sigma; indicates summation; sum of terms of index i.

Special functions

$J_0(x), J_1(x),$ $J_n(x).$	Bessel functions. The notation recommended is in G. N. Watson's *Treatise* (1922), as endorsed by E. P. Adams in the *Smithsonian Tables*, (1922).
$B_1, B_3, B_5, \ldots$ $B_1, B_2, B_3, \ldots$	Bernoulli numbers and polynomials.
γ	Gamma; Eulerian (Mascheronis) constant (0.5772—).
$\Gamma(x) =$ $\int_0^\infty x^{-1}e^{-x}\,dx$	Gamm function of the positive number n; also called the factorial function.
$B(m, n) =$ $\int_0^1 x^{m-1}$ $(1 - x)^{n-1}\,dx$	Beta function of any two positive numbers m and n.
$\Gamma x^{(n-1)} =$ $\int_x^z x^{\,n}e^{-x}\,dx$	Incomplete gamma function.
$B_x(m, n) =$ $\int_0^x x^{m-1}$ $(1 - x)^{n-1}\,dx$	Incomplete beta function.

T A B L E 13 Decimal equivalents

Fractions, in.	Decimals, in.	mm.	Fractions, in.	Decimals, in.	mm.
1/64	0.01562	0.397	33/64	0.51562	13.097
1/32	0.03125	0.794	17/32	0.53125	13.494
3/64	0.04687	1.191	35/64	0.54687	13.891
1/16	0.0625	1.588	9/16	0.5625	14.288
5/64	0.07812	1.984	37/64	0.57812	14.684
3/32	0.09375	2.381	19/32	0.59375	15.081
7/64	0.10937	2.778	39/64	0.60937	15.478
1/8	0.1250	3.175	5/8	0.625	15.875
9/64	0.14062	3.572	41/64	0.64062	16.272
5/32	0.15625	3.969	21/32	0.65625	16.669
11/64	0.17187	4.366	43/64	0.67187	17.066
3/16	0.1875	4.763	11/16	0.6875	17.463
13/64	0.20312	5.159	45/64	0.70312	17.859
7/32	0.21875	5.556	23/32	0.71875	18.256
15/64	0.23437	5.953	47/64	0.73437	18.653
1/4	0.2500	6.350	3/4	0.750	19.050
17/64	0.26562	6.747	49/64	0.76562	19.447
9/32	0.28125	7.144	25/32	0.78125	19.844
19/64	0.29687	7.541	51/64	0.79687	20.241
5/16	0.3125	7.938	13/16	0.8125	20.638
21/64	0.32812	8.334	53/64	0.82812	21.034
11/32	0.34375	8.731	27/32	0.84375	21.431
23/64	0.35937	9.128	55/64	0.85937	21.828
3/8	0.3750	9.525	7/8	0.875	22.225
25/64	0.39062	9.922	57/64	0.89062	22.622
13/32	0.40625	10.319	29/32	0.90625	23.019
27/64	0.42187	10.716	59/64	0.92187	23.416
7/16	0.4375	11.113	15/16	0.9375	23.813
29/64	0.45312	11.509	61/64	0.95312	24.209
15/32	0.46875	11.906	31/32	0.96875	24.606
31/64	0.48437	12.303	63/64	0.98437	25.003
1/2	0.5	12.700		1.000	25.400

SOURCE: National Bureau of Standards.

T A B L E 14 Elements and symbols

Name	Symbol	Name	Symbol
Actinium	Ac	Beryllium	Be
Aluminum	Al	Bismuth	Bi
Americium	Am	Boron	B
Antimony	Sb	Bromine	Br
Argon	Ar	Cadmium	Cd
Arsenic	As	Calcium	Ca
Astatine	At	Californium	Cf
Barium	Ba	Carbon	C
Berkelium	Bk	Cerium	Ce

TABLE 14 (Continued)

Name	Symbol	Name	Symbol
Cesium	Cs	Nobelium	No
Chlorine	Cl	Osmium	Os
Chromium	Cr	Oxygen	O
Cobalt	Co	Palladium	Pd
Columbium (niobium)	Cb	Phosphorus	P
Copper	Cu	Platinum	Pt
Curium	Cm	Plutonium	Pu
Dysprosium	Dy	Polonium	Po
Einsteinium	Es	Potassium	K
Erbium	Er	Praseodymium	Pr
Europium	Eu	Promethium	Pm
Fermium	Fm	Protactinium	Pa
Fluorine	F	Radium	Ra
Francium	Fr	Radon	Rn
Gadolinium	Gd	Rhenium	Re
Gallium	Ga	Rhodium	Rh
Germanium	Ge	Rubidium	Rb
Gold	Au	Ruthenium	Ru
Hafnium	Hf	Samarium	Sm
Helium	He	Scandium	Sc
Holmium	Ho	Selenium	Se
Hydrogen	H	Silicon	Si
Indium	In	Silver	Ag
Iodine	I	Sodium	Na
Iridium	Ir	Strontium	Sr
Iron	Fe	Sulfur	S
Krypton	Kr	Tantalum	Ta
Lanthanum	La	Technetium	Tc
Lawrencium	Lw	Tellurium	Te
Lead	Pb	Terbium	Tb
Lithium	Li	Thallium	Tl
Lutetium	Lu	Thorium	Th
Magnesium	Mg	Thulium	Tm
Manganese	Mn	Tin	Sn
Mendelevium	Md	Titanium	Ti
Mercury	Hg	Tungsten (Wolfram)	W
Molybdenum	Mo	Uranium	U
Neodymium	Nd	Vanadium	V
Neon	Ne	Wolfram	W
Neptunium	Np	Xenon	Xe
Nickel	Ni	Ytterbium	Yb
Niobium	Nb	Yttrium	Y
Nitrogen	N	Zinc	Zn
		Zirconium	Zr

TABLE 15 Temperature conversion table

C	F	C	F	C	F	C	F
−75	−103	40	104	155	311	537.8	1000
−73.3	−100	43.3	110	160	320	550	1022
−70	−94	45	113	165	329	593.3	1100
−67.8	−90	48.9	120	165.6	330	600	1112
−65	−85	50	122	170	338	648.9	1200
−62.2	−80	54.4	130	171.1	340	650	1202
−60	−76	55	131	175	347	700	1292
−56.7	−70	60	140	176.7	350	704.4	1300
−55	−67	65	149	180	356	750	1382
−51.1	−60	65.6	150	182.2	360	760	1400
−50	−58	70	158	185	365	800	1472
−45.6	−50	71.1	160	187.8	370	815.6	1500
−45	−49	75	167	190	374	850	1562
−40	−40	76.7	170	193.3	380	871.1	1600
−35	−31	80	176	195	383	900	1652
−34.4	−30	82.2	180	198.9	390	926.7	1700
−30	−22	85	185	200	392	950	1742
−28.9	−20	87.8	190	204.4	400	982.2	1800
−25	−13	90	194	225	437	1000	1832
−23.3	−10	93.3	200	232.2	450	1037.8	1900
−20	−4	95	203	250	482	1050	1922
−17.8	0	98.9	210	260	500	1093.3	2000
−15	5	100	212	275	527	1100	2012
−12.2	10	104.4	220	287.8	550	1148.9	2100
−10	14	105	221	300	572	1150	2102
−6.7	20	110	230	315.6	600	1200	2192
−5	23	115	239	325	617	1204.4	2200
−1.1	30	115.6	240	343.3	650	1250	2282
0	32	120	248	350	662	1260	2300
4.4	40	121.1	250	371.1	700	1300	2372
5	41	125	257	375	707	1315.6	2400
10	50	126.7	260	398.9	750	1350	2462
15	59	130	266	400	752	1371.1	2500
15.6	60	132.2	270	425	797	1400	2552
20	68	135	275	426.7	800	1426.7	2600
21.1	70	137.8	280	450	842	1500	2732
25	77	140	284	454.4	850	1537.8	2800
26.7	80	143.3	290	475	887	1550	2822
30	86	145	293	482.2	900	1593.3	2900
32.2	90	148.9	300	500	932	1600	2912
35	95	150	302	510	950	1648.9	3000
37.8	100	154.4	310	525	977	1650	3002

NOTE: $F = (C \times \frac{9}{5}) + 32$; $C = (F - 32) \times \frac{5}{9}$.

T A B L E 16 Weights and measures

Linear measure	Square measure
12 inches = 1 foot	144 square inches = 1 square foot
3 feet = 1 yard	9 square feet = 1 square yard
5½ yards = 1 rod	272¼ square feet = 1 square rod (or
40 rods = 1 furlong	1 square perch)
8 furlongs = 1 mile	30¼ square yards = 1 square rod (or
320 rods = 1 mile	1 square perch)
5,280 feet = 1 mile	160 square rods = 1 acre
3 miles = 1 league	640 acres = 1 square mile

Cubic measure	Wood measure
1,728 cubic inches = 1 cubic foot	16 cubic feet = 1 cord foot
27 cubic feet = 1 cubic yard	8 cord feet = 1 cord
24¾ cubic feet = 1 perch	128 cubic feet = 1 cord

Liquid measure	Apothecaries' fluid measure
4 gills = 1 pint	60 minims = 1 fluid dram
2 pints = 1 quart	8 fluid drams = 1 fluid ounce
4 quarts = 1 gallon	16 fluid ounces = 1 pint
	8 pints = 1 gallon

Dry measure	Apothecaries' weight
2 pints = 1 quart	20 grains = 1 scruple
8 quarts = 1 peck	3 scruples = 1 dram
4 pecks = 1 bushel	8 drams = 1 ounce
8 bushels = 1 quarter	12 ounces = 1 pound
8 quarters = 1 load	
2 loads = 1 last	

Linen-yarn measure	Cotton-yarn measure
300 yards = 1 cut or hank	120 yards = 1 skein
2 cuts = 1 heer	7 skeins = 1 hank
6 heers = 1 hasp	18 hanks = 1 spindle
4 hasps = 1 spindle	

Ale and beer measure	Wine measure
4 gills = 1 pint	4 gills = 1 pint
2 pints = 1 quart	2 pints = 1 quart
4 quarts = 1 gallon	4 quarts = 1 gallon
9 gallons = 1 firkin	10 gallons = 1 anker
2 firkins = 1 kilderkin	18 gallons = 1 runlet
2 kilderkins = 1 barrel	42 gallons = 1 tierce
1½ barrels = 1 hogshead	63 gallons = 1 hogshead
2 hogsheads = 1 butt	84 gallons = 1 puncheon
2 butts = 1 turn	2 hogsheads = 1 pipe
	2 pipes = 1 turn

T A B L E 16 *(Continued)*

Miscellaneous weights and measures

56 pounds = 1 firkin (butter)	4 inches = 1 hand
112 pounds = 1 quintal (fish)	18 inches = 1 cubit
280 pounds = 1 sack (flour)	4,840 square yards = 1 English acre
80 pounds = 1 bushel (coal)	
140 pounds = 1 boll (oatmeal)	6,250 square yards = 1 Scottish acre
3 bushels = 1 sack	
24 sheets = 1 quire (paper)	7,840 square yards = 1 Irish acre
20 quires = 1 ream (paper)	12 dozen = 1 gross
10 reams = 1 bale	12–18 hundredweight = 1 hogshead (tobacco)

Metric measures of surface

1 hectare (10,000 square meters) = 2.471 acres
1 are (100 square meters) = 119.6 square yards
1 centare (1 square meter) = 1,550 square inches

Surveyors' measure

7.92 square inches = 1 link
100 links = 1 chain
80 chains = 1 mile
100,000 square links = 1 acre
10 square chains = 1 acre

Troy weight

24 grains = 1 pennyweight
20 pennyweights = 1 ounce
12 ounces = 1 pound

Avoirdupois weight

$27^{11}/_{32}$ grains = 1 dram
16 drams = 1 ounce
16 ounces = 1 pound
25 pounds = 1 quarter
4 quarters
or 100 pounds
(United States) = 1 hundred-weight
112 pounds
(Great Britain) = 1 hundred-weight
20 hundredweight
or 2,000 pounds
(United States) = 1 ton
2,240 pounds
(Great Britain) = 1 long ton

Mariners' measure

6 feet = 1 fathom
120 fathoms = 1 cable
$7\frac{1}{2}$ cables = 1 mile
5,280 feet = 1 statute mile
6,080 feet = 1 nautical mile

Angles or arcs

60 seconds = 1 minute
60 minutes = 1 degree
90 degrees = 1 right angle or 1 quadrant
360 degrees = 1 circle

Metric measures of length

1 myriameter (10,000 meters) = 6.3127 miles
1 kilometer (1,000 meters) = 0.62137 mile
1 hectometer (100 meters) = 328 feet 1 inch
1 decameter (10 meters) = 393.7 inches
1 meter = 39.37 inches
1 decimeter = 3.937 inches
1 centimeter = 0.3937 inch
1 millimeter = 0.03937 inch

index